D1456017

SIGNING THE DECLARATION OF INDEPENDENCE *(From Trumbull's painting in the rotunda of the capitol, Washington, D. C.)*

The Real America in Romance

THE STARS & STRIPES

THE AGE OF INDEPENDENCE

1763-1783

EDITED BY

EDWIN MARKHAM

AUTHOR OF "THE MAN WITH THE HOE, AND OTHER POEMS,"
"LINCOLN, AND OTHER POEMS," "VIRGILIA, AND OTHER
POEMS," "THE POETRY OF JESUS," ETC.

VOLUME IX

Art Edition

NEW YORK   CHICAGO

WILLIAM H. WISE & COMPANY

MCMXII

W. F. HALL PRINTING COMPANY, CHICAGO

THE STARS AND STRIPES

THE AGE OF INDEPENDENCE

THE American Revolution was precipitated by a people fired with a passion for freedom that could not wait to calculate the possibility of disaster. There was no weighing of chances at Lexington and Concord; no balancing of the possibility of success when thirteen disunited colonies with conflicting interests took up arms against a great and thoroughly organized empire. Wise statesmen would have asked for time to ponder, but had the yeomen of New England doubted, they must have despaired. Had they hesitated, the glory of opening a new era for America would have been lost. The conduct of the trainbands at Lexington and Concord was the culmination of the tendencies which the free air and boundless horizons of America have always induced in her children, a passionate yearning for the opportunity to work out our own salvation, free from the fettering traditions of Europe.

Yet the Fathers of the Revolution realized — and that not dimly — that they were fighting the British Crown, not the English people. The yearning for civil liberty was in the heart of England and Scotland no less than in the heart of the thirteen colonies. Rebels though the Americans might be in Tory estimation, still they never lacked able and eloquent defenders in the British Parliament. It was Pitt himself who distinguished between the lack of success that left a fleeing foe rebellious, and accorded to an enemy advancing with triumph on his banner the greater name of revolutionist. The pervading spirit of the British people was shown when it was found to be impossible for the tyrannical George to recruit an army among his own subjects for the overthrow of America, forcing him to the pitiful expedient of hiring Hessians to fight the battles of Hanoverian despotism. While the American Revolution was a military contest between the two governments, it was in no sense a conflict between Americans and Englishmen. The struggle was between two antagonistic principles of government, and victory for the younger nation conferred greater freedom upon the elder. Only gross ignorance of the spirit of the two peoples can find in such a war the slightest justification for any bitterness between the two countries.

Instead of throwing into a solid mass detailed accounts of all the battles of the conflict, their causes and effects, the methods of the modern novelist have been employed in "The Stars and Stripes" with the hope of giving the story a human interest that cannot be put into the usual historical narrative. From its beginnings in the Boston Massacre to the final triumph at Yorktown, not the glowing facts of history alone but the natural tendency of the human mind to follow the fortunes of the hero absorbs the reader's attention and aids him in fixing the entwined narrative in memory beyond the possibility of forgetfulness.

Previous volumes show the preparation for this great drama; in them the seeds are sown for a ripened harvest. Out of the smaller strifes of the colonies there emerges a unified and welded people, not yet used to its nationality, setting too much store upon liberty and not enough upon the restraints needful for successful government, but still one people, one nation, marching forward under the inspiring banner of the Stars and Stripes to fulfil its destiny.

CONTENTS

7

ILLUSTRATIONS

THE STARS AND STRIPES

THE STARS AND STRIPES

CHAPTER I

A NIGHT IN MARCH

A BAND of boys was abroad in the streets of Boston Town. It was 9 o'clock on the night of March 5, in the year 1770. Overhead was the moon, so crisply clear in the twanging winter air. and so near it seemed as though men might have reached up and made it ring with the sticks they carried. Underfoot was newly fallen snow, soft, white, enticing. It was a fit night for lads to be abroad.

GEORGE WASHINGTON (*From the Stuart portrait*)

But it was not mirth nor mischief that brought them forth to throng the streets. So much might have been inferred from their eager and excited talk as they hurried over the flagging, covered thinly with snow. For the time was teeming big with events, and the promise of greater to come. It was a time when lads were men, and men in their excitement little more than lads.

Massachusetts was at outs with his Majesty George III, King of England. Boston, the apex of the colony, had long borne the burden of the King's displeasure. Nine years before, fiery James Otis had made resistance to the navigation acts, which the Government had endeavored to 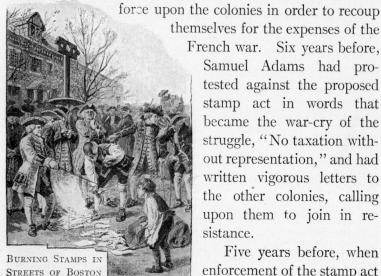 force upon the colonies in order to recoup themselves for the expenses of the French war. Six years before, Samuel Adams had protested against the proposed stamp act in words that became the war-cry of the struggle, "No taxation without representation," and had written vigorous letters to the other colonies, calling upon them to join in resistance.

Five years before, when enforcement of the stamp act was attempted, the Sons of

BURNING STAMPS IN STREETS OF BOSTON
(*From a drawing by A. B. Frost*)

Liberty had dragged the effigy of Oliver, the King's stamp officer, through these very streets, to hang it with much enthusiastic ceremony; they had demolished the stamp office; they had sacked the home of Chief Justice Hutchinson, because of his Toryism.

Sisters and mothers of these same lads, calling themselves Daughters of Liberty, had abjured the use of tea in protest against the tax laid upon it. Their fathers and uncles were members of that assembly which had been dissolved by the royal will because it refused to rescind other letters written by Samuel Adams, attacking and defying Parliament for imposing taxes.

So things had gone from bad to worse, until, on a day in June, 1768, British officers seized John Hancock's sloop *Liberty* at a wharf in Boston for breaking the importation laws. Then the people, or such of them as did not feel the restraints of the more orderly element, rose in riot.

The answer to the riot came in the shape of red-coated soldiers, two regiments of them, under Colonel Dalrymple; and the appointment of the hated Hutchinson, Tory townsman, as lieutenant-governor. Since then the troops, although refused quarters by the town, had been in the midst of them at the King's expense, barracked about town.

The situation was scarcely to be borne; the soldiers themselves were odious, seeking to provoke the townspeople by studied effrontery and insolence, leading dissolute lives and insulting citizens in drunken fashion. The idea that their presence expressed was even more insufferable; it was the idea that the King would force upon them by might what he could not establish over them by right.

Now the tension of nearly two years had been drawn taut within three days, and peace thus strained

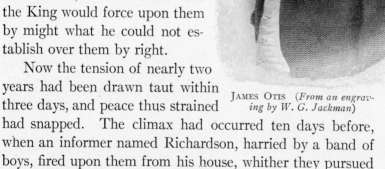

JAMES OTIS (*From an engraving by W. G. Jackman*)

had snapped. The climax had occurred ten days before, when an informer named Richardson, harried by a band of boys, fired upon them from his house, whither they pursued him, killing one and wounding another.

On Friday, March 2, there was a fight at Gray's ropewalk between soldiers and workmen. The soldiers, severely beaten, swore vengeance. Saturday they prepared for it, fashioning bludgeons; for it would not do to shoot. They warned their friends to be off the streets Monday night, when they would take vengeance on all who might be abroad.

Lieutenant-Colonel Carr of the 29th made no effort to restrain his men or keep them in barracks, though he knew of their threats. Neither had Lieutenant-Governor Hutchinson endeavored to guard the peace. The streets were full of soldiers that night, cursing, swaggering, striking with clubs and sheathed cutlasses those who failed to evade them, and challenging citizens to combat.

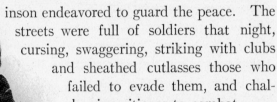

The group of lads discussed these matters in loud voices as they passed through the streets. Some of them had just come from Murray's barracks, in Brattle Street, where there had already been an affray.

THOMAS HUTCHINSON (*From a portrait attributed to Copley*)

"Come, let us get guns!" cried one, excitedly, hearing how the soldiers had threatened to bayonet and kill citizens. "Let us arm ourselves. Let us not be shot down like cowards!"

"We shall not be shot down," returned another, a tall lad and straight, with resolute step, who held his head high. He had said scarcely a word before, yet he was their leader. About him was a subtle manifestation of forcefulness that made his comrades defer to him.

"How know you we shall not be shot, then, John Stevens?" rejoined the first, with a trace of mockery in his tones.

"Because, as you are aware, the soldiers may not shoot without order from civil authority,

GOVERNOR HUTCHINSON'S HOUSE, BOSTON
TAKEN DOWN IN 1830

this being a time of peace, and who is there will give them
the order to fire on citizens?" answered the leader, evenly
enough.

"I doubt not our traitorous governor would be right
glad to bid them kill us."

"And as for arming," John Stevens continued, paying
no heed to the fling, though it was well received by the others,

FANEUIL HALL IN 1775   (*From an engraving by C. B. Hall*)

"have you not been sufficiently told that we must not make
open resistance to our oppressors, lest we seem to lose our
advantage of right?   It is for us to obey the law, that we
may look to the law for our redress.   If we destroy it, upon
what shall we depend?"   It was a day when lads spoke
with the tongues of elders.

"On our swords!"

"The time is not yet ripe."

Silenced for a moment, the lads turned into King Street
and toward the custom house, which was hard by, at the
corner of Exchange Lane.   The crisp night was filled with
the sounds of distant voices; there were little sporadic out-

breakings of tumult where soldiers rioted through the streets, seeking victims to beat with their cudgels.

A boy ran to them, weeping. "A band of ruffians, coming out of the main guard, beat me down a moment since, though I begged them not to kill me," he cried. They saw it was his wrath, more than his hurt, that made him cry. Angry words came from them with imprecations and epithets.

"Listen!" The voice of John Stevens bespoke silence.

Out across the night came the clangor of a bell, in wild alarm; the sound sent the flesh creeping on the bodies of the young patriots.

" 'T is the bell of the old brick meeting-house in King Street."

"What is the meaning of it!"

"Come. There is a fire. Let us hasten. The soldiers are burning the town."

"Hush. 'T is but a warning to the citizens, to let them know the soldiers are turned loose," asserted John Stevens.

"Look! Who is there?"

A crowd of men swung into King Street and turned toward the custom house. The moon glinted from musket barrels; in the light from the moon and the reflecting snow, the lads made the men out to be British soldiers.

"Come, let us follow. They are returning to their quarters." The quarters of the main guard was near the custom house.

"We will pelt them with snowballs. Huzza!"

Whistling through their fingers, huzzaing, scoffing, and jeering, the young Americans fell into pursuit, making missiles of the snow as they went; for even in such times youth will assert itself.

The bell still rang from the old brick meeting-house; startled men were hurrying into the streets from their houses.

BRONZE PANEL OF THE BOSTON MASSACRE, FROM THE CRISPUS ATTUCKS MONUMENT,
BOSTON COMMON

"The red scoundrels are abroad!" screamed the lads, running on to their pelting.

"Look! Yon is fellow that knocked me down, not a half-hour since," cried the boy who had joined them.

They were now close to the custom house.

"Which one is that?" demanded John Stevens.

"Yonder sentinel, against the corner of the custom house." His finger singled him out.

"How came that about?" The concourse stopped to hear, making out new game; for the band of soldiery had reached the barracks too soon for the promised fun.

"Why, when Captain Hitchcock went forth anon to stop the fray at Murray's barracks, I did call out after him, 'There goes a mean fellow who hath not paid my master for dressing his hair,' the truth of which you may well learn from my master himself over the way there; whereupon this rogue set upon me with his musket and beat me about the head. See, you may feel the welt he raised." The boy jerked off his hat to display his wounds, making the most of his elevation into heroics; for the others were pressed admiringly about him.

With a whoop, the band broke toward the sentinel.

"Kill him!" they cried. "Kill the bloody-backed scoundrel!"

They fell to pelting him with the snowballs they had prepared for the other soldiers.

John Stevens, following slowly, joined them. Beneath the light of the moon there was a cold gleam in his eye; his lips were tightly drawn; his head was lowered in the intensity of his feeling.

The sentinel, helpless against the storm of snow that swirled upon him, growled a curse and loaded his musket.

"The lobster is going to fire!" cried the lads, pressing closer.

From a shadow lying along the building a man passed swiftly to the side of the soldier, reaching out a warning hand.

"If you fire you must die for it," he said, solemnly.

" 'T is Henry Knox!" exclaimed Stevens, recognizing the voice of the one who spoke.

BOSTON MASSACRE, MARCH 5, 1770　(*From the Painting by Alonzo Chappell*)

"Huzza for Henry Knox!"　His companions took up the cry.

The soldier was sullen.　"I don't care," he growled. "Damn them, if they touch me, I 'll fire!"

"Fire and be damned!" said a voice from the group, augmented constantly by men and other boys who came running up to the scene, stirred from home by the ringing of the bell.

The soldier pointed his musket, and snapped the trigger, thinking to frighten them.　They hooted him for it, and fell to pelting him more than ever.

"We 'll knock him down for snapping!" exclaimed one lad, deriding the sentinel.

The crowd increased, pressing closer "Lobster! Bloody-back! Murderer! Hireling! Infamous scoundrel!" They knocked against his musket; they threatened him with sticks. "The coward dare not fire!" they cried, taunting him.

John Stevens, standing back, looked on. His hands were clenched at his side, "First let us try the law, as we are told," he repeated to himself, "and then — "

"Stand off!" The soldier, alone against the press, was becoming frightened.

"Turn out, main guard!" He was terrified. His voice was a shriek. Over in the barracks, across the way, they heard his scream.

A door burst open; in the room within were figures of soldiers; some of them came clattering forth, accoutered and equipped. Their feet creaked in the snow; they hurried toward the solitary sentinel, pressing the citizens away roughly. They were seven, two of whom were of the number that had been discomfited at the ropewalk on Friday, and who had sworn vengeance. With them came Captain Preston. Making their way to their comrade, they turned upon the threatening citizens.

THE OLD STATE HOUSE, BOSTON

The bell in the old brick meeting-house stopped ringing; for a moment there was a hush, tense, potential.

The voice of Henry Knox broke the silence. "For God's sake," he said, addressing Captain Preston fervently, "take your men back again; if they fire, your life must answer for the consequences."

"I know what I am about," retorted the captain, gruffly. In his voice was a flaw; he was nervous.

The gathering men walked before the circle of soldiers, backed against the custom house; it had become the work of men now.

"You are cowardly rascals for bringing arms against naked men!" they called, angrily. "Lay aside your guns, and we are ready for you!" They carried sticks in their hands.

They stirred closer to the soldiers, knocking against the muskets.

"Are the soldiers' guns loaded?" asked Richard Palmes, a citizen, getting close to Captain Preston.

"Yes, with powder and ball."

"Are they going to fire upon the inhabitants?" pressed Theodore Bliss, another citizen.

"They cannot, without my orders."

The taunting of the crowd increased.

"Come on, you rascals! You bloody-backs! You lobster scoundrels! Fire, if you dare!"

Some one threw a stick. It struck against the musket in the hands of Montgomery, one of those who had been worsted on Friday at the ropewalk, and who on Saturday had vowed vengeance He leveled his gun. There was a flash, a crash. Crispus Attucks, citizen of Boston, subject of the King, lay dead at the hands of the King's soldiers.

Another fired, and another; the noise echoed up the streets, through the town, down the ages.

Black figures lay on the ground, with crimson patches spreading softly across the trampled snow.

Not in all the brave history of Massachusetts was greater courage than now. For now, with their fellow-citizens lying dead at their feet, and their murderers at hand, the men of Boston forebore. Theirs must be patience; theirs must be constancy to higher purposes of truth and right, and not present retribution. The time was not ripe for rebellion and revolution. Independence was an idea yet to be taught by their oppressors.

Groaning with horror and anguish, uttering the low, awful noise of many men in a rage, those who had seen this thing done drew back; not in fear for their lives, but in fear lest they do that which they might rue.

One there was who did not draw away, but stood stiff and straight where they had been, confronting the soldiers. It was John Stevens. His eyes were fixed on a black figure that lay, stirring slightly, and groaning, on the ground.

For a space he stood immovable. Breaking at last into a low cry, he passed to the side of the recumbent figure, the muskets of the soldiers, swung level, pointing at him. He gave no heed, but knelt, bending over the wounded man.

Kneeling still, he raised his head; from his waist and his body upright. His clenched hands were at his side. His face was like a rock as he turned it toward the soldiers. Their guns were lowered; they had been told to desist.

GRAVES OF THE VICTIMS OF THE BOSTON MASSACRE
IN THE OLD GRANARY BURYING GROUND, BOSTON

Like a face of rock it was, save that there glared and flared in the depths of the eyes a light that was not the light of the moon.

"If there is a God above, and a hell beyond, this is not the end, but the beginning," said John Stevens. His voice was hollow, low, almost a hoarse whisper; but the soldiers could hear it. Hearing it, they laughed.

He bent over again, thrust his arms about the figure, and staggered to his feet, bearing it upon his shoulder. In the place where it had been was a spot that spread and gave up into the moonlight a thin, sick vapor.

While the angry populace, aroused by the shooting, were surging about the murderous soldiers, threatening them, they were reinforced by the entire 29th, and when Governor Hutchinson, hastening to the scene, was beginning his hard task of pacifying them, a youth, forgotten and alone, staggered through a narrow lane of Boston with a heavy, heavy burden.

He came to a little cottage. A candle burned in the window, as though to light home the householder. The lad lifted the knocker. The sound of it, falling, echoed through the rooms. There was the sound of a woman's voice within.

"Who is it?" she asked.

"It is John, mother. It is I."

The bolt slid; the woman fumbled the latch.

"And where is your father, John?"

The latch gave way; the door swung open; the mother, all forgetful of the cold, stood in the doorway.

The son answered her. "He is with me," he said.

CRISPUS ATTUCKS MONUMENT, BOSTON COMMON

CHAPTER II

TIMES OF TUMULT

"GENTLEMEN, by your very good leave, I will pledge you a toast!"

Lieutenant Lucas Hempstead, of the 17th Lancers, lifting high his glass of punch, although it was clear he had already had too much, looked with half a leer at the group foregathered about him. They were half a dozen young officers of the British army; their flaming coats, encrusted with gold embroidery and heavy with cords and medals, gave a flash of color to the stately room in which they stood. Lounging about the great bowl of punch that rested amid the sparkling ranks of cut glass on the sideboard, the roistering group for the moment had the room to themselves, save for two young men in civilian clothes, so quietly engaged in conversation in a far corner of the room that their presence was not heeded.

The scattering clatter of the

33   ALEXANDER HAMILTON (*After the painting by Colonel Trumbull*)

others subsided by degrees; clearly he who proposed a toast was the leader of the revel. Waiting, with poised glass, until all had filled and were attending him, he proceeded. "Gentlemen and brother officers, I pledge you our hostess, Mistress Robert Stevens, sometime the Widow Osborne, and sometimes the devil knows what! May her life be full of days, and her days be full of life!"

The gentlemen and brother officers, being in mellow mood, received the toast uproariously.

"'T is highly fitting that we should drink deep to that!" cried one, tossing off his glass with a flourish, "for if there is one who is a friend to England and to such swaggering braggarts as ourselves, that one is the Widow Osborne."

"'T is well said, to wish that her days may be full of life," quoth another, a slim, dark man, with a scar above his left eye, and the only one out of uniform; "for, had you wished that her —"

"Tush, Francis," interrupted Lieutenant Hempstead, jocosely perceiving by his manner what the other would say; "your tongue ever runs upon an evil jest. Is it not enough that this poor, rich, old man hath found a young wife without our making merry over it?"

"Old he is, forsooth, and rich," commented another, speaking through the ready laughter that followed everything Lieutenant Lucas saw fit to say. "But how make you out that the Widow Osborne is young, when she already has a daughter of one-and-twenty?"

"Put me no question concerning the ways of women," Hempstead returned, with the manner of one of superior wisdom.

"I had rather thought the daughter had been the subject of your toast, Lieutenant Lucifer," suggested he whom they called Francis, with a shrewd glance at the man he addressed, comporting little with his light way of speaking.

Lieutenant Hempstead shrugged his shoulders and blinked despairingly. "Thaw me out an iceberg with your words and your glances, friend Francis," he said, "and I will find warmth in the heart of the fair Sophronia."

"Nay, then, but can you tell me how she managed this bit of business?" came a question from one of the officers. "In truth, it is a far step from being the widow of a clergyman to being the wife of a rich banker."

"'Managed, man!" retorted Lieutenant Hempstead, bending on the other a look of compassionate reproof. "Have you not seen her? Need you be told aught, on top of that?"

JOSEPH WARREN   (*From the painting by J. S. Copley in Faneuil Hall, Boston*)

"She is a famous beauty, I grant you that, and noted for her charms," returned he who sought enlightenment. "But there are some who hint that the adjectives would be more fitting if they underwent some change in the matter of prefix and suffix. I have heard mothers with marriageable daughters, and daughters with marriageable mothers, protest that she is little better than an adventuress."

"Adventures she has had, no doubt," returned Francis, "but 't is long odds from having adventures to being an adventuress. For my part, I am well content to take matters as they are, and to come to her balls without picking and choosing; for, though they snarl at her in their boudoirs, the beauties of the land must perforce purr in her ball-room, would they keep favor with their men."

"Ay, and here we may find a brew the fame of which has reached the hearts of select circles in London and is sung on the far frontier of Virginia," added Lieutenant Lucas, reaching his hand forth for another glass of the punch as he spoke. "Come, fill me your glasses, and I will give you yet another toast that ye may drink!" They filled. Lieutenant Hempstead swept them with a gesture of indolent grace. "Long life to our friends, and confusion to our enemies!" he said.

Setting down his glass empty, Lieutenant Hempstead became aware that the two who had been talking in a corner of the room, and whose presence had been forgotten, had come to the sideboard, where they now stood, waiting to be

SAMUEL ADAMS (*From the painting by J. S. Copley in Faneuil Hall*)

served by the two negroes in attendance. One of them, a handsome youth of seventeen, sharp faced, with an expression of high intelligence, was too much absorbed in his own thought to heed what went on about him. The other, several years his senior, a tall fellow, broad of shoulder, earnest of mien, with a native dignity in his carriage and manner, had clearly heard the toast, and was looking thoughtfully at the one who proposed it.

"Perchance, sirrah, when you have had your fill of staring, you will drink my toast," said Lieutenant Hempstead, insolently, returning the look of this one.

The eyes of all turned toward the two.

"Haply you think ill of it?" went on Lieutenant Lucas, when the one he addressed vouchsafed no reply.

"I think that the confusion you drink to your enemies may find its way into your own head," answered the stranger.

The young lieutenant, subordinated for the moment by the self-possession of the other, glared balefully at him, at a loss for speech. His companions stood by observing the trend of events with varying degrees of amusement; they knew what came of baiting Lieutenant Hempstead; they were content to let the quarrel brew between him and the American. But before the Englishman could find word or deed commensurate with his resentment, that occurred which diverted the attention of all from such petty matters as strife between individuals.

"You talk of fighting, then!" cried an excited voice, close at hand. "Fight! Fight! Why, you will as soon fight as a bed of oysters, and shall be as easily swallowed if you attempt it! What shall a pack of farmers do against the regulars of England? They would not stand through the echoes of our first volley! They would not even stay to be taught a lesson, but would run like sheep!"

It was a major of British infantry who spoke so hotly.

LORD CHATHAM (*From the portrait painted by Richard Brompton*)

He was one of a group at the moment approaching the sideboard; a fiery, wiry warrior, with snapping eyes and a thin, sharp mouth. Major Pitcairn it was, he who was to become famous as the one whose first pistol shot precipitated the fighting at which he now scoffed, and who was to forfeit his own life to the valor of the farmers and yeomen he now despised.

The one to whom he spoke most directly, a man past middle years, tall, courtly, of distinguished bearing, was Doctor Joseph Warren, of Boston, an illustrious patriot and a leader in Massachusetts. With them were Major Jack Hempstead, brother to Lucas and husband to Margaret Stevens, now a fat, joyful little officer, whose spirits were clearly extinguished for the time by the bitter words of his fellow-officers, and Robert Stevens himself, now grown old, with benign countenance and white hair. He was sorely troubled by what the fiery Pitcairn had said, the more so because, as host, he desired peace between his guests.

But it was more than strife among the guests then present that was hinted in the remarks of the British officer. For the night was a night in October, in the year 1774, and the times were heavy and brooding. Even as he spoke, the colonies were full of a smouldering wrath, ready to break forth into a flame against England for the wrongs she had done. Even as he spoke, in every town and village from the coast of New England to the last settlement along the frontier, determined men lay sleeping with loaded muskets leaning against the door-post and ears trained to hear the signal shot that should call them forth to fight for their rights and their liberties. Nor was the spirit of liberty unknown outside of New England. In the South the spark had been kindled by such broad-minded men as Christopher Gadsden, who sought to wipe out the sectional feeling between the colonists and unite them on the common plane of Americans. Feeling burst into flame at the eloquence of Patrick Henry, who warned King George in the beginning of the example of Tarquin, Cæsar and Charles I. Even as he spoke, leaders from all the colonies save

PATRICK HENRY DELIVERING HIS CELEBRATED TARQUIN AND CÆSAR SPEECH IN 1775 (*From the painting by P. F. Rothermel*)

one were assembled in Carpenter's Hall, Philadelphia, in the
First Continental Congress, considering how best to protect
the liberty of the colonies from the assaults upon it by King
George of England and his ministers.

That is why the words of the little British major struck
ominously upon the ears of those who heard, and made them
forget the strife that lay between individuals alone. For
those who heard, British and American alike, knew well
that the minds of men were hot; that few could point out
the way leading to better feeling, and fewer still could incline
their hearts to follow it.

There was a silence; a tense, strained silence, electrical
with potentialities. Those already about the punch bowl
merged into those who came, foregoing word of greeting;
in times of crisis the conventions break down.

Abruptly was the silence broken. Bursting into the
center of the group newly formed, the youth of seventeen,
who had been one of the two unnoticed in the room during
the roistering of the young English blades, confronted the
officer who had spoken. His eyes flashed; his lips quivered
with emotion.

"You go far wrong there!" he cried, striving to keep his
passion and his voice in leash. "Our men have stood their
ground beside the best regulars of England, on many a
bloody field, and will stand as well against them! Who was
it saved the broken fragments of Braddock's army from
annihilation if it was not Colonel Washington with his
Virginia yeomen? Who fought side by side with the red-
coats at Louisburg and Ticonderoga? Who stood with
Wolfe on the Plains of Abraham? Whose courage and
sacrifice brought luster to British arms on many a field,
and extended England's empire to the frozen seas of the
north, if it was not these contemned and despised provincials? Go to your history, sir, if they are not ashamed to

CARPENTERS' HALL, PHILADELPHIA, WHERE THE CONTINENTAL CONGRESS
FIRST MET

write it in England, and learn how well we will fight for our rights, if you put us to it!"

Erect, blazing, defiant, this slip of a boy stood among the warriors of England, the incarnate spirit of the colonies. Astonished, admiring, they looked upon him for a moment, voicing no word. It was Lieutenant Hempstead who spoke first.

"Ay, my little gamecock," he said, sneering at the lad, "we know —"

"My name, sir, if you care to address me, is Alexander Hamilton, of this province," interposed the lad, with vigor.

Hamilton was born of Scotch and English parents in the Island of Nevis, British West Indies; on his mother's side was a strain of French blood. He had only recently come to America, but already, despite his extreme youth and foreign birth, he was looked upon as a leader. Some months before this, in July, Hamilton took the platform in a public meeting held in one of the fields of New York and astonished his audience with a clear and fervent exposition of the rights of the colonists. Within a few days he had written a pamphlet defending the Continental Congress, in reply to Tory attacks, that had attracted immediate and wide-spread attention, and was being attributed to various leaders of the patriots; for in those days such work was done under classical pseudonyms.

"Let me tell you, then, Alexander Gamecock," went on Lucas, insolently, "that we know somewhat of history over-seas; but, mark my word, it will be a different matter when these same yokels stand in front of British regulars, rather than behind them."

"Belike they shall be as often behind them again, if it comes to that," observed the young man with whom Lieutenant Lucas had been on the point of a quarrel, anticipating the retort of his companion.

INTERIOR OF CARPENTERS' HALL

"As for you and your fellow rebels!" cried Lucas, turning hotly on him, in spite of the efforts of his brother, the major, to mollify him, "I should feel my sword as deeply sullied if I thrust it into the entrails of a swine as I shall if I am obliged to sheath it in the flesh of these blundering bumpkins!"

"You are as like to do the one thing as the other, I should say," returned the civilian serenely.

Beside himself with rage, Lucas took a step forward, and in another instant would have given himself over to some rash act, had not his brother and one or two of his companions interposed and prevented him. The American eyed him calmly as he struggled with his guardians; the others sought to avert a clash in whatever way seemed to them most promising. In the end, Lucas was prevailed upon, half by persuasion and half by force, to take himself off to the ball-room, whither he departed, grumbling and cursing, and swearing vengeance.

"Nay, Major Pitcairn," said Major Hempstead, with a sigh of relief when Lucas had been led way, "the lad is more than half right," indicating Hamilton with a nod,

" WITHIN THESE WALLS HENRY, HANCOCK, AND ADAMS INSPIRED THE DELEGATES OF THE COLONIES WITH NERVE AND SINEW FOR THE TOILS OF WAR"

and casting a deprecating look upon the other Americans, as though he would erase the memory from their minds of the ill-advised words of his brother. "I myself fought by the side of these same provincials and know their mettle. Our good host had a son who died as fine a death as ever British soldier died on field of battle. Egad, it fair makes my eyes swim to think of it. But we waste much idle talk. Let us hope the test will never come. For my part, I conceive these ardent patriots of the soil to take matters much too seriously, and incline toward making a mountain out of a mole-hill."

"By Heaven, that they do," agreed Major Pitcairn. "We do but ask them for a few pence apiece, and we bring the whole starving pack yelping about our heels. We do but levy a slight impost on some few things that are brought into their country, and straightway they close their ports against us, like the obstinate mules they are. And when we sought to raise a pound or two by placing a stamp tax on deeds, such a cry arose as you would have thought we came with an invading army to lay them by the heels!"

"To us it seemed more nearly that than anything else," returned Doctor Warren, with perfect patience. "You gentlemen both reflect a view of the matter, which, broadly entertained among the English, is one of the most obstinate obstacles to an understanding between the mother country and her colonies. The King, the Parliament, the Tories, and many of the Whigs believe that we quarrel over taxes because of the money at issue. They think that with us it is a question of pounds, shillings, and pence. The money is nothing; the course we take is like to cost us vastly greater treasure than the taxes entailed, unless our cousins across the water speedily come to some better comprehension of what we contend for. It is a principle that is at stake; the fundamental principle of constitutional liberty; the principle that no man shall be taxed without his consent.

That is a right guaranteed to Englishmen under the constitution; it is a right for which not one of you would fail to fight, if it were threatened. If Parliament had asked us for money, we would have given it, gladly, according to our means. But Parliament demanded it of us by force of law, and we refused, maintaining that to tax us without our consent was to strike at the tap-root of liberty. As Lord Chatham, our champion in Parliament, has said, if we shall consent to it, we shall drag into slavery not only ourselves, but the people of England as well. If that much could be made clear to your countrymen overseas, a grave danger would be removed."

PATRICK HENRY   (*After the Sully portrait*)

"I quite agree with the statement of principle made by Doctor Warren," interposed Robert Stevens, when Major Pitcairn was about to retort; "but I cannot think otherwise than that we shall lose more than we gain if we stubbornly refuse a compromise for the present. I have great faith that matters may yet be adjusted."

"Compromise!" cried the fiery Pitcairn, taking his third glass of punch from a negro servitor. "Here is the only compromise!" He touched the hilt of his sword as he spoke. "Your attitude, gentlemen of America, is preposterous, and your action insurrectionary! You of Massachusetts, sir," turning to Doctor Warren, "are little better than rebels, and should be treated accordingly."

"Gentlemen! The war has not begun!" cried Major Hempstead, with a jocular turn to his tongue, as being the best means of averting a rupture.

"Perchance we shall all be better satisfied if Major Pitcairn will endeavor to substantiate his remarks with some few instances," suggested Doctor Warren suavely, seeking a way out.

"Ay, Major Pitcairn, for our own comfort let us have proof that we are rebellious and seditious, if you must call us so," added Alexander Hamilton. His companion held his peace.

"Proof you shall have, and plenty of it," rejoined Major Pitcairn, pausing only to drain his glass, an operation interrupted by the heated turn the talk had taken. "To put away the question of taxation for the present, what say you of your behavior toward the governors we sent over, with every one of whom you picked quarrels?"

"We say that they were tyrannical in their methods, without sympathy for our institutions, or consideration for our feelings," replied Doctor Warren, calmly.

"And that they overrode our liberties without let or hindrance, beyond what little we were able to place in their way," added Hamilton.

Major Pitcairn let fall an oath of impatience. "Insubordination!" he ejaculated. "Rank insubordination! If you defend such conduct, doubtless you can find some excuses for the disgraceful riot in your town when a band of ruffians threw certain cargoes of tea into the harbor?" This to Doctor Warren.

"The affair was in no sense a riot," returned Doctor Warren, passively. "We were forced to such a course.

To have permitted the landing of taxed tea would have been to acknowledge that our principles had failed. It was a last resort, after all other means to prevent the discharge of the cargoes had been exhausted. The affair was orderly; it was in no sense a riot." Major Pitcairn could scarcely repress his indignation at hearing the matter defended. "I think," went on Doctor Warren, "it will be necessary to call your attention to the lamentable occurrences in Boston on the fifth of March, four years ago, when our citizens were shot down by British soldiery in the streets, to show you how far we are from being rashly rebellious in our behavior."

"The thing was nothing," rejoined Major Pitcairn. "An ordinary street broil, in which some half a dozen lost their lives; deservedly, no doubt."

At the words, the face of the young man from Boston went white with rage; but he said nothing, not daring to trust himself in speech.

"To you it may seem nothing, but to the people of Boston it was much," replied Doctor Warren, looking toward the other. "So much that they call it there the Boston Massacre, and hold the day sacred to the memory of those slain. Do you think that the populace of Boston, easily able to overwhelm and annihilate the two regiments of troops then stationed there, were riotous and seditious when they thoughtfully restrained themselves from wreaking vengeance? Do you think a turbulent and angry people would have subsequently defended the culprits with their ablest lawyers, and acquitted all but two of them in a court of law?"

"Supine and cowardly behavior," retorted Major Pitcairn, inconsistently enough.

Again the face of the young man from Boston exhibited signs of intense passion; and again he held his peace.

"You are raising many fine points," said Francis at this juncture, easily. "For my part, I consider the matter quite plain. When one who is a friend of his sovereign is pursued through the streets with cries of 'Tory, Tory,' and pelted with clods, it is high time to confess that the conduct of the people is insurrectionary, and to treat it in that light. Even our good host here, Mr. Stevens, has suffered from the violent prejudice that runs like a plague through the country."

At this covert attack on his patriotism, Robert Stevens winced and grew once more confused. Again he was saved by Major Pitcairn. "I will not maintain that you are all a turbulent people," he said, with a trace of good taste. "You are not all ready, perhaps, to go into the street and lead mobs after the fashion of the one that destroyed Chief Justice Hutchinson's home. But the best of you are little better, sir!" he went on, vehemently. "You preach sedition. You incite the people to mutiny. Sam Adams, sir, is little better than a ruffian; he plots against the Crown. If I were to have my way, I would hang Sam Adams on Boston Common and let the crows pick at him."

"Our debate grows acrimonious," observed Doctor Warren, evenly, before the others had opportunity to retort upon the rudeness of the British major. "We do not desire, I am sure, to engender bitterness by futile discussion between individuals. If any hope of readjustment remains, it will be much better if negotiations are left exclusively to the representatives of the interests concerned."

"Representatives!" cried Major Pitcairn, growing more acrid every moment. "What talk is this of representatives! There are no representatives; the matter lies between the King and his subjects!"

CHRISTOPHER GADSDEN
(*From an etching by Hall*)

"And his subjects, so please you, are represented by their delegates in the Continental Congress, now sitting in Philadelphia," amended Hamilton.

"The Continental Congress is an outrage, an insult to King George!" returned Major Pitcairn, vociferously. "It is unlawful; it is treasonable, it is abominable, and should not be tolerated!"

"Since when has it been unlawful for free Englishmen to meet together for a discussion of their affairs?" asked the young man from Boston, ironically.

"That is another point," rejoined Pitcairn. "This is a union of the colonies,

GEORGE WASHINGTON   (*From the full length portrait by Colonel Trumbull in Yale College*)

and a union of the colonies is beyond the law. It spells treason."

"And has twice been sought by the Lords of Trade," commented the man from Boston.

"But not for offense against the Crown," argued Major Hempstead.

"Ay, Major Hempstead hath hit it," said Pitcairn. "This Continental Congress, as you are pleased to dignify it, is a disorderly and unlawful gathering, brought together to plot and conspire against the Crown. It should not be tolerated; it should be dispersed at the bayonet's point. If they have the audacity to contravene the will of the

King, they should be taken to England in chains and hanged!"

Hamilton and his friend looked at each other, hearing these words. "The hangman is like to have much business on hand then," observed the latter.

"How so?" asked Major Hempstead, amiably, ever ready to promote peace. "What may you mean?"

"Why, only that the Continental Congress has, within a day or two, uttered a declaration of rights, claiming for all America, in the name of all Americans, a free and exclusive power of legislation in their provincial legislatures, where their rights could alone be preserved in all cases of taxation and internal policy."

"How know you that?" cried Doctor Warren, in sudden excitement.

"Is it news to you, then?" rejoined the other. "Friend Hamilton here has this moment told me of it, the word having come to him this evening as he prepared to come to this ball."

"Yes, yes," went on Doctor Warren. "What more word is there?"

"Why, so far, they call for the repeal of eleven acts of Parliament hostile to our liberties, and prepare addresses to be sent to the King, the people of Great Britain, and the inhabitants of British America," answered Hamilton. "Moreover, they bind the several provinces into an association for insuring commercial non-intercourse with Great Britain. So far have they already gone; more will come hereafter."

A silence fell upon them,— an awed hush. It was Major Pitcairn who broke it. His voice was solemn, sober, quiet, now. "By Heaven, gentlemen, when next we meet it is like to be in war!" he said.

"Ay, war!" echoed the young man from Boston.

A stillness fell upon them all; they exchanged neither word nor look, the constraint between them growing tense and tenser.

There was the sound of a lovely, lute-like voice, the swish of silken skirts, and Mistress Robert Stevens stood among them, magnificent in the mature beauty of womanhood. "For shame!" she cried, lightly, with exquisite charm of tone and manner. "Do you conspire to ruin my entertainment? The very heart of it languishes; come, back to your duty!" With that she swept away on the arm of Major Pitcairn, and the party slowly dispersed.

INTERIOR OF SAINT JOHN'S CHURCH, RICHMOND, VIRGINIA, WITH THE PEW MARKED IN WHICH PATRICK HENRY MADE HIS FAMOUS "GIVE ME LIBERTY OR GIVE ME DEATH" SPEECH

CHAPTER III

THE MAN FROM BOSTON

CONCERNING Mistress Robert Stevens, sometime the Widow Osborne, and sometime, as Lieutenant Lucifer would have it, "the devil knows what," much more was told in New York than was known. For a time before her marriage to Robert Stevens, the wealthy banker of the city, the Widow Osborne was a famous beauty and noted belle. Whether she was an adventuress is largely a question of terms. It must not be denied, however, that she had experienced adventures, largely matrimonial, and had progressed by reason of them from obscurity to the headship of one of the most aristocratic and prominent households in New York province.

Aside from those evidences of wisdom that come with adventures, largely matrimonial, there was no sign of her experiences about Mistress Stevens other than a daughter Sophronia, by common consent surnamed Osborne. How a young woman

THE SPIRIT OF '76 (*From a drawing by Darley*)

of twenty-one, as Sophronia was, could be accounted for is a problem that must be left for solution to the ingenuity of women, and the charity of men.

With all of this Mistress Stevens concerned herself little at present; for, despite the purring snarls of half the women in New York, she had come swiftly into her own since her marriage with the rich banker. She had preserved a beauty remarkable in one of her years — she was only forty, at

53

that — which, combined with a knowledge of human nature, a fascinating past, and charm, made her an assured favorite with the men; the women, in sheer self-preservation, were forced to come to her.

Therefore, in spite of many things, and because of many things, the best of the town and province were present at this ball, given by Mistress Stevens to the officers of the British regiments on garrison duty in the town, on this night in October, 1774. The ball-room, stately in its architecture, superb in its appointments, was aglow with light and ahum with revelry. Innumerable candles, fluttering and flickering in the perfumed air from highly wrought brackets on the paneled walls, from elaborate silver candelabra heavy with dangling prisms of cut glass, flooded the room with a soft, yellow light that shone mellow and warm upon beauty and chivalry, on broadcloth and lace, on patch and powder, on slipper and shoon. Over it all rang laughter; through it all floated the music of the

FANEUIL HALL, BOSTON

dance. For why should the heart of youth be sad, even
though war impends?

In an alcove between two pillars of the wall, half hidden
by palms and potted plants from the gay throng on the floor,
a young man, dark, handsome, impetuous in manner, was
talking in low and earnest tone to a beauty, pink and white,
of dancing blue eyes and a wealth of hair that strove still
to be brightly brown, even through the weight of powder
piled upon it. Her blue eyes danced the more as he continued pouring his words into her ear; when he paused at
last, she rippled merrily.

"Tush, boy," she cried, tapping her ebony fan playfully against his full lips. "Cease your pretty prattle, or
you will have me loving you in spite of myself; and that
I should never do, for we are cousins, you know."

"Nay, how are we cousins?" returned the youth, his
face full of the woe of first love unrequited.

"How, child?" made answer the young woman, merrily.
"Why, forsooth, did not my brother, Major Hempstead,
wed with Mistress Margaret Stevens, daughter of Robert
Stevens, and are not you, Master Fontaine Stevens of Vir-
ginia, one of the same great family who are all cousins?
Wherefore am I not your cousin, sirrah?"

"You do but mock me," replied the youth, distressed.
"There is no consanguinity. Nancy! Nancy!" he
went on fervently, striving to grasp her hand, which eluded
him without seeming to. "You drive me mad! Give me
some manner of answer. Let me know at least what my
fate is. It cannot be harder than this uncertainty. I love
you! A thousand times, I love you!"

His voice faltered in his appeal. She looked at him for
an instant with compassion.

"Why, lad, how you talk!" she cried, making her eyes
dance again with mischievous mirth, as being the best

device in the circumstances. "Why, I might be your god-mother for the years that are between us. Now, I warrant me you have not yet turned your teens, and yet you talk of love to her who was one-and-twenty this very week."

"That is nothing!" he cried. "You know it is nothing! You only mean to put me off!"

"Well, then, if that is nothing," she replied, archly, "you must bear in mind that I am of the accursed English race, whom you and your friends choose to hold as enemies!"

"You are more my enemy than you believe," he answered, compressing his lips and fixing his eyes longingly upon hers, "if you taunt me so; for you will strike at all that makes my life worth while. As for being my country's

enemy, if you were a Joan of Arc and came at the head of conquering invaders I would still love you."

"Fie upon you, traitor!" she cried, with pretty playfulness, striking his hand with her fan, "you cannot love me, lad, so much, love

JOHN HANCOCK   (*From the painting by Copley in Faneuil Hall*)

you not honor more," making a quick adaptation of Colonel Lovelace's song.

Fontaine, conscious and chagrined, was struggling for a reply, when the voice of a third person broke upon them. "Zounds, but you have well hidden yourself, Mistress Nancy!" cried the intruder. "Were not my heart a better guide to you than my eyes I should scarce have found you."

Looking over his shoulder, Fontaine saw behind them a slight, dark man, somewhat under

HANCOCK HOUSE, BOSTON (*From a drawing by J. Davis*)

what under thirty, with a slender face, beady black eyes, brows that came close together, thin, tight lips that seemed ever ready to sneer, and a scar on his temple running across his forehead at such an angle as to heighten a certain sinister, cynical expression that pervaded his countenance. Turning toward the young Virginian as he finished, the man eyed him with insolent curiosity. Fontaine, rising to confront him, felt his own gaze falter before that of this shrewd-looking man as he endeavored to return the stare, and grew confused and angry, wondering how long the man had been there unnoticed.

"Master Francis, it would appear that you do not know my cousin, Fontaine Stevens, of Virginia," said Nancy, witnessing the play

At the word cousin, she looked roguishly at the youth,

who colored more deeply. Francis, following the look with
his keen eyes and observing the blush that rose to meet it,
made no sign, further than to compress his lips more tightly
and to bring his brows more closely together.

"I am pleased to meet Master Francis," said Fontaine,
but his answering glare, both at her and at Francis, was
baleful enough, as he turned upon his heel and left with as
scant courtesy as his Virginia breeding permitted.

Pausing for a moment at the edge of the floor, Fontaine
gazed about him, uncertain where to go. The splendor of
the room had a pacific effect on the boy's choler. His
anger ran down as swiftly as it had arisen, and he looked
about for some social diversion, being of strongly gregarious
instincts. It was an interval between dances; a group of
young people, among whom he saw none of the red-coats
that were so odious to him, stood at the opposite side of the
room. He made his way toward them, burying his grief as
he went beneath a smiling countenance.

The group comprised several colonial belles and two
or three young patriots, one of them dressed in the blue
uniform of the Massachusetts militia. With them was
Sophronia Osborne, silent, contained, aloof, watching with
her deep-set eyes and listening covertly to what was said.
Her manner might have been mistaken by an indifferent
observer as diffident. The indifferent observer would have
been wrong; it was rather a cool, deliberate, calculating
reticence; the attitude of a looker-on. At her side was the
youth who had exchanged words with Lieutenant Lucas,
clearly under the restraint of her presence.

Fontaine, bowing slightingly to Sophronia and to him
who stood silently beside her, joined them and soon fell into
small talk. He had not been long among them when the
strains of Sir Roger de Coverley floated across the ball-room,
and the group scattered to join in the dance. Fontaine,

THE OLD STATE HOUSE, BOSTON, MASSACHUSETTS. THE ROSETTE MARKS
THE SPOT WHERE THE BOSTON MASSACRE OCCURRED, MARCH 5, 1770

reminded of his late partner, was not in the whim to take
another at once, and remained behind with the Massachusetts
militia-man, who likewise was not in sportive humor. Close
to them, unnoticed, Sophronia and her companion still
stood, silent, save for a chance sentence now and then
between them.

"'T is enough to make one's blood boil over to be
bandied and bullied by these jackanapes in scarlet as I
have been this evening," said the militia-man, angrily,
when the dancers had gone, addressing himself to Fontaine,
to the exclusion of the other two standing near them. "Because it suits me to wear my uniform they scoff at and insult
me till I can bear it no longer. 'T is a wonder that the wife
of an American would tolerate them in her house, much
less give a ball in their honor at such a time. For my part,
I incline toward the whispers that say she has Tory leanings."

Sophronia, unobserved, smiled blandly at this charge
against her mother. Fontaine, with southern chivalry
and family loyalty, forebore to discuss the evidence against
her; a circumstance indicating how closely his own views
coincided with those of his companion.

"If these blustering British officers reflect the temper of
England, it means war," he said, avoiding the other point.

As he spoke, Francis passed with Nancy Hempstead
on his arm. "And if this blooming British maiden reflects
the beauty of England, it means surrender; what say you,
Monsieur Fontaine Stevens of Virginia?" he called, tauntingly, over his shoulder, as they swept past.

Fontaine, without words for an answer, glared after
them. He was too angry to observe the look that Nancy
fixed upon the youth with Sophronia; the look, half surprised, of admiration and interest; the look of one who
sees more than she thought ever to see in a man. Not so
Sophronia. Watching the scene without any appearance of

watching, she saw the expression on the face of the English girl; and through half-shut lids, she beheld the countenance of the man beside her.   In his eyes was a trace of surprise too, and the light of one who glimpses a new universe; of one to whom, for the first time, one woman stands forth from all other women, solitary, alone, individualized.   All

this Sophronia saw, and noted well.

"Who is that insolent fellow?" demanded Fontaine, when he could speak.

"An impudent Tory of the town, well known to be a rogue," returned the other.

"I hope I may meet with him in field of battle," quoth Fontaine, direfully.

"You are little likely to," said his friend, "for he is one of these back-handed rascals

GEORGE III OF ENGLAND   (*From the painting by Sir Joshua Reynolds*)

that ever work in the dark. He is in repute of being much of a spy upon the Americans hereabout, who heartily detest him.   Bah!" went on the militia-man, "my soul is sick with it all!   What say you to a glass of punch in the room below?"

Fontaine said nothing; for answer he took the other's arm, and was about to lead the way, when the militia-man, catching sight of the youth with Sophronia, paused.   "Will you come?" he said; in his tone there was more of a civility toward one who was entitled to it than cordiality.   Whether the other failed to detect the perfunctory nature of the invitation, or whether he chose to take the opportunity to escape his companion, should not, as a matter of gallantry, be told.   It is only needful to record that he went.

The three of them, weaving among the dancers, made their way to the dining-room. Francis, having resigned Nancy to the partner that succeeded him, was already there, drinking with Lieutenant Lucas. Observing the three approaching, he did not wait until they were close, but called out to them, across the room.

"What, Culver," he laughed, addressing the one who wore uniform, "are you still in your rebel rig? I should have thought that you were taught better taste ere this."

"It seems an evil taste enough that leads you to flout the uniform of the cause you yourself should be openly espousing!" cried Fontaine, taking the retort upon himself, hot with memories. "For my part, I cannot see that you are better than a traitor, and an enemy to your country."

"How now?" rejoined Francis, turning to him in mock surprise. "Do you speak of traitors? 'T was not a quarter of an hour since that I heard you offer unconditional surrender to one of the enemy. Belike, if I espoused a cause, I would be

HEADQUARTERS OF THE BRITISH GENERALS, 1775-76, IN BOSTON

more true to it." He said it with a flippant unconcern that made his scorn more biting.

Fontaine was beside himself. "My friend, Captain Culver, will wait upon such friend as you may select," he snapped, amateurishly, trembling with the excitement of his first affair of honor.

Francis gazed quizzically upon his youthful face. "I shall trouble no friend of mine in the matter," he purred, with lids wrinkling in amusement. "I shall choose the place and weapons at once. I will fight you to the death to-morrow, boy, after your daily slumber; and let the weapons be paper pellets. As for the place, none suits my fancy better than the Bowling Green."

"Nay, you may better that," interposed Lieutenant Lucas, laughing a maudlin laugh. " 'T would be well were you to fight him with a laurel switch, such as my mother used on me when I was a naughty boy."

"If it be true that your legs have known the laurel,

THE BOSTON TEA PARTY (*From the painting in the Massachusetts State Capitol by Robert Reid*)

which, from your behavior, I much doubt, 't is like you shall have no better knowledge of it," retorted he who had fenced with him before. His words, deliberate and quiet, were wholly unprovoked.

Lucas, who had not yet noted the third member of the party of Americans, turned on him with the accumulated rage of their previous encounter.

"An you are not the utter cur your words would make you seem," he cried, "you shall soon have opportunity to taste my valor. If there is a friend of yours who will undertake the mission, doubtless he can find Master Francis at his leisure. I wish you a very good evening."

Bowing with elaborate politeness, he turned and paced toward the door, followed presently by Francis, who paused only long enough to draw a card from his

OLD SOUTH CHURCH, BOSTON (*From an early engraving*)

packet, which he pressed into the hand of Fontaine, with a supercilious leer. Fontaine, whose demeanor toward the Boston man had hitherto been indifferent to the verge of rudeness, looked at him with surprised approval. With the look went a question.

"Do you desire that I should act for you?" he asked.

"It is not needful that any one should act."

"You mean that you will not meet this fellow?" incredulously.

John nodded affirmation.

"That you will brook his insults? That you will make no attempt to salve your honor?" Incredulity was making way for disgust, for contempt.

John Stevens seemed on the point of speaking, of explaining, but refrained, manifestly with an effort. For a space there was heavy silence; presently, with only a nod of farewell, John left the room.

Fontaine watched him through the door. "Is it thus you of Massachusetts fight your battles?" he sneered, turning to help himself to a glass of punch.

To the insinuation the militia-man vouchsafed no reply, other than to fill a glass of punch and drink with Fontaine, in silence.

VIEW OF BOSTON IN 1774, FROM DORCHESTER HEIGHTS

CHAPTER IV

A QUESTION OF COURAGE

THE last reveler had scarcely left the scene of the night's ball, and the dull October day was little more than a promise low in the east, when John Stevens rode from among the houses of New York City and turned into the road that led through Harlem, and so into northern New York, or, by a turn, into Connecticut.

His heart lay heavy within him as he rode along through the grey dusk. He could not free his thoughts from the episode of the preceding evening. He could not avoid reflecting what ill opinion those familiar with the circumstances would have of his valor, a consideration that would move any man of proper pride and sensitive honor.

But then . . . . that was a part of the sacrifice. Since

FREDERICK LORD NORTH (*From the portrait by Romney*)

the night he had borne his father home from the fatal scene at the custom house, four years before, he had made many sacrifices in the cause of the liberty of the people, and was ready to make more. If it served the cause for him to bear a message from Joseph Warren to the committee of

67

WARREN'S ORATION

safety in Boston; if it served best that he should set out with it on this one morning, of all mornings, he should rather be thankfully glad of his office than otherwise. He was truly grateful for one circumstance, at least. He consoled himself that he had known his errand soon enough on the night before to avoid involving himself in any engagement he could not fulfil.

Events since that fateful night in March had grown big, and John Stevens had grown with them. Bringing back his father to die in their little cottage on the crooked lane in Boston, he became in that hour the man he and his mother had lost. His labor provided them both with their daily needs; his quickly maturing mind was their counselor in their small affairs.

What time he had from the necessity to provide he spent in laboring for the cause of liberty. Always he had been heart and soul a lover of the principles so firmly advanced by the New England leaders; now he became in body one of the more active workers. Youth that he was, already he had been accorded more than one task of honor and trust; already he was close to the leaders themselves. He was one of the party of Sons of Liberty to throw the tea into Boston Harbor only the year before; he was a member of the committee of correspondence for Boston; and now he was a messenger between Doctor Warren and John Hancock, on business both important and intimate.

It is necessary to go back. Boston was in duress. She

had incurred the King's displeasure anew. Indeed, she had never ceased to call it down upon herself. After the massacre, as the people called it, there was a lull. The inhabitants, with heroic self-control, refrained from violence against the soldiers. Sam Adams wrought upon Governor Hutchinson to the end that the soldiers were removed to the Castle, in the harbor. Captain Preston and the privates were tried. John Adams and Josiah Quincy defended them, with the approval of the more sober citizens. Two of the soldiers were convicted of manslaughter, but were subsequently pardoned.

The next crisis had been in 1772, when the King decreed, through his subservient Parliament, that all judges, who were appointed by the Crown, should receive their pay from the same source, instead of from the provincial legislatures. It left them beyond the control of the people, direct or indirect.

Samuel Adams arose to the occasion. He organized committees in the neighboring towns, to correspond with each other, and to consult concerning the best methods of resistance; for they were bound to resist. The system grew, until in time there were committees of correspondence in all the large cities of all the colonies. It was the beginning of mutuality; the first dawn-break of union.

Then followed the trouble over tea. Lord North repealed all the impost taxes excepting those upon tea. But the people would not permit tea to be brought to America. On the other hand, the ministry, constantly beset by the complaints of merchants, determined that the Americans should receive it. To this end, vessels were loaded and sent

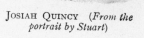

JOSIAH QUINCY (*From the portrait by Stuart*)

to the several colonies, consigned to certain agents. The consignees in Charlestown, Philadelphia, and New York, resigned under pressure. But those in Boston refused to do so. That is what brought the first great climax of the struggle to the city that had been the center of disturbance from the beginning.

When the tea arrived, in three vessels, the situation was taken in hand by a series of town meetings, held in the Old South meeting-house. A watch was set upon the vessels to prevent the landing of the tea, while efforts were making to have it returned to England. Every legal means failed; the crisis came. Seven thousand people were gathered in and about the Old South Church. Samuel Adams came among them, returning from his last futile effort, — an appeal to Governor Hutchinson. "This meeting can do nothing more to save the country," he said solemnly.

An awed hush fell upon the assembly. They knew, those who were there, that the law had failed them in their fight for their rights. What should be their course now?

As they questioned each other, the Mohawk war-whoop sounded outside the door, and a band of fifty men, dressed as Indian warriors, filed past the entrance. Swiftly out-stripping the crowd that followed, they ran to Griffin's wharf, where the ships lay. Before 9 o'clock the 342 chests on the three vessels were cut open and the tea thrown into the water. Under the brilliant moon there was no sound as the work progressed, save the click of the hatchets and the plash of the tea as it fell into the bay.

England was furious when she heard. Boston must be made to pay for her insolent insubordination. To that end the regulating act, comprising five laws, was passed by Parliament. By the first, the port of the town was closed until the East India company, whose tea had been thrown into the harbor, should be indemnified. Marblehead was made the port of entry. By the second act, the charter of Massachusetts was annulled; by the third, provision was made that any soldier, magistrate, or revenue officer indicted for murder, might be tried in England; by the fourth, all legal obstacles to quartering troops in Boston were obliterated; by the fifth, as an indirect blow, territory claimed by Massachusetts as far west as the Ohio was given to Canada, and the Catholic religion was permitted there. Many minor matters, all oppressive to the colony, were involved in the several laws. All were to take effect June 1, 1774.

THE OLD SOUTH CHURCH, BOSTON

They did take effect, constructively, on that day. General Gage, with four regiments, arrived in Boston in April, 1774, to see that they should. But from that day forth, Massachusetts never again acknowledged the sovereignty of Great Britain. The regulating act was defied; councilors appointed by the King were coerced into resigning; courts held by the royal judges were prevented from transacting business; town meetings, against which Gage issued a manifesto, were more fully attended than ever; 20,000 armed men assembled in forty-eight hours following an alarm that the soldiers had fired upon citizens; the militia stood ready: the minute-men were prepared to answer liberty's call at a moment's notice; everywhere was there a determined spirit of defiance and resistance. Gage had said that with four regiments he could subdue the show of rebellion; now his four regiments were almost in terror in the midst of the storm they had provoked. From without came support and assistance. The several colonies regarded Boston as suffering in the common cause; the rancor that had been shown against her might at any time be turned to blast their own rights; provisions and supplies came in abundance; Marblehead, officially appointed a port of entry, instead of taking advantage of the opportunity to get business from her rival, opened her warehouses to the Boston merchants. Salem did the same.

GENERAL THOMAS GAGE

Then came the Continental Congress, first proposed by the Sons of Liberty, in New York. Samuel Adams, locking the doors of the room in Salem where the Massachusetts Assembly had convened, introduced resolutions calling the Congress to meet at Philadelphia in September; while the governor's secretary roared at the door with a writ dissolving the assembly, the resolutions were passed, and the first decisive step toward the United States of America had been taken.

September 6, five days after the Congress convened, a convention of the towns of Suffolk County passed resolutions, drawn up by Doctor Warren, declaring that a king who violates the rights of his subjects forfeits their allegiance,

that the regulating act was null and void; that all officers
appointed under it should resign; directing the tax collectors
to refuse to pay over money to Gage; advising the towns to
choose their own militia officers; and threatening the governor that any political arrests would be met by the seizure
of King's officers as hostages. It was an announcement of
rebellion. When the resolutions were enthusiastically adopted by the Continental Congress, with assurances that the colonies would sustain Massachusetts, even by force, those
glorious events were set in train which resulted in the formation of the Union
and the triumph of
republican ideas in
America.

GEORGE GRENVILLE (*After the portrait by T. Phillips*)

All along the way
as he rode to Boston
John found the feel-
ing of the people
wrought to a high
pitch. On the one
hand were the patri-
ots, as they called
themselves, sustain-
ing the action of the
Continental Con-
gress, promising sup-
port to Boston in her
fight, and talking
high. On the other
hand were the loyal-
ists, whom the others contemptuously called Tories, maintaining the King's position.

Militia and companies of minute-men he found on every
green and common, training for war. Whole towns turned

out to greet him as he passed through the country-side; he was one newly come from New York with word of the Congress; he was the friend of Hancock and Adams, of Warren and Otis. All along the way was a will to fight, when the time came. Even his ardent heart could have desired no more.

Coming to Boston at last, he found heavy stress there. The Assembly of Massachusetts, in disregard of Gage's orders, had met at Salem on September 8 and organized themselves into a provincial congress, with Hancock as president. Adjourning to Concord, it was in the old church there that those stirring speeches were made by Hancock, Adams, and other patriots which did so much to hasten the Revolution. Even when he reached Salem, going there from Boston, they were forming a committee of safety, with Doctor Warren at its head, for the purpose of gathering arms and munitions, and preparing to resist England by force, if necessary. Of this committee he was made one.

It was high time. Boston was cut off from the water by the port bill. Not so much as a scow of hay from the Medway could discharge at her docks. Business was at a standstill. Grass grew between the cobbles in the pavements. There was hardly food enough in the town to sustain life; what there was had to be brought on carts from a distance across the Neck. Some came all the way from Connecticut.

More than that, soldiers were in the streets again, more insolent than they had been at first, and stronger. General Gage commanded, both as military and civil officer. There was constant friction; the situation was surcharged with electricity.

Throughout the winter the people of Massachusetts remained passive, ready to fight, but well schooled in the doctrine that the first blow must come from England. But though they made no open and forceful resistance, they

JAMES OTIS MAKING HIS FAMOUS SPEECH AGAINST THE WRITS OF ASSISTANCE (*From the painting by Robert Reid in the State House, Boston*)

utterly ignored the authority of Great Britain, giving no heed to the administration of Gage or the attempted enforcement of the provisions of the regulating act.

March 5 came, the anniversary of the massacre; a day held in honor for its associations. Following the custom, a meeting was held in Old South Church to commemorate the death of Boston citizens at the hands of British soldiery. Word had gone forth from British headquarters that he who addressed the meeting did so at peril of his life. Doctor Warren, hearing the threat, begged to be permitted the honor. It was accorded him. The church was so crowded that he was obliged to reach the pulpit through a window, by means of a ladder. Hancock and Adams, against whom threats of arrest for treason had been made,

JOHN ADAMS (*From the painting by Gilbert Stuart*)

were present, calmly, deliberately defiant. The meeting itself was a challenge of Gage's proclamation against town meetings; he might have broken it up consistently with his own view of the case. But he forebore; the audience was too serenely passive to be safely tampered with.

Out Concord way there dwelt one Ezra Stevens, of the same family whose lines of kinship now lay like a web over the colonies. A farmer's lad he was, tall, awkward, bashful, in the midst of his teens. And minute-man he was, for all his youth, having long arms and stalwart legs, and a heart of fire beneath his homespun shirt. On a day in mid-April, Ezra drove a cart into Boston, laden with food for the citizens, who were cut off from the water by the port bill; at the tail of the cart were two fat oxen, the elder Stevens's contribution to liberty.

THE OLD CONCORD CHURCH, WHERE THE FIRST PROVINCIAL CONGRESS WAS HELD, HANCOCK PRESIDING

Having disposed of his provender, which, be it understood, was without money and without price, young Ezra, with many flutterings of the heart, betook himself to the house of Lawrence Averill, a man of consequence in the community, and a kinsman of the Stevens family, being the grandson of Elmer Stevens of Virginia and the nephew of Robert Stevens of New York. It was not Master Averill's importance in the town that fluttered Ezra's heart, though that in itself might well have been sufficient. It was the thought of Catherine Averill that twitched him,—Catherine Averill, whose little, dark, oval face, whose ruddy lips, whose raven curls, whose night-black eyes had turned his heart to a warm, quivering throb since the day when they first played together as children, on a visit between their cousin parents.

Coming at last to the house, which stood upon a hill over-looking the harbor and Charlestown beyond, Ezra would have taken a turn or two to revive his courage had he not perceived Catherine herself standing in a window, and been perceived of her. In two moments more he stood within the drawing-room.

But if he had been tremulous and ill at ease before, his embarrassment now was utterly blasting. For Catherine was not alone. With her in the room was another maiden, older, sedate, who looked at him out of amused blue eyes, reading his secret, and who shook a bright brown head of hair at him when the young lass introduced her as Mistress Nancy Hempstead.

As though that were not enough, there was also in the room a dashing young British officer — elegant, insolent, scornful. At him Ezra looked with instant hate and dis-trust, subordinated by awe of his fine airs; for his boyish fancy pictured him as a rival, formidable, insufferable.

"My brother, Lieutenant Lucas Hempstead, Master Ezra Stevens, of Concord," rippled Nancy Hempstead, when Catherine hesitated.

"Another Stevens, say you?" returned Lieutenant Lu-cas, lightly eying the lad with a leer and a sneer. "Ecad, they are like to be enough of them hereabouts, for it is my experience of them that they take sufficiently good care of themselves never to come into any danger.

"I had not thought to mention it; until now it has slipped my mind," went on the lieutenant, in reply to his sister's look, taking a pinch of snuff at the same time, with elabo-rate elbow. "I make no doubt you are a cousin of one

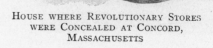

HOUSE WHERE REVOLUTIONARY STORES
WERE CONCEALED AT CONCORD,
MASSACHUSETTS

John Stevens, of Boston?" He interrupted himself, turning to address the lad. "You are about of a limb," eying the other whimsically, to his eminent annoyance.

Rambling on, he ceased, as though it was not worth while following the subject. He was recalled to it by the tense voice of Catherine, begging him to go on.

"Ah, to be sure; I had quite forgot," he said, with a show of being reminded. "I was about to explain to my sister that once upon a time I had arranged an affair of honor with this same John Stevens,— don't scold, Nancy, I beg of you, do not scold, — which he had the good discretion to avoid. The matter fell out by night; the next day not so much as a scrap of paper was left to show which way he had gone. I had quite forgot. Tell me, boy, is your cousin quite well? Is he here? Ecad, I hope I shall not encounter his wrath!" He shuddered with mock terror, bursting out at last into a languid laugh.

Ezra could endure no more. He forgot Catherine, he forgot the English girl, this man's sister, who had listened to her brother with manifest annoyance; the man himself, supercilious, insulting, had no more terror for him. He thought only of his cousin John, his knight, his hero, his demigod! On his quavering voice there arose words, hot, burning, resentful, fearless; young America spoke to young England in the tone and temper that was to echo across the land for seven long and weary years; almost eloquent he was, in his boyish way. For a space he stormed at the British lieutenant, defending his blood, and the bravery of his cousin; threatening, defying, scornful, angry. As abruptly as he had begun, he ended, suddenly left

THE MINUTE-MAN, CONCORD, MASSACHUSETTS
(By Daniel C. French)

conscious when his wrath spent its first force. Blushing, stammering something to Catherine, he turned swiftly upon his heel and departed, the girl following him in a tumult of excitement.

"Bless my body and soul!" cried Lieutenant Lucas, when the two had gone. "Bless my body and soul! I am likely to find amusement in Boston, after all!"

Nancy Hempstead, gazing upon the retreating figure of the youth as he passed up the street, made no answer, pondering many things concerning young men of America.

KING HOOPER HOUSE, DANVERS, MASSACHUSETTS, GENERAL GAGE'S HEAD-
QUARTERS

CHAPTER V

A SON OF LIBERTY

TWILIGHT shadows, creeping over the town of Boston on the evening of April 18, 1775, stole into a sparsely furnished room in the heart of the city and gathered about the face of the woman who lay bedridden there. Many years had spent themselves upon her; the bitter struggle to live, of which the room was eloquent, sorrow, and bodily pain had left their marks. Her thin hair, smoothed across her brow, was past white, and turning yellow with extremity of age; her face was meager and pale, her cheeks sunken. In her wasted hand, resting on the counterpane, she held her Bible, a finger between the leaves. She had been reading until the light failed. Now her eyes were closed; she was alone, and there was no one to set a light for her. The barest necessities of life were about her — nothing more, except a row of hooks on which hung a blue uniform, a sword, a brace of pistols, and a powder flask.

PAUL REVERE   (*From the portrait by Stuart*)

Lying there silent, solitary, with shut eyes, with finger

marking the place where she had ceased reading, she heard the sound of footsteps on the flags without the door. The latch rattled; the door creaked, opening; in the square of grey light which it framed from the twilight stood the silhouette of a man, spacious, young, graceful. Her eyes, opened now, brightened at the sight.

"Ah, John, you have come at last," she said, caressingly. "I had grave fears lest something had befallen you."

"Nay, mother," made answer the man, bending to kiss her with tender affection; "is it not grievous enough that I must leave you for so long, without your adding that to my burden?" It was a selfish appeal; the son of this woman knew none other would reach her.

"Forgive the heart of a mother, lad," said the woman; "I will try to be braver."

"'T will not be many days now ere the twilights lengthen, so that you will not be left in such gloom," the young man went on, leaving the topic as easily as he might.

He struck a

THE OLD NORTH CHURCH, BOSTON

light as he talked, and brought the candle to the sewing
stand, at the head of the bed, shielding the flame with
his hand until it burned steadily. She looked eagerly at
his face with the glow of the lighted candle upon it; her
mother's eye caught an expression in it that set her staring.
It was not a handsome face; it was too ruggedly strong
for that. The mouth was large and firm; the chin was
heavy, thrusting forward — the chin of one not easily to
be put aside. The nose was long and prominent, the
head high and broad, the eyes steely blue, with the light in
them of high purpose, almost of inspired enthusiasm. In
them, too, was the light of deep grief, and trouble. This
it was that caught her attention.

"There is news, John!" she whispered, clutching at
his arm, studying his features with keen scrutiny.

"News!" he returned, quickly. "Have you heard
news?" He was without guile; it was easy to see that he
sought to put
her off. Other
eyes than a
mother's
would have
perceived so
much.

PARSON CLARK'S HOUSE AT LEXINGTON, WHERE HANCOCK
AND ADAMS WERE ROUSED BY PAUL REVERE
THE NIGHT BEFORE THE FIGHT

"Nay, son
how should I
hear aught?
But I know
by your face
that there is
something afoot. What new trouble has arisen?"

He looked swiftly at her, to see how much she might have
guessed. "'T is enough to make one sober, having these
red-coated soldiers under foot from dawn till night," he said,

still striving to put her off. "These are heavy times, mother, and we cannot tell what is ahead of us."

"No one has come to harm? No news from England? They have not made good their threat to arrest Adams and Doctor Warren?" She went through the questions swiftly.

"No, mother," he said, with hesitation, turning away.

"John," she called after him, before he had crossed the room, "I know that you do it in the kindness of your heart, but you must not hide these things from your mother, boy. Because my body is weak you must not think that my soul is not strong. 'T is my fight as well as yours, son, and 't is not right that you should keep me from doing my part."

He returned to the side of the bed and took her hand. "Well, then, mother, you have fairly guessed it," he said, frankly. "I would not have alarmed you; but the order has gone forth to take Samuel Adams and John Hancock, who are at Lexington, and send them to England to stand trial as traitors. The regulars are planning to leave Boston to-night and to march out to-morrow morning to capture them — if they can —" he interjected the provision with deep significance in both tone and look "and perchance they will destroy the stores of powder and shot that the Sons of Liberty have gathered at Concord, having learned through some traitor that they were there."

"What are the plans? What will be done to prevent it?"

For answer he turned to the inner room, and pointed his hand at the sword hanging there.

"Must you go?" she asked, bravely.

A tremor ran through his great frame. He looked at her pityingly. "Would you have me stay?" His voice was low. He spoke with terrible earnestness.

"God bless you, John, I would have you lying dead at my feet first!" she cried, fervently, tears of pride and of grief starting in her eyes.

He brushed his hand across his cheeks and looked again at the sword in the other room before he spoke. "Cousin Averill will take care of you," he said, a quaver in his voice. "He was with us; he will see that you come to no want if I should not return."

"Tut!" she said, waving away the thought. "Never mind me, son; that is my part of the fight. Tell me, what will be done?" Their Puritan stock stood them in good stead in this hour of trial.

"The Sons of Liberty are watching the regulars," he answered, quietly. "When they leave Boston a lantern is to be hung in the belfry of the North meeting-house for a sign, one lantern if the regulars march across the Neck, and two if they go by boat to Charlestown. Paul Revere and William Dawes will ride through the countryside by Roxbury to give the alarm and warn Adams and Hancock. The minute-men will muster; we have long expected something of this sort.

PAUL REVERE'S HOUSE IN BOSTON

"Yes," he went on, standing erect, his voice rising and his face glowing with the vigor of his emotions, "we shall be ready for them. The magnificent day is at hand! It will be war,— glorious war for our rights. We have waited long for them to strike the first blow, and now the hour has

come. Let the regulars go forth; we shall be ready for them
with a baptism of fire and blood!"

His face was afire with high devotion; his voice rang
loud and clear in the room. His mother, listening with
bated breath and kindled eye, grasped the edge of the bed
in the intensity of her response.

"Ah!" she murmured, "would that I had a score of
such sons to give to such a cause!"

The fervor of his patriotic passion still burned in his eye,
his arms were still upraised in gesture, when the latch rattled,
and the door swung wide. Out of the darkness there stepped
into the light of the candle, fluttering in the draught of the
open door, Catherine Averill and another, a young woman.
They stood near the door, the two who had entered, forgetting to close it, looking at John Stevens, erect, beautiful,
magnificent in the emotion that welled within him. At
sight of the one with Catherine, barely discernible in the
wavering light of the blown taper, the heart of the young
patriot fell into turmoil; for there he saw her whom he had
glimpsed at the ball in New York the autumn before; and
he stood dumb, like one overcome by a vision, seeing too
much.

In the eyes of Catherine Averill, as they still stood staring,
there was utter devotion, hero worship, adoration. In the
eyes of her companion there was nothing; but in her thoughts
there was much. This, then, was John Stevens; he whose
memory had haunted her since that
night six months before; whose
face had looked down to her from
clouds; in whom she had had a
vision of all mankind. This
was the one whom she had
prayed, with a blush upon
her cheeks, that she might

PAUL REVERE'S HOUSE IN WATERTOWN,
MASSACHUSETTS. HERE THE FIRST
CONTINENTAL NOTES WERE
PRINTED BY REVERE

see again. And this, too, was the one who had fled from meeting her brother! She found her heart sinking with disappointment at the thought that this man had failed the test of personal courage.

"We intrude?" she ventured, at last, taking her gaze from the son to glance at the bedridden mother. "I, at least, intrude. I did but come with Catherine to accompany her through the streets on an errand. I will await her without."

"Nay, nay," cried the woman on the bed; "that you shall not do. 'T is only an old woman and her son you find; you are fully welcome. John, lad, can you not place a chair for — our visitor?" She hesitated for a moment as a sign to Catherine that she had not made them known to each other, but the child was much too preoccupied to observe.

Not so Nancy; glancing first at her young companion, and seeing that Catherine gave no heed, she turned with a smile upon the bedridden woman; a smile friendly, inspiring confidence, winning. "I am Nancy Hempstead," she said, simply, "an English girl."

John Stevens stopped midway in bringing a chair; stopped and stared abruptly at her, when he heard the name. In his face was a look of injury, of resentment, of anger, as though she had offered him a deliberate affront in bearing that name, and in being English; a look of suspicion, almost of dislike; and, withal, a trace of disappointment. But neither about his mouth nor in the depths of his steel-blue eyes did she find any lack of courage.

"She came here with her brothers, Major and Lieutenant Hempstead," explained Catherine, feeling the feminine necessity to resolve the unusual. "Her brother, Major Hempstead, married Margaret Stevens, daughter of Robert Stevens, of New York, you know."

THE OLD NORTH BRIDGE, CONCORD, MASSACHUSETTS

The girl paused awkwardly. A constrained silence fell upon them; they looked askance, none being wishful to behold the face of another. It was the mother who saved the moment. She reached forth her withered hand and drew that of Nancy Hempstead toward her. "I like your face, girl," she said, honestly. "Sit; for are not we English too?"

Nancy, with native simplicity, carried the withered hand to her lips, and took the chair John had brought her. The man, with face of iron, ignored her. "Come, child, what have you in the basket?" he asked Catherine, gently, extending a hand to relieve her of it.

"Some bits of chicken, and some bread," replied the girl, looking wistfully into the set face of the man, understanding nothing. "Mother thought Aunt Helen would be alone to-night. Are you going away, John?" with deep solicitude.

"My duties are many," he returned, taking the basket toward the hearth. "I can never know when I shall be forced to be away for a day, or a week." His voice fell into sadness; that the child perceived, with dread and awe.

He knelt by the side of the hearth, kindling a fire; Catherine beside him silent, thoughtful, watching him wistfully. By the bed sat the English girl, talking in low tones of many things with the striken woman, casting a glance now and then toward the two by the fireplace.

"John!" Catherine whispered, her voice tense with excitement; "do you know — her brother?" She could scarce speak the words. "Were you going to fight him, once?"

"How know you that?" He turned upon her with sudden surprise; she, being a child, with worship for him, was altogether frightened, believing him angry.

"He — he told us!"

"Us did he tell?" rejoined John, with a grim accent.

Her heart cried out a question. Why? Why? Why had he not fought? Why? There was a reason; she must know it. She must know it, or perish. For her life she could not ask him.

"May I not help you?" The voice of Nancy, standing close behind them, came into their silence. "Shall I brew a dish of tea, Master Stevens? I am famous for my tea." She said it with a desire she did not conceal from him, of establishing a truce between them. She could with difficulty have found words more ill advised.

Swiftly, with lightning grace, the man stood to his full height before her; not until now had she known how tall, how magnificently tall he was, so perfect were his proportions. His eyes were cold and hard as they fixed hers; his jaws set; his nostrils quivered. "Tea!" he said, at last, with manifest restraint. "There is no tea in Boston, nor in all the colonies!"

"No tea!" cried the English girl, missing his meaning, and speaking lightly, in her confusion before his ominous look. "Why, however do you live without tea?"

"We shall better live without tea than without our liberty," rejoined the man, still repressed, "and if it comes to that, we shall better die without it, than to surrender our rights in the purchase of it."

Instantly the girl knew; she had touched a wound; she had blundered. "I had forgot," she stammered, blankly.

"Perchance it is easily forgotten on your side the sea," answered the man.

Catherine looked timidly from one to the other, hoping for peace between them. The aged mother leaned across the bed's edge, anxious — too anxious to find voice. On the fire, a bit of chicken sputtered unheeded in the pan.

Suddenly, as the English girl met the gaze of the steel-blue eyes, her confusion and chagrin fell from her; she

answered him firmly, boldly, word for word, look for look.
"It is not just, it is not fair, that you make me suffer the
resentment and prejudice you bear against my people,"
she said, with a slight flush of excitement in her cheeks.
"You condemn me without trial. You have many warm

PAUL REVERE'S RIDE (*From the painting by Robert Reid in the State House.
Boston*)

friends in England. Do you not know that William Pitt,
Lord Chatham, arose from a sick bed to plead your cause
when Grenville imposed the tax you speak of? I had
not understood the significance of it until you opened my
eyes to-night. Do you not know that the eloquence of
Burke was enlisted in your behalf? Have you not heard
that Lord Hillsborough, Lord Rockingham, Lord Beau-
champ, the duke of Grafton, the duke of Richmond, have

EDMUND BURKE (*From the engraving by J. Chapman*)

taken your fight into Parliament? Are you ignorant of what Conway and Barré have sought to do for you? There are many of the English people who have warm sympathy for you."

She spoke so low in her earnestness that the mother on her bed could not catch the words, though the room was small and she endeavored to hear. The soft violet eyes of Catherine fluttered from one to the other as Nancy spoke. The man listened, impressed with her sincerity.

"Is not a brother of yours major of the troops who are sent here to destroy our liberty?" he said, after a pause. "And is not another brother of yours, Lieutenant Hempstead, one of the British officers who endeavored to break up the meeting that we held on March fifth last in the South Church to commemorate the anniversary of the Boston Massacre? It was he, if I mistake not, who boasted that any one who spoke to us that day did so on peril of his life; it was he, I know, who most flagrantly and wantonly insulted the brave Doctor Warren because he dared to address an assemblage of law-abiding citizens gathered in their place of worship to honor their dead."

The mother, hearing her son's words, listened breathlessly for the reply.

"Massacre, do you call it?" returned the girl, driven into defense in spite of her wish to be friendly. "'T was instead a disgraceful riot, I take it, in which the soldiers fought for their lives against an unruly mob!"

John drew himself up, fixing her with his eyes, which

narrowed to cold points. "My father was one of those in the unruly mob who were slain in the riot," he said ironically, an ominous ring in his voice.

The girl recoiled as though he had struck her, turning white and clasping her hands. "I did not know! I did not know!" Her voice was half a moan, as she turned piteously toward the mother.

"Indeed, you did not know," broke in the aged woman from her bed. "We had long endured the intolerable conduct of the soldiers, and when a brutal sentinel knocked down a barber's boy for his boyish jesting, it was more than human flesh could stand. The soldiers had long insulted and abused us; that was too much. But there was no riot; there were anger and protests, and some throwing of snowballs, but our citizens held their temper better than you can know. But the soldiers fired — and they brought my husband home to die in my arms!"

She covered her face in her hands and turned her head on the pillow. John, hastening to the side of the bed, comforted her with word and caress. Catherine, in tears, turned to the hearth and bent over the warming food. Nancy, passing slowly to the chair where she had left her shawl, threw it about her shoulders.

"I am sorry," she said, simply. "I did not know. I had never stopped to think that those who were killed by the soldiers had wives — and sons — at home. I am learning much." There was silence. "I am sorry that my brothers' soldier-duty brought them here." There was a cry in her voice, a cry for their mercy. "I

THE OLD BELFRY AT LEXINGTON,
FROM WHICH REVERE RANG
THE ALARM

am sorry I came with them. I did not know. I have no one left to me but them, and so I came. I hope you can learn to forgive me, and them. It was not I who brought them. They had no choice but to come."

The woman on the bed, recovering her composure, turned toward the girl. in whose voice was genuine grief. "Nay. do not go." she said, seeing that Nancy was about to leave.

The girl looked at John, who stood peering through the window. Turning, he met her gaze. "We have blundered, both," he said, a softness creeping slowly into his eyes. "Will you not stay?"

"I want to stay," she answered; "I want to understand these things better. I hear only our side. It is too hard for us to realize that you are guided by a sincere purpose, that you have honest convictions. We only hear you abused and vilified." She looked at John still, as though she saw in him a new truth, and marveled at it.

His mother, who had watched him with anxious interest while he looked through the window into the night, breathed with relief when he returned to the hearth, without further word to Nancy.

"We have endured much, and my son feels strongly," she said to the girl, with a woman's instinct to apologize for her men.

"I admire him for it," Nancy reassured her. Her following glance showed how much.

At the fire Catherine knelt over the supper she had brought for her aunt. "I am making it ready, John, dear," she said, tenderly, relieved in

TABLET MARKING THE SPOT WHERE REVERE WAS CAPTURED

a measure of the distress and anxiety that had held her during the scene that had just closed. She looked wistfully up into his rugged face. The expression of admiration in her eyes was intensified and deepened. He did not see the look. He did not have a word for her as he turned and strode back across the room to where Nancy had resumed her seat by his mother.

"I know how they talk," he said, abruptly taking up the last words she had said to him. "I know how they feel toward us. It is because they know they have wronged us. They call us ruffians and rogues, rebels and rioters, trying to make themselves believe they have justification." He spoke half to himself, fervently, full of thought. Nancy was glad that he had changed his pronoun in speaking of the English.

"If these things were better understood, think you not there would be hope of adjustment?" she ventured.

"How can there be hope, when the King and his ministry pursue their oppressive course with such reckless obstinacy?" replied the Son of Liberty, growing fervent as his thoughts returned to the subject of his country's wrongs. "They deprive us of our legislatures and take away our charter, making us serfs and vassals. They tell us that our town meetings, by which we have governed ourselves locally from the beginning, shall do no more than elect town officials, and that we can make no laws in them. They complain of our committees of correspondence. The committees are nothing but a means of discussing our affairs, one with another, and keeping our friends informed of the course of events. They assail those who champion our rights. Otis, whose truth-speaking hurt, was brutally beaten by the King's soldiers in a coffee-house; now his reason is dethroned, and he wanders harmlessly through the fields; but the words he spoke live on. They accuse

Samuel Adams and John Hancock and Doctor Warren of stirring up strife and discontent, because they dare to speak the truth. If it had not been for the cool restraint of these men the people would have risen in violence long ago. And now they send word that these men must be arrested and brought to England to stand trial for treason! Let them try it! Let them try it!"

Silence fell upon them all again. The man passed once more to the window and searched the night. His mother, watching him breathlessly, saw him turn quickly. In the look that he gave her she read what he had seen. He was calm, fatefully calm. The light of excitement had given place to the light of high purpose in his eyes. He came toward Nancy.

"Our leaders are gathering at Philadelphia, where the second Continental Congress will soon convene," he said, solemnly. "Militia and minute-men train in every town. The sons of our fathers are   Sons of Liberty; the daughters of our mothers are   Daughters of Liberty. Our

THE BRITISH MONUMENT MARKING THE POSITION OF THE INVADERS AT THE
CONCORD FIGHT, WHERE THE FIRST BRITISH BLOOD WAS SHED

lives are dear to us, but worthless without our right to order
them as we will. We pursue the ways of peace to the end.
When the ways of peace fail, there will be war. Until
the last shred of flesh is beaten into the dust, or until liberty
triumphs, there will be war; the land will be a wilderness,
or it will be the home of freedom; and the glorious day is
at hand when the issue will be tried!"

In the midst of silence he passed into the inner room.
There was no sound in the cottage, save a light metallic
rattle and the noise of a window shutter opening and closing
on creaking hinge. In the midst of silence, he reëntered.
As the door swung wide, the mother saw that sword and
pistols and powder-flask were gone from the hook. He
bent over her, kissing her on her withered cheek.

"God bless you, my son," she whispered.

He opened the outer door, and was gone into the night.

THE MONUMENT AND COMMON, LEXINGTON, MASSACHUSETTS

CHAPTER VI

STIRRING THE HIVE

NIGHT! Soft darkness lay hushed over the town of Boston. It settled thick in the angles of her streets; it gathered dense beneath the walls of her houses, enveloping citizen and soldier, patriot and Tory, hiding many sores and laying its cool cheek soothingly upon many a heated heart. It lay heavy at the foot of the steeple of the North Meeting-house; it hung across the waters of river and bay, spangled with a few lights on the British war vessels there at anchor; it spread over the lowlands toward Cambridge; it climbed the heights behind Charlestown; it merged river and town, farmhouse and field beyond, in one vague and silent shadow.

Although it was not yet 10 o'clock the streets of Boston were already nearly deserted. Only a few belated pedestrians shuffled along the flags, avoiding the guard when they could; only a few flickering lights still shone through chinks in cottage shutters. Soldiers, in couples and squads, or singly, stalked through street and lane, low-voiced and with little speech between them. In the environs they were more numerous and active, for the order had gone forth that no one should be permitted to pass through the lines to leave Boston on this night.

The sound of ships' bells sang into the darkness from the river; 4 bells of the night watch. "Ten o'clock, and all is well!" The cry of the lookouts passed from ship

CAPTAIN JOHN PARKER (*By Henry Hudson Kitson*)

9

to ship. Out upon the sheen waters of the river that lay grey beneath the starlight crept many shadows, silent and mysterious. There was the faint splashing of oars; muttered cries of those who gave orders, smothered beneath their breath. Tiny sparkles of starlight, coming and going, glanced from the shadows; now and then was heard the clash of steel or the butting of wood against wood. It was the British soldiers crossing to Charlestown.

Beneath the foot of the steeple of the North Meeting-house, where the darkness lay heavy, there swiftly gathered a half-dozen of those who had lately loitered through the streets, avoiding the guard where they could. Terse, tense whispers passed among them; the church door opened; the blackness within swallowed the group. Their feet struck gently against the steps that climbed to the belfry, awakening sepulchral echoes through the empty building. The steps grew fainter; they passed higher into the church-tower. There was silence, fol- lowed by the crackling blow of flint on steel. A light burst forth in the belfry, fluttered, settled, and shone with steady gleam out above the slumbering roofs. It was the signal light of the Sons of Liberty, to tell the patriots that the regulars were marching toward Lexington and Concord; it was a signal light to the world telling that Liberty had set her torch alight, a flame that

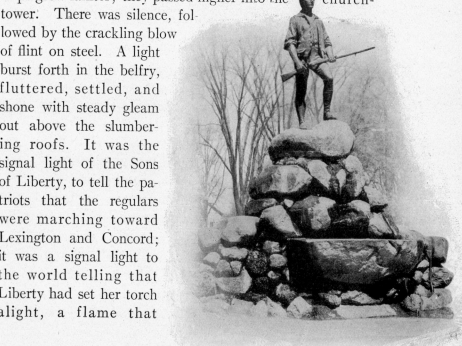

MONUMENT TO CAPTAIN JOHN PARKER, COMMANDER OF THE MINUTE-MEN AT LEXINGTON

neither blood could quench nor the storms of battle extin-
guish.

A solitary man, standing watchfully by the side of his
horse in Charlestown, seeing the light, swung into the saddle
and hurried northward, urging the animal with whip and
spur. It was Paul Revere, engraver and watchmaker of
Boston, patriot, and hero of song and story. Swiftly he
rode along the dark
road that led to
Medford.

SEWALL HOUSE, BURLINGTON, MASSACHUSETTS,
IN WHICH HANCOCK AND ADAMS TOOK REF-
UGE IN THEIR FLIGHT FROM LEXINGTON,
APRIL, 19, 1775

Farmers, hearing
the clatter of his
horse's hoofs, threw
open windows and
thrust out their heads
to learn what it was
about. "The regu-
lars are out!" came
a cry through the still
night. Before they could question further the rider was
gone in a cloud of dust and a tumult of hoof-beats.

The cry rang through the streets of villages and echoed
among the hills. "The regulars are coming! The regulars
are coming!"

All along the way he went the quiet countryside was
stirred into a wake of excitement and commotion; men
hastily pulling on their clothes and rushing into the street,
muskets and swords in hand; young men tumbling out of
their sleep to join the whispering groups; women hurrying
through the dark with shawls drawn about their pale faces.

In the midst of the starlit waters that lay between Boston
and Charlestown there passed a dinghy, swiftly propelled
by the arms of its solitary occupant. John Stevens, having
seen the light from the window, was making his way with

glad heart and humming soul to take his place in the ranks of the defenders of liberty. He had snatched the pistols and the sword from the grass where he had thrown them through the window; he had dodged along the streets to the waterside, the weapons beneath his coat; he had climbed into the dinghy, provided beforehand, and now, his weapons lying in the bottom of the craft, he was going forth to battle for freedom.

The lookouts on the British craft hailed and challenged him. He paid no heed, save to laugh within himself. His prow crunched against the gravel on the further bank. He leapt ashore, snatched up his weapons, and made his way to a house that stood apart from the Medford road. A light in a window above answered to his knock. There were whispered words. A man emerged, half dressed, and lead the way to his stables. A horse was saddled. John Stevens, swinging himself upon the animal's back, clattered through the night.

Twelve o'clock! From Charlestown through Medford, along the way Revere had gone, lay a seething, boiling wake of determined men, hurrying after him. At Lexington Samuel Adams and John Hancock lay sleeping in the house of the Reverend Mr. Clarke. Eight militia-men stood guard before the door. The rattle of hoofs came to their ears. They lifted their guns, peering through

BUTTRICK HOUSE, CONCORD, MASSACHUSETTS, FRONT OF WHICH THE AMERICANS FORMED AND MARCHED TO CONCORD BRIDGE the night. Out of the darkness came a horseman, rushing toward them with a cry in his throat.

"What do you want?" demanded Lieutenant Monroe, in charge of the militia.

"I am Paul Revere, and I want to see Hancock and Adams," replied the rider, loud-voiced and excited.

"You can't go in," answered Monroe, as Revere made for the door. "Make less noise, there! They are asleep."

"Noise!" cried Revere. "You'll soon have noise enough! The regulars are coming!"

A window in the second story was thrown open. John Hancock leaned from the sill.

"Who's there?" he cried. "Is that you, Revere?" He recognized the voice as sleep passed from his brain. "Let him in, Lieutenant Monroe!"

A few hasty words in the dining-room; Adams, Hancock, the Reverend Mr. Clarke listening while Revere hurried through  the burning story; and the messenger was gone, riding through the night again with the cry in his throat: "The regulars are coming! The regulars are coming!" On he rode, calling up the inhabi- tants, until he

THE OLD NORTH BRIDGE AT CONCORD, MASSACHU-
SETTS; THE MONUMENT TO THE MINUTE-MEN
IN THE DISTANCE

fell in with a party of British officers and was captured and taken back to Lexington.

"Ring the bell! Spread the alarm! Get out the militia! Alarum! Alarum!" shouted Hancock, snatching his gun and dashing to the door. His sweetheart, Dorothy Quincy, listened at the head of the stairs. "We shall be ready for them," he shouted to her.

"We must not fight to-night, Hancock," said Adams, laying hand on the shoulder of his impetuous friend; he whom the British called a "terrible desperado." "We

THE BATTLE OF LEXINGTON   (*From the painting by Alonzo Chappell*)

belong to the committee of safety and to the Continental Congress; there is other work for us to do."

Out across the night clashed the village bell, crying with clamorous tongue: "The reg-u-lars are com-ing!! The reg-u-lars are com-ing!!"

House and cottage burst into light; men came running to the doors; the cry ran from mouth to mouth: "The regulars are out! The regulars are out!" Half dressed, wide eyed, excited, the militia gathered at Buckman's tavern, muskets in hand, talking excitedly and peering down the road that led from Medford.

Far away the British column crept silently through the

night, wondering at the signs of life they saw. Beacon lights glared from every hilltop; signal shots rang across the still darkness, dying away in the distance with tiny crackle. They were discovered. Like a fire that is set in dry grass, like the ruffled stir that flies across a placid lake beneath the morning breeze, spread the news of their coming.

THE STRUGGLE ON CONCORD BRIDGE   (*Drawn by Alonzo Chappell*)

Their hearts beat high, uncertain what it might mean. But whatever it might mean, there could be no harm in precautions, and Lieutenant-Colonel Smith, who held command with Major Pitcairn of the marines, sent a messenger from Medford to bring up reinforcements from the garrison in Boston.

Ezra Stevens, returning that evening from his journey to Boston and the encounter with the British lieutenant, had lain long awake. His heart was heavy. The words of the young officer whispered in his memory, impeaching the honor and courage of his cousin John, his hero. That was enough; but to that was added the gnawing black thought that this gay and gallant dandy, wrought out in fine cloth and braid of gold, was close to his beloved. Behind it all, casting him into utter gloom, was the haunting vision of the look that had been on Catherine's face when this same John was assailed.

The clock struck 12, and still he slept not. One, and he was still wakeful. He was falling at last into a doze, when the bell cried out again. He stopped to count the hour. One! Two! Three! So late? Four! Five! Five? It was pitch dark; by five the sky should be grey. Six! How could he have slept so long, scarcely having slept at all? Seven! Eight! What was the meaning of this?

Out across the night sky rang a shot, mingling with the humming drone of the echoing bell! Another shot; and another! A low cry, coming from afar; the cry of men shouting! "The regulars are out!" That was the meaning of it!

He leapt from his bed, his heart in his mouth. The day had come; the day they had awaited long and patiently. Down along the sky, as he dressed, rang the punctuated shots, a minute between each; the signal of the minute-men! Loud clanged the bell, ringing the hour of glory!

Through the dark, musket in hand, ran Ezra Stevens, toward Concord.

Half-past four! The first

BUCKMAN TAVERN, LEXINGTON, MASSACHUSETTS, THE RALLY-ING-PLACE OF THE MINUTE-MEN ON THE NIGHT OF APRIL 18, 1775

grey of dawn was in the east. The minute-men of Lexington were drawn up on the village green in front of
Buckman's tavern. Captain John Parker commanded
them. They waited in eager impatience; destiny was at
hand.

A man on a horse whirled up to them. It was John
Stevens. Captain Parker knew him.

"They are not a mile away," said Stevens, glancing at
the assembled minute-men with a light of joy in his eye.

"Did you see them?"

"I came all the way from Charlestown ahead of them.
They went on the back road through the marshes to avoid
discovery." He grinned at the trick the Sons of Liberty
had played on them.

"How many are they?"

"I don't know; about a thousand. Where are Adams
and Hancock?"

"On the way to Burlington," whispered the captain.

Unlearned in the arts of war, but knowing how to die,
the minute-men stood on the green, tense with excitement.
A wonderful silence fell upon them as they gazed along the
road over which the British were approaching. The slanting
rays of the sun touched the tops of the elm trees in the common. The mumble of distant steps filled the air. A
column of red-coated regulars wheeled flashing into sight,
rank on rank, file on file. With even tread they came, the
sun glinting along their bayonets and gleaming warm on
their ruddy uniforms. They swung into line with admir-
able precision. The sun shone on their faces, and on the
faces of the patriots drawn up opposite them on the common with looks pale and stiff with emotion. An officer,
Major Pitcairn, rode forward from the end of the line.

"Disperse, ye rebels!" he cried. "Damn you, why
don't ye disperse?"

THE BATTLE OF LEXINGTON (*From the painting by A. H. Bicknell*)
"Where the embattled farmers stood, and fired the shot heard round the world"

"They are too many for us," said Captain Parker, who was a soldier, knowing what war was. It was not lack of courage that spoke in him; for he had scaled the Plains of Abraham with Wolfe. It was wisdom.

There was not a tremor in the irregular line of minute-men. Hopeless against so many, they stood their ground. It was superb! It was splendid! It was prophetic.

"Fire!" cried Major Pitcairn.

There was no movement of the redcoats.

"Fire!" he cried again, and discharged his pistol.

The guns of the regulars swept into a level line. There was a sheet of flame, a swirling cloud of smoke, a crashing of the air.

"The time has arrived!" cried John Stevens, exultation on his face. "They have made us free!"

To the right and to the left of him men tottered and reeled, tumbling to the ground; their blood sank into the earth — the first libation poured out to liberty. Of those who fell eight would rise no more and ten would bear a scar to the grave.

"Disperse!" Captain Parker gave the order, calmly, without fear, knowing it was best. The men scattered. The regulars marched on.

Ezra Stevens leaned on his musket beneath the liberty pole at Concord. It was approaching 7 o'clock. The stores were safe, for the most part. Some of the cannon were dragged into a field and buried; even now a farmer plowed above them, to hide the scar where they had been secreted. Barrels of flour were hidden about in barns, beneath the hay; powder and balls were smuggled away by housewives.

From far and near, the minute-men were coming; the hive was stirred. Wild rumors flew from mouth to mouth. Ezra, listening, breathed fast, his eyes glowing. In them were tears; tears of joy, of emotion.

"There they are!   The regulars!   The regulars!"

Looking, the lad beheld a sight that checked the
currents of his blood for a space.   Rank on rank, weary,
dusty, the British soldiers wheeled down the road, to stop
before the meeting-house.   A suppressed murmur ran like
a sigh among the men of Massachusetts; there was the
mutter of musket butts stirring on the ground, like sentient
things.

"Let us stand our ground!"   It was the Reverend
Mr. Emerson who spoke, minister of Concord, whose
grandson was to sing the praises of that day.

Major Buttrick commanded the militia.   "We are too
few, as yet," he answered.   "We will cross the river, and
await reinforcements."

Reluctantly, eager to try the issue, the men followed
him.

Smoke rose from the yard of Colonel Barrett's house;
a detachment of regulars was burning the gun carriages

THE LINE OF THE MINUTE-MEN: THE HERRINGTON HOUSE IN
THE BACKGROUND

there. The minute-men fretted, impatient to be at the foe. "The Acton men are on the way; they are almost at the bridge. It is held by a handful of regulars. We can drive them like chaff." A mutter ran down the lines. "Wait!" roared Major Buttrick.

"The men of Sudbury are not a half-mile away! Quick, and we can cut off the redcoats at the bridge!" A man, disheveled, hot with riding, came into their midst on a tottering steed; the quivering flanks of the animal dripped. At the sound of the man's voice, Ezra looked again at him, and perceived, through the grime of his journey and the strange look of exultation in his eyes, that it was John Stevens.

CONCORD BRIDGE (*From the painting by Edward Simmons in the State House, Boston*)

"Whence do you come?" Major Buttrick, to whom the rider was known, asked the question.

"From Boston, through Lexington."

"What is the news?"

"Have you not heard the news? The regulars fired on the men of Lexington. Eight of them were killed!"

A low shout arose from the throats of the little band; a cry of rage; a pæan of triumph. The hour had come when they might strike back, before the world.

"Forward!" It was Major Buttrick gave the order.

"Forward! Forward!" It ran down the line, to lose itself at last in the rush of hastening feet.

Before them, as they neared the bridge, still hidden from them by trees and hills, the air burst asunder in a splintered crash of thunder. It was the sound of musketry; the shots "heard round the world," said the grandson of the minister Emerson, who kept pace now with the man of Concord. Silence fell upon the little band; silence broken only by fall of feet upon the ground.

Around the foot of a hill they swung, tense, grim, breathing hard. Glorious sight! There stood the men of Acton and Sudbury, face to face with the British foe. About them lay their dead; Captain Davis, and half a dozen others. To the bridge dashed the Concord men, supporting those already there. "Charge! Charge!" Ezra beheld a bulking figure, agile, with the

COLONEL BARRETT'S HOUSE, AT CONCORD, MASSACHUSETTS

grace of a panther, spring into the forefront and out upon the narrow bridge, a score following him. From the opposite shore flashed a sheet of red; the leaping air surged against the breasts of the soldier-farmers. The smoke whirled away; the leader of those on the bridge was far across, triumphant, magnificent. Ezra, looking, beheld that it was John; he who had feared to meet his foe!

Against the trained fighters of England, victors in many bloody fields, against the veterans of Europe, the mad band of patriots dashed across the bridge; dashed into the ranks of bayonets, beating them down, shouting gloriously; pressed the seasoned warriors; slew them with rifle-butt and ancient sword, and drove them back to their fellows formed before the meeting-house!

The British had done nothing that they set out to do. For a space of time they waited in the roads of Concord, angry and sullen, unwilling to abandon their errands. From every side came the minute-men, the bees whom the regulars had stirred up, ready now   to sting.
Reluctantly the col-
umns turned back
along the road
by which they
had come
that same
morning.
Too late!
On every
hillside,
behind each
stone fence,
at each corner,
were yeomen
pouring skillful

THE WRIGHT TAVERN, BRITISH HEADQUARTERS AT
CONCORD, MASSACHUSETTS

fire into the British ranks; marksmen to whom the gun was as familiar as the plow. The British were struck at by a foe against whom they could not strike back. Men fell groaning from the compact ranks. Their comrades hastened on, leaving them writhing in the road. They were brave; they were willing to fight; they answered the fire as well as they could, but the task was hopeless. Before them lay twenty miles of ambuscade; twenty miles of angry, swarming bees.

Ezra, skirting behind the hills with a company of militia to intercept the British at Merriam's Corner, knelt behind the stone wall, panting, waiting for them to come. One touched his arm. He looked. It was John. Between them was no word; only a glance. The thing they did that day was above speech.

Grim, determined, pitiable, the redcoats came in sight, huddling in the road. Those behind the wall, resting their guns, waited.

THE MONROE TAVERN, LEXINGTON, MASSACHUSETTS, HEADQUARTERS OF PERCY ON APRIL 19, 1775

Ezra, picking out his man, ran his eyes over the quarry. Of a sudden he cursed, with virgin lip, and horribly. John glanced for an instant at him. His eye was afire; his teeth gleamed between set lips.

"There he is; the cur!" muttered the lad, aiming his piece.

John followed the leveled barrel. Before it, a fair mark, leading his men, strode Lieutenant Lucas Hempstead, his coat thrown open, his face drawn with fatigue and thirst; but brave, as a soldier of old England should be brave.

In the instant that Ezra's gun spoke, John struck it upward with his fist. "Him you must not kill!" he cried, as he leapt to his feet and ran ahead.

Each one for himself, aiming with deadly deliberation, the Americans fired. An answering volley battered against the stones, or made music above their heads. Rushing from his shelter, loading as he ran, Ezra hastened ahead, stopped, fired again; ran on, loading, stopped and fired, and so through the glorious noontide of that day. And so, too, through the early afternoon. Minute-men from distant towns, panting

MERRIAM'S CORNER, CONCORD, MASSACHUSETTS

and half fagged, joined the others on the British flanks,
forgetting their exhaustion. From the front and rear,
from both sides, swept a murderous hail of lead. They
had stirred the hive deeply, the regulars; and
deep was the avenging sting in their ranks.
They were running now! Ezra, forgetting his fatigue, forgetting the sleepless
night that lay behind him, raised a
mighty shout of joy and ran abreast
of them, loading and firing as he ran.
Into the streets of Lexington fled the
British, their eyes rolling, their tongues
hanging from their mouths; for the day
was hot, though it was April. It was a
rout, a red-coated rabble that staggered
into the common where they had fired upon the patriots when the day was young.
Ah, how old was the day now!

HUGH EARL PERCY

The hot sun beat down upon them; the dust choked
them; the stinging of the bees thinned their ranks; there
was no hope! They stopped in despair. Stopping, a glad

THE RETREAT OF THE BRITISH FROM CONCORD   (*From the painting by Alonzo
Chappell*)

shout arose feebly from the parched lips of the desperate
band, for along the road up which they had so proudly
marched in the early morning came Lord Percy with 1100
regulars and two cannon!

Now there was a moment of rest. The reinforcement
formed a hollow square. The fugitives cast themselves
down on the cool grass within it. But the day was not
ended. With each minute came new recruits from neighboring towns. The news had traveled far; the Sons of
Liberty had done their work well. Contingents from twenty-
three towns joined in the fight before night. Doctor Warren
and General Heath arriving at 3 o'clock, the minute-men
took up the fight once more, and the retreat began again.

All through the afternoon it continued. Minute by
minute the militia pressed harder upon the flanks of the
British. Again the invaders broke into a run, helpless
against the desultory onslaughts of the foe, who came from

ONE OF MANY MONUMENTS COMMEMORATING THE HEROIC DEEDS OF APRIL
19, 1775

behind, who circled ahead, who attacked them again from the front, with a zeal that never faltered. It was not until Percy reached Charlestown that the regulars were safe from destruction or capture. And they came not a moment too soon, for Colonel Pickering with 700 fresh troops from Essex was already at Winter Hill, and must have compelled their surrender if he had intercepted them.

Thus ended the stirring of the hive. Two hundred and seventy-three of the British were missing,—killed, wounded, or captured; of   the Americans, ninety-three! And thus began the   glorious dawn of liberty in the land.

THE FIRST REVOLUTIONARY MONUMENT IN AMERICA: HERE LIE THE
EIGHT MEN WHO FELL ON APRIL 19, 1775

CHAPTER VII

THE MOTHER OF ONE

IT was the afternoon of June 17, 1775. In the town of Boston was a hush, a significant silence, as though very eternity paused in its rush to behold that which was taking place there. From hillside, from roof-top, from balustrade and balcony, from upper window and domitory, citizens, bent with eagerness, scarcely breathing, gazed with irresistible fascination across the waters of the Bay to the heights behind Charlestown.

It was a terrible, a magnificent sight that the people of Boston were gathered to behold. In the dark of the previous night the Americans had thrown up a redoubt and breastworks on Breed's Hill, behind Charlestown. Thence their guns commanded the city and the Bay; thence they must be dislodged, or the English must abandon the town. Wherefore 3000 regulars had crossed the river to Charlestown, to drive them out.

It was Colonel Prescott of Pepperell, a veteran of the French war, who commanded the patriot force behind Charlestown. Breed's Hill, where he had come in the night, was nearest the water and the most commanding in the ridge that ran back from the town. At his right and behind him, was Bunker Hill; beyond Bunker Hill the ridge ran to the surface and pinched out at Charlestown Neck. The position was critically dangerous; the British vessels could move so as to command the rear, and British forces

121

MAJOR-GENERAL ARTEMAS WARD

could be landed to occupy the Neck and compel a sur-
render.	Only the blundering obstinacy of Gage and Howe,
who scoffed at the thought of employing strategy against
a rabble handful of peasants, prevented such a calamity
The strategic oversight of Colonel
Prescott was in a measure reme-
died by General Israel Putnam, who, arriving during the
night, fortified Bunker Hill,
securing a partial line of retreat.   In the course of the
forenoon, Stark came up
and occupied a position
behind a rail fence at the
extreme left, to prevent a
flanking movement in that
direction.   His defence was
strengthened by piling hay
against the rails.   The
American forces in all numbered about 1800.

The event was the culmination in a long series that took

ISRAEL PUTNAM (*After a
sketch by Trumbull*)

its beginning when the British went
forth and stirred the hive on April 19.
The swarm of minute-men they brought about their ears
that day did not return to their homes when Percy reached
the shelter of the ship's guns at Charlestown.   Exultant
and glorying, they remained under arms to fight for their
liberties, for the die was cast.   Others came to their aid.
From New Hampsh're and Vermont they came; from
Connecticut and Rhode Island; the entire country rose
in arms.

Israel Putnam, plowing his field at Pomfret, Connecticut,

on the morning of April 20, hearing the news of Lexington and Concord, unharnessed his team, mounted and rode a hundred miles to Cambridge before noon of the next day, leaving the militia to follow him. There he met John Stark with men from New Hampshire. Captain Benedict Arnold, organizing a company of sixty volunteers on the college campus at New Haven, reached Cambridge with them April 21st. By Saturday there were 16,000 determined men surrounding Boston, under the command of Major-General Artemas Ward. Gage was hemmed in.

Nor was the effect of the news local. The New York committee of correspondence, hearing it, made protest to the city of London, declaring that the horrors of civil war could not drive them from their rights. Pennsylvania immediately took steps to organize and drill a provincial militia.

GENERAL SIR WILLIAM HOWE   (*From an English print*)

The Irish and Scotch of Mecklenburg County, North Carolina, declared that the act had thrown authority into the hands of the several provincial legislatures, and that the Continental Congress should assume direction of them.

Far more vital was the effect it had on the Continental Congress itself, when it convened in Philadelphia on May 10. Although this body was merely advisory in its functions, and although there was no organization of central authority, the Congress took steps that bound the several provinces into United Colonies, a character that they held throughout the ensuing struggle and until the formation of the Union; a character under which the war was waged and won.

Now there was no division of interest. With Massachusetts must stand or fall the hopes of all the colonies. Congress, tacitly representing them all, took over the responsibilities of the army that had gathered about Boston, naming it the Continental army and assuming charge of it.

Their next step was the most fateful and fortunate in the history of the country, to that time. They appointed Colonel George Washington of Virginia, who was a delegate from that colony, to command the Continental army. In placing a Virginian at the head of the New England army they welded together the several links of the chain. The choice was opposed for political reasons by some. John Hancock, who had been made president of the Congress, desired the appointment and had many supporters from New England, but when the matter came before the body for final decision the vote for Washington was unanimous.

Not only did Congress effect a master-stroke in politics in choosing Washington; they also placed in command the only man who could have carried the war to a successful issue. Infallible judgment, perfect balance, complete devotion, indestructible courage, utter unselfishness, faith, hope and charity, went to make up the majestic manhood within whose hands they placed the destinies of their country.

While these things went forward at Philadelphia, the army about Boston was not idle. A cordon was firmly placed about the city, and a complete siege by land was begun. Nor was this all. Captain Benedict Arnold, realizing the importance of getting possession of the command of the Hudson River, obtained from the Massachusetts Congress a commission as colonel with authority to organize a body of troops in the Hampshire hills and capture Ticonderoga and Crown Point, on Lake Champlain, in the highway formed between New York and Canada by the Hudson River and Lakes George and Champlain.

Setting out on this expedition, he found that Captain Ethan Allen of Vermont had already started on the same errand with a body of Green Mountain Boys. He joined as private after some bickering over the command of the forces. Allen, coming opposite to Ticonderoga on the night of May 9 and finding that there were not boats enough to carry his entire command across, went with those whom he could take, surprised the guard, entered the fort and compelled its surrender "in the name of the Great Jehovah and the Continental Congress." Seth Warner with another band of Green Mountain Boys accomplished the same result at Crown Point.

On May 25 General William Howe arrived at Boston, bringing with him Clinton, Burgoyne, and 10,000 men. Howe was sent from England to supplant Gage in command of the British troops and had been chosen for politic reasons. He was known to be more fa- vorable to the American cause than Gage, and was well

GENERAL WARD'S HOUSE, SHREWSBURY MASSACHUSETTS

liked by the colonists, both for himself and because he was the brother of that beloved Lord Howe who had fallen at the head of the British and colonial troops in the attack on the advanced lines of Ticonderoga in the French war.

Gage took such courage from their presence that he awoke from the apathy and fright into which the Concord

GENERAL ISRAEL PUTNAM'S BIRTHPLACE, DANVERS, MASSACHUSETTS

affair had thrown him, and when still in authority issued a proclamation offering pardon to all but Adams and Hancock if they would lay down their arms, but threatening dire things if they refused. The proclamation was received with ridicule. The answer was the American troops, now thrown across Charlestown Neck, threatening the entire British force in Boston.

All day long Boston had been in turmoil. Citizens and soldiers were awakened at daybreak by the sound of heavy firing from the ships at anchor in the bay. The officers of the fleet, discovering the enemy fortifying the heights beyond Charlestown as soon as it was light, opened upon them with full broadsides. From window and rooftop, from the waterfront and the hills of Boston, the people of the town watched the bombardment, noting that their compatriots continued the work with pick and shovel.

Gage, Howe, Clinton, and Burgoyne were in a flurry of consternation and amazement. They knew the strategic value of the position assumed by the Continentals; Gage had contemplated its occupation. Long and earnestly did they deliberate the situation. "Three thousand men can drive them," said Gage. "They will not stay to fight." Soldiers ran through the streets; drums beat; bugles called to arms. Now, at 3 o'clock in the afternoon, the 3000 red-coats were across the river forming for the assault.

A group of men and women, hushed and expectant, was clustered on a balcony jutting out from the second story of the house of Lawrence Averill, gazing with the rest, in fascinated interest, at the drama on the heights of Charlestown, across the waters of the bay. In all Boston was not a group more tense; for here were those whose sympathies were with the British, and those to whom the patriot cause was dearer than life itself.

There was Margaret Hempstead, daughter of Robert Stevens of New York, come to Boston to be near her husband, Major Hempstead, who at the very moment was with the attacking party. There was Nancy Hempstead, sister to the major and to Lieutenant Lucas, English born and taught, following the fortunes of her brothers in the war. There was Lieutenant Hempstead himself, carrying his arm in a sling because of a wound he had received in the fight at Lexington, and wearing the British uniform. There was Isaac Francis, the Tory, come all the way from New York that he might be by the side of Nancy.

These stood that afternoon on the balcony of the patriot Averill's house; for the tenacity of race was still too strong between English and provincials, the open hostility between England and the colonies still too new in the habits of all to sunder the slight bonds of blood that were between them and their host. With them, trembling for the companions that consanguinity had thrust upon them, were Mistress Averill and her daughter Catherine.

In the room from which the balcony opened, propped on many pillows and straining to see through the windows, lay Helen Stevens, mother of John. They had brought her there when her son did not return after the fight out Concord way, the better to care for her; now she lay in the midst of her son's enemies. To her came Catherine from time to time with messages, and Nancy, in whom womanhood exceeded a regard for political differences.

Three o'clock! The group on the balcony was hushed in expectancy. Catherine Averill, trembling and faint, crept to the bedside of Helen Stevens, and crouched there.

"Can you see?" she whispered. "They are moving up the ridge now. They are about to attack!"

"God be with us!" murmured the woman.

There was a silence, broken only by the distant roar of the broadsides from the fleet, and the volleys of the regulars.

"Do you think he is there?" asked the girl, with frightened voice, looking into the woman's face.

"Ay, child, he is there," made answer the other, stoutly. "I know he is there!" There was no need to call his name between these two.

Another silence, made more deep by a lull in the firing.

"Look again, child, look again!" whispered the woman, clasping her hands in prayer.

Catherine went softly to the doorway. The red ranks crept up the hill against the very face of the redoubt and the long lines of breastworks. The sight held her, fascinated. She called over her shoulder to the helpless woman, telling her what she saw.

The sound of firing passed from the air. The British

soldiers crept up slowly, near and nearer to the crest of the hill, amidst an awful lull.

"The regulars are almost at the fort!" cried Catherine over her shoulder to the woman on the bed, "and our men do not fire. Oh! why do they not fire?"

In the instant that she spoke a flash of flame leapt from the crest of the   ridge, a belling swirl   of smoke

FORTIFYING BREED'S HILL ON THE NIGHT OF JUNE 16, 1775 (*From the drawing by Darley*)

rolled toward advancing soldiers and a crashing roar smote against their ears.

"See! Look!" cried Catherine, distraught with excitement, "they melt away; they fall in heaps; they turn; they fly! Aunt, the British fly!" She ran to the bed and threw herself down by the side of the prostrate woman, burying her face in her hands and weeping with emotion.

"He is there!" whispered the woman, exultantly, laying her hand upon the slight shoulder of the girl.

Nancy, in the doorway, looked with trembling lip from

the face of Lucas to that of Francis, they were staring, speechless and stunned, at the sight of British soldiers fleeing down the distant hill.

"If I were a man, and saw that, I should no longer bide with a pack of women!" she said to Francis, indignantly, remembering only that she was English.

"Hold your tongue, girl!" he retorted hotly, blushing with mortification. "There are ten thousand soldiers in the town; what should I do if I went?"

A moan came from the blanched lips of Margaret Hempstead. She sank against the body of Mistress Averill. "My husband! Oh, my husband!" she sobbed; for Major Hempstead was with the assaulting troops.

They bore her within the room and placed her in a chair.

The air shook with the reverberations of the guns of the fleet, firing on the American works.

"Look you!" cried Francis, presently, alone with Lucas on the balcony for the moment, while the other sought to comfort and encourage Margaret. "They have set fire to the town, the cursed rebels!"

"Nay, you are wrong there, Francis," returned Lieutenant Lucas. "'T is our own shot have done that."

Vast volumes of black smoke arose above Charlestown; in a short time the 400 wooden houses were all ablaze.

"They are advancing again!" cried Lucas. "Now shall we see what regulars are!"

Far away on the green hills those who watched saw the lines of the British moving once more upon the American works; they saw the rolling smoke from their volleys and heard the crash of musketry. They saw the lines advance until, in the distance, they were merged into the line of earthworks; they saw the flashing of the patriot volleys in the very faces of the redcoats; they saw the gallant troops

THE BATTLE OF BUNKER HILL *(From the painting by John Trumbull)*

of England waver and wither; they saw those who were left, straggle down the hill.

"We have driven them again!" cried Catherine, running to the woman on the bed, in an ecstasy. "We have beaten them back! He is safe! He is safe!"

The woman, with eyes aloft, murmured a prayer of thanksgiving. On the balcony Lucas Hempstead, with an oath of wrath, placed an arm about Margaret to support her. His sister, looking with wonder from him to Francis, saw him pale and speechless, staring wide-eyed at the marvelous sight.

Lucas supported Margaret to the bed, where she sank beside the older woman. Catherine was stroking the wrinkled face of her aunt in a rapture of joy and relief. "My boy; my brave John!" the mother was whispering.

A deeper scowl settled on the face of Lucas as he saw the light in Catherine's eyes at sound of the name. The fancy that this slip of a girl had awakened in him when he had first seen her leapt into a flame of desire when he beheld her so moved by the thought of another. Such was his selfish nature.

An hour passed. Margaret, recovering composure, was sitting in an armchair facing the door, from which the others stood aside that she might see. Francis, standing with Nancy in the balcony, had recovered his spirits and was making flippant talk of the affair across the water, promising much from the forthcoming adventure that the British soldiers were preparing to make. Lucas, scarcely removing his eyes from Catherine, who fluttered between the doorway and the bed, was absorbed in his own thoughts. Madeline Averill, torn with conflicting emotions arising from the presence of her husband's enemies beneath their roof, stood silent and apart.

It was 5 o'clock. There was another lull in the firing

of the ships, preceding the third assault. The British, formed and arrayed, moved forward.

"Now, look you, they are clipping their wings!" cried Francis, pinching Nancy's cheek playfully.

The British columns, reinforced, moving toward the hill, turned to the right and advanced in greatest force against the fence bolstered with hay. Howe was ready to concede that the Yankees could fight, and was making a flank movement.

No word was spoken among the watchers. Catherine, absorbed in the sight, forgot the woman on the bed. Closer and closer to the entrenched patriots moved the veteran ranks. Closer and closer, up to the very works. Once more the lines of red merged into the line of earthworks; once more those who watched waited for the terrible onslaught of the American musketry, — and for what might follow.

But there was scarcely a shot. "Merciful Heaven, why do they not fire!" cried Catherine, beneath her breath.

She did not know that barely half a keg of powder remained to all that gallant line of defence. She did not know that they had only their naked courage now to oppose against the bayonets of the foe; that they waited in sheer desperate heroism for the final moment.

"Thank God, we drive them at last!" breathed Lucas Hempstead, revealing in the tone of his voice how great was his relief to see success come finally to his arms, betraying the fear he had of those at whom he scoffed.

Little heads of the red torrent that swept against the American breastworks could be seen trickling over and spreading in the space beyond; heads that gained volume and size, like tiny streams that lick through the walls of a dike. A sob of dismay burst from the throat of Mistress Averill. Catherine, groaning, shut out the sight with her hands. Nancy uttered a cry of gladness. In the last analysis she was an Englishwoman, and these men who fought and won so valiantly were English.

"Now God be with him in his hour of need!" came a hoarse voice from behind them. Turning, they saw the bedridden woman standing at their backs. "Good God,"

THE BATTLE OF BUNKER HILL (*From the painting by Alonzo Chappell*)

she went on, "keep his face to the foe! Take his soul unto Thee, if Thou must; but let him be brave to the last, let him be brave to the last!"

They led her back to the bed and laid her gently upon it. "Tell me," she pleaded, "do they fly? Is the day lost? And what of him? Is he safe?"

Nancy, standing beside her, soothing her as best she could, forgot that she was an Englishwoman, and knew only pity for this mother. With the pity there came surging into her consciousness the realization that in the land her peo- ple had come to subdue were many such mothers; that among those against whom her brother had marched that day were numbered not one hero such as the young man she had seen in the plain cottage with this woman, but hundreds; — yea, thousands! The thought filled her with sorrow and dismay, leaving a profound wish that all might be different.

From the balcony came the glad cries of Lucas and Francis as they watched the British troops pour in a solid stream over the opposing works, and fold the struggling Continentals back on Bunker Hill.

"The redoubt is carried!" cried the two. "Look! they are pressing close to the rear. They will cut them off! God! What a sight! You can see them running across the Neck! Now will the impudent beggars yield, I fancy! Ho, to be there with a sword!"

"'T is true; they fly. We are beaten," said the stricken woman, calmly. "But the end is not yet! The end is not yet! They may drive us from an hundred fields, but they cannot drive us from our rights!"

Catherine, kneeling beside the bed, buried her face in the covers and wept. Nancy arose softly and went out upon the balcony where the two men were exulting in the defeat of the enemy.

"For shame," she whispered, laying her hand on her brother's sleeve. "Have you no pity? Spare this woman; her son was one of those who fought!"

"Spare her!" snapped Lucas. "I would soon show you how I would spare the mother of rebels!"

"Nay, Lucas," laughed Francis, in exuberant spirits again, looking whimsically at Nancy, "speak not too rashly; for you are like to be the brother of a rebel, if signs fail not. Your lovely sister here has too tender a heart for this old woman and her fractious son."

"The woman is dying!" whispered Nancy to her brother, with deep reproach, paying no heed to the other.

"Eh?" exclaimed Lucas, with a whistle. "Close the door, then."

Without another word Nancy returned to the room, closing the door behind her to shut out the sound of the men's voices. There was deep silence about the bed, where Catherine and her mother knelt. Nancy stood apart with bowed head.

"My boy! My son!" she heard the woman saying. "Are you there? Tell him to be brave," she went on, addressing those who knelt beside her. "He has no mother now, my John; but tell him that her soul fights

CAPTURE OF FORT TICONDEROGA   (*From the painting by Alonzo Chappell*)

with him in the good fight. And tell him that if he is called, his mother has gone before to await him. Bless him and love him for me!"

A stifled sob from Catherine.

"Nay, child, weep not for me," said the woman, laying her hand gently on the raven locks. "I am but an old woman, and my time has come. Her eyes fell upon Nancy. "You are English, but you are good," she said. "You have been kind to me, and my heart goes out to you. I could wish you were not English; I could wish that my son could find such a one as you among his own people."

"Nay; we are all one people," whispered Nancy, not

thinking of the significance her words might have, desiring only to comfort the woman. "We shall soon be one again, at least."

"If all were like you we might be," answered the woman, her voice growing more faint with every word; "but now it is too late. You have seen my son; there are many, many more as brave as he, and the breach will never close."

She paused for breath to continue. There was silence in the room; silence in the streets of Boston; a horrid stillness on the distant field of battle. There was dismay among the victorious British soldiers; the despised provincials had withstood, more than once, the determined onslaught of veteran troops. There was exultation in the hearts of the defeated men of New England; not until their ammunition failed them had they been driven by their redoubtable enemies. Death in its most shocking forms proved the valor of both antagonists; death, peaceful and attended, was approaching the pallid woman within the room. She spoke.

"If he dies, I shall have done all a mother of one could do; if he lives, I

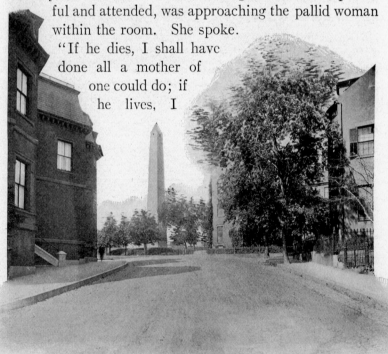

shall have done all. I am content. I could wish to see the day, but God wills it otherwise."

"Do not say that," pleaded Nancy, the tears streaming down her face. "You shall live; the war will end, and he will come back. You shall have many happy years together." But the plea was futile.

The aged woman only smiled, and closed her eyes. "I am weary," she said, and fell into a slumber.

From that slumber there was to be no awakening on this earth.

BUNKER HILL MONUMENT, CHARLESTOWN, MASSACHUSETTS

CHAPTER VIII

THE SON

"I WISH we could sell them another hill at the same price," remarked General Nathanael Greene to John Stevens, who had been with Prescott at the redoubt. He stood by the side of James Otis, who had wandered in his mania from his sister's farm at Watertown, borrowed a

MAJOR-GENERAL NATHANAEL GREENE
(*From Trumbull's portrait*)

musket, and lifted his voice once more against England on tongues of flame, with speech of lead. Twice he saw the British lines reel under the murderous fire of the Continentals; he had lingered until the last after the enemy carried the works; he had seen Doctor Warren die with a bullet through his forehead. Reluctant to abandon the field, he had gone away with the final stragglers still elated.

The Americans lost the hill, but at such cost to the enemy in men and morale that Vergennes, the French minister of foreign affairs, exclaimed that with two more such victories England would not have an army left in America. Ten hundred and fifty-four British, a full third of the men engaged, were killed and wounded; every officer on Howe's staff was cut down, and only one of them survived. Pitcairn of hated memory was slain. The American loss was 449, about one-fourth of the total force under fire.

It was a strategic victory for the British nevertheless; if the redcoats had not driven the Americans from their position the evacuation of Boston would have been forced forthwith. But the moral effect of the fight, however, was all on the side of the Americans. The British soldiers and officers found that the Yankee "peasants" could fight; better than French regulars, some of the officers declared. On the other hand the minute-men were elated. They knew that, had their powder held out, they would have continued to repulse the British as long as they continued to come against their front.

Franklin, but lately returned from England where he had spent several years in the interests of peace, now declared that England had lost her colonies forever. And Washington, journeying from Philadelphia to take command of the army, remarked that there could be now no doubt that the liberties of the American people were assured. Arriving at Cambridge on July 2, the next day he took command of the American forces under the elm still standing on Cambridge common. The new commander-in-chief was housed temporarily with the president of the college until more commodious quarters could be made ready for him. John, seeing the lofty bearing of the man, the high intelligence of his countenance, the expression of sublime devotion and deep, calm determination as he took the oath of office, gave his faith utterly to the new leader.

In the town of Boston General Howe, assuming command of the British forces, hesitated to strike another blow, remembering well the lesson of Bunker Hill, and suffered the work of organization that Washington set on foot straightway to go on without interference. The Continental army was not yet an army. It was a concourse of men held together only by a common purpose. The militia-men were under enlistment contracts with their several communities for terms of various lengths; all of them short. Other than their muskets and rifles they had no equipment. Powder was scarce; the commisariat was nothing. The army of 16,000 men subsisted for months on provisions brought in without method or system from the surrounding country. There was no drill, no discipline, no recognized central authority such as is necessary to the morale of an army. To remedy these defects was the first task of Washington.

Troops and leaders had already begun to arrive from other colonies. Congress sent a force of 3000 militia-men from Pennsylvania, Maryland, and Virginia. Among them was Daniel Morgan with his famous Virginia riflemen; men who could hit a squirrel at a range of 300 yards when on the double quick. Morgan was a man of Welsh descent, of gigantic stature; courageous, sacrificing, schooled in the wild campaigns of the French war; Indian fighter and back-woodsman, with the soul of a chief and the heart of a woman.

Benedict Arnold, fiery, impetuous, brave, was one of the officers about Washington. John Stark was another, much like Morgan in native shrewdness, rough simplicity, and courage. The commander of the New Hampshire contingent was General John Sullivan, a wealthy lawyer of Durham, member of the first Continental Congress, cultured, of some ability as a statesman, faithful and brave as an officer but without brilliant military qualities. Nathanael Greene of Rhode Island,

WADSWORTH OR PRESIDENT'S HOUSE, CAMBRIDGE, OCCUPIED BY WASHINGTON UNTIL THE VASSALL HOUSE WAS PUT IN READINESS FOR HIM

destined to achieve fame as a commander second only to
Washington, beginning life as a blacksmith, had struggled
through a lack of opportunities to become a man of culture
and scholarly attainments. With a rare ability to master
knowledge was combined a sweetness of temper and purity
of heart which had lifted him into the high estimation of
his fellow-citizens. Henry Knox, the bookseller of Boston
and a close friend of Greene, joined the army as colonel of
artillery and soon became one of Washington's most devoted
followers.

Among all the forceful and interesting men with the
army, perhaps no one was more picturesque than General
Israel Putnam. The story of his having entered a wolf's
cave, crouching and crawling, to slay the beast in a hand-to-
hand fight, while not authenticated, has in it the elements
of truth that leave it entirely consistent with his character.
It is a thing he would and could have done, if he did not
actually do it, and so has its value as an index to the temper
of the man. Thrilling adventures with the savages, including a narrow escape from death by torture in the French
and Indian War, added to his reputation as a daring fighter.
But he proved to be better as a fighter than as a leader, and
in the strenuous elimination of the unfit that was to follow
he was soon relegated to garrison duty. Under the leadership of these men whose fame has come down to us John
Stevens consecrated himself to the sacred cause of liberty.

Two there were of the generals associated with Washington whose present fame was to dwindle; these two were
Horatio Gates and Charles Lee. Both were Englishmen
possessed of estates in Virginia. Gates was nothing more
than foolish and vain, perverted by a narrow selfishness that
resulted in great harm and much disheartening intrigue.
Charles Lee was far more dangerous to the cause of liberty.
He had served in the Seven Years' War and afterward in

Europe as a soldier. His reputation preceded him, and
he was received with enthusiasm, the greater because he
hailed from Europe, a circumstance that prejudiced the
Americans toward him. He was rough, slovenly, pompous,
loud-voiced, cynical, morose, and insulting. These characteristics rather added to his prestige than otherwise, being
interpreted as the eccentricities of genius. He had no faith
in humanity, and cared nothing for the cause of America.
His object and desire was to win fame and position for himself; a motive that was to lead to dire consequences before
the cause should be won.

The task that confronted Washington was heavy and
trying. There was no organization of government behind
him; there was no money; there was little sympathy from
the people, who did not understand that it was necessary
to create an army out of the motley gathering of men under
him before he could offer battle. Although the Continental
Congress had adopted the army, it could do nothing more
for it than to suggest to the colonies what they should sever-
ally do. It could neither levy taxes nor beat up recruits.
Realizing the necessity of a firmer form of government,
Congress recommended to each of the colonies that they
establish their former legislatures, ignoring the authority
of England. Samuel Adams suggested that they might as
well declare their independence at once, and urged such a
move. Franklin, always ahead of his time, endeavored to
unite the colonies after somewhat the same plan that he had
proposed before the Albany convention.

Massachusetts was the first to follow the suggestions of
the Continental Congress. In July a legislature was formed
on the basis of the old charter that had been taken away, the
people voting for delegates in their town-meetings. James
Bowdoin was made president of the council and thereby
chief executive of the government. John Adams was chosen

The Elm at Cambridge, Massachusetts, where Washington Took Command of the American Army, July 3, 1775

chief justice. The authority of the King was virtually disallowed. A tax of $40,000 for the support of the army was levied on polls and real estate, and bills given for $1000 more. With this help Washington continued the work of organizing the army.

The lines, sixteen miles long, lay from the Mystic River on the left across the base of the Charlestown peninsula to the bay on the right, covering the Dorcester peninsula. Lee commanded the left, and General Artemas Ward the right wing. Washington himself, with head-quarters at Cambridge, assumed per-sonal control of the center. Works were thrown up in parallels, and Boston was fairly beleaguered. Her supplies could not be cut off, because the Americans had no fleet; but the British army was effectually cooped up in the town and could do nothing.

MAJOR-GENERAL CHARLES LEE
(*From the engraving by G. R. Hall*)

July had come, and was nearly gone. John Stevens, now captain of militia in position before Cambridge, sat before a hut made of twisted boughs, revolving in his mind many things. For the most part, his thoughts were of his mother, with whom he had had no communication since he left home, on the night before the Concord fight. His grief and anxiety were heavy upon him this afternoon; he was ready to risk much to see her again.

Another train of thought, quite as disturbing to his peace, persisted in his mind. Do what he would, he was not able to ignore the memory of Nancy Hempstead. When he

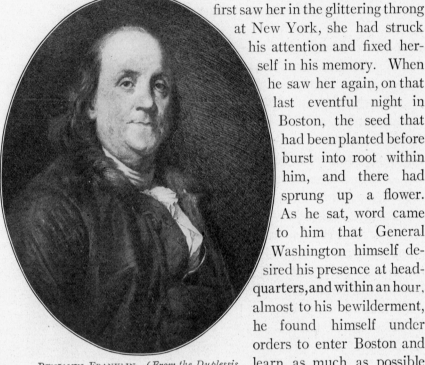

first saw her in the glittering throng at New York, she had struck his attention and fixed herself in his memory. When he saw her again, on that last eventful night in Boston, the seed that had been planted before burst into root within him, and there had sprung up a flower. As he sat, word came to him that General Washington himself desired his presence at headquarters, and within an hour, almost to his bewilderment, he found himself under orders to enter Boston and learn as much as possible about the disposition and

BENJAMIN FRANKLIN (*From the Duplessis portrait in the Boston Museum of Fine Arts*)

force of the enemy there. General Knox had recommended him for this difficult and honorable service. Filled with pride, he set about his task as soon as darkness fell.

A man, large, erect, and quick of step, was walking through the streets of Boston that night, without stealth, as one having business abroad at that hour of the night. Turning abruptly at the shadow of a tall house, he disappeared into a secluded way, little more than a lane, narrow and crooked, and paused before a cottage; the cottage where Helen Stevens and her son John had dwelt before that night when he went forth to Lexington and Concord. A gleam of light came from beneath the door; clearly the sight of it disturbed his equanimity, complete and assured until now. Still as the night, he stood with his ear close to the door, listening.

After a little his hand rested on the latch; noiselessly, he raised it; without sound, slowly, the door swung open, letting the light through in ever widening vertical strip — wider, until there was space for him to pass; and he stood within. A rushlight burned at the hearth; no one was by it; so far as he could perceive, the room was empty. He could not see the bed; a shadow cast by the foot of it, obscured the pillows.

"Who is there?" A voice, the voice of a woman, low, startled, but restrained, as though the one who spoke wished to avoid waking another, came from the shadow on the bed.

The intruder stood still, speaking not a word; clearly, if he sought any one, it was not the one who had spoken.

"Who is it?" the woman repeated; startled still, but fully controlled. Whoever spoke had courage — great courage, for now she arose and came toward the in-

HOUSE OF BENJAMIN FRANKLIN AT No. 7 CRAVEN STREET, LONDON

truder. Her face was in shadow; the man, standing motionless by the door, could not see it. Nor did he try; for his chin was upon his breast, and his hat over his brows, as though he would not be known too soon. But he was known, nevertheless; hide his face as he might, none who had seen those shoulders, that frame, could forget.

"John Stevens! Is it you?" exclaimed she who came softly from the bed.

She was wrapped in loose flowing robes; that much could be discerned in the dim light. Though she had been lying on the bed, she was dressed. From that circumstance, from the rushlight burning on the hearth, from her speaking softly, rather than calling for help against the intruder, it was to be inferred that she watched over the sick. Evidently the visitor thought so; he looked swiftly, anxiously, toward the door of the inner room, which stood closed. But if there was a heartsick question on his tongue, he did not voice it. He only asked, as he shut the street door, governing his tone by hers, "Who is it speaks?"

"It is I, John Stevens," was the answer. "Do you not know me?"

"I cannot believe that I know you," he returned, cautiously.

"Nancy Hempstead?" she ventured, tentatively, as though she would see what effect the information might have upon him.

"Ha!" he exclaimed, under his breath. "What do you here?" And then, before she could answer, another question, made up of several, as being of more import: "My mother? What of her? Is she here?"

There was a moment of silence; clearly the girl found it hard to answer.

"She is not here," she said, at last. "When you did not return, we took her to the Averills."

"Is she well?"

"And I, lest the place fall into evil hands, came here to stay; I could not live longer beneath that roof, with the war going on," she explained, choosing to answer his first question and avoiding the others.

"My mother; tell me of her?" In the face of John was the fear he felt.

Nancy dreaded still to tell him. "I felt I had the right," she stammered, swiftly, post- poning the moment. "Surely, I cherish the place above many who might have come; for I loved your mother greatly . . ."

"You loved her?" cried the man, but softly, speaking the past tense of the verb as though it held fate.

She came closer to him, with a swift movement, through pity for him; it was as though she would have

MAJOR-GENERAL HENRY KNOX

soothed him with her hands, with her lips. For a moment of silence their eyes met. He understood. He knew now.

"How did she die?" His voice was hollow; but it was brave, with the strength of a strong man meeting grief.

Her hands rested on his arms as she told him; she did not try to keep them from resting there; it seemed natural and right that they should so rest, when she delivered the messages from his mother, her last on earth. Softly, in tones of tender sympathy, she told him how the woman had followed the fortunes of the fight; how she had passed away when the fight was lost; how her last thoughts had been of him; how she had blessed him, and invoked their love for him, telling them to make him brave; and how, at the last, she had gone with a smile, and a tear. But there was one thing she did not tell; though her heart beat full of the memory of it.

Without a sound, he stepped past her and knelt at the side of the bed. He knelt there long, pitiably still, no moan, no sigh, no sob passing his breast. When at last he arose, she, who had stood apart, respecting his grief as a thing sacred, knew that it was buried; that there must be no further word concerning it between them.

"May I ask you how it is that you have come?" she said, seeing him standing again.

"Being of the enemy, it is your right," he replied, stiffly, as though there must be nothing more between them, now that her message was given.

VERGENNES, FRENCH MINISTER OF FOREIGN AFFAIRS

"Say not so!" she cried, softly, with a hurt in her tone. "Why do you look upon me as an enemy?"

Ill at ease, he made no reply.

"Is it because I am in this house that you hold enmity against me?" she asked.

"I have given that no thought," he answered, honestly. He must be honest in all things, this John, as he must breathe.

"Or is it because my brothers fight against you?"

"Would not that be enough?"

"No!" Decisively, finally, she spoke.

He was silent. "Can we not be friends?" she said.

He was silent still, for a space. "I am content," he answered; and then, quickly: "I desire it."

She held forth her hand; he took and pressed it warmly.
"I must go," he whispered, letting it fall abruptly.
"Are you safe here?"
He smiled grimly. "Nevertheless, I must go," he said. "We who war can scarce wait for safety."

He was at the door; **she close behind him, lingering;** he was opening it softly; a strip of black night was along its outer edge, when there was a stirring within the inner room. Before the two could do more than look at each other, and toward the communicating door, it flew open, and Lucas Hempstead, his head bound in white, with a long grey cloak about his shoulders, emerged into the dim light.

"Now, what the devil is the meaning of this!" he cried, querulously; his voice was ragged and husky from drink; his face, vaguely discernible in the half-light, was bloated and red. John knew now why it was that the rushlight burned; why it was that the sister, lying on the bed fully dressed, watched and waited; why she had not cried out her alarm when a prowler entered from the night. With the knowledge, came a great pity for her and resentment against this brother; the incongruity of which, in him, he did not stop to consider. With the resentment arose again the feeling of repugnance he had experienced from the first, which had been submerged since in the larger hates of the war.

"What the devil does this fellow mean, coming here in the middle of the night!" went on the young Englishman, before the others could frame an answer. "And what the devil do you do, entertaining visitors in the dark?"

"It is one who came to inquire for your health," explained the sister, laying a restraining hand on John's sleeve, fearing lest he betray himself into danger. It was for him she told the untruth; he knew that, half consciously, —and wondered thereat afterward, when he recalled the scene.

THE DEATH OF GENERAL WARREN (*From the bronze doors of the Capitol at Washington, by Rogers*)

"A pretty time he takes to pay his visits!" snarled Lucas, approaching. "Who is my solicitous friend?"

John, seeing him come, and desiring to take to himself the responsibility of his presence, stepped forward to meet him, disengaging Nancy's hand from his sleeve as he advanced.

Lucas, peering into his features as he came closer, knew him. "In God's name, what do you here?" he cried, in a frenzy of anger. "Nay, I know your errand," he went on; "you come as a spy, and by my sword, so you shall hang as a spy!"

With that he strode to the door, flung it wide, and shouted into the night: "What, ho! The guard! Treason! A spy! Help, ho! The guard."

John, standing calmly in the center of the room, suffered him to make the outcry, forbearing to lay hand upon Nancy's brother. Not so the girl. Clutching his arm as he passed, she clung to him, striving to silence his lips with her hand.

In vain, from a far distance rose an answering cry, and the dim noise of a stir among men.

"Brother! What have you done?" cried Nancy, in terror, when he came back from his outcrying. "He came to seek his mother, who once lived here, and stopped while I told him concerning her!"

The girl grasped his wrist as he started across the room to seek his weapon. John, who had heretofore stood calmly by, to see that no harm came to her, listening the while to the noise of running men, coming ever nearer.

"Confound your impudence!" snarled the lieutenant. "Is this your regard for your honor, and your brother's? You are little better than a — "

That word was not spoken; it died in his throat, choked there with the breath that formed it by the hand of John.

"Unutterable dog!" roared the American, forgetting himself; forgetting the sister, whom they struck away in their struggle; oblivious to the sound of hurrying footsteps that echoed through the night from no great distance. "Retract, or by Heaven, you shall never speak word more!"

"Nan! Nan! My sword! My pistol! Quick! He is killing me! Run the rascal through!" Lucas struggled horribly to mouth the words, as the two writhed together.

Her name brought a return of self-control to John Stevens; he realized the presence of a woman; his brain recoiled from the thought that the woman was the sister of the man. He cast his adversary from him, with some force, for the two were close locked together. Lucas, reeling, fell, striking heavily against the floor, where he lay still, with rolling eyes. The sound of footsteps was in the narrow street; men, calling, hurried up and down to learn whence the alarm had come.

With a little sob of fright, Nancy knelt beside the prostrate man. "He lives," she whispered, turning to John. "He is not dead! Flee!"

The hastening feet were back and forth, before the door; voices were calling there. John moved no foot.

"You can do nothing! He lives! Go! They are at the door!"

THE GRAVE OF JAMES OTIS IN THE OLD GRANARY
BURIAL GROUND, BOSTON

Still he stood, gazing at her, and at the one prostrate at his feet; the aroused soldiers, having passed the door, were returning to it. She rose to her feet; she placed her hands —he had never noted how fair and soft they were —upon his shoulders. Her face was a prayer.

"If for no other reason, go because your country needs you!" Her voice was low, throbbing, intense; men were within paces of the door. "You are a brave people all," she went on, tumultuously. "You are passing brave! Flee; your country needs you!"

"My country?" — with surprise.

"Ay, your country, and your cause!"

Scarce knowing what he did, he took the upturned face between his hands, and kissed the pale forehead. With one stride, he was at the hearth, and, overturning the rushlight, with another he was at the door. As the dying light flickered and went out, he threw it open.

Bristling there, blacker lines against the black night sky, were bayonets of the King's soldiers! The men were upon him, seeking the alarm.

THE GRAVE OF PAUL REVERE IN THE OLD GRANARY BURIAL GROUND, BOSTON

CHAPTER IX

THE MAN OF FIRE

JOHN STEVENS, emerging from the cottage, pressed the soldiers roughly away, as one having authority over them. "Laggards!" he growled, fiercely, "you come late with your aid, God wot! The fellow is within; take him to the guard-house,—if he lives. I myself will report the matter at headquarters." He spoke as one having the right to command.

They, unsuspecting, entered the house he had quitted, leaving him alone in the street. With such haste as was seemly, he passed along the narrow way and turned into the first lane that offered.

The noise of a commotion about the cottage he had just left reached his ears as he hastened stealthily up the dark lane; the cries of soldiers, and the voice of Lucas raised in angry expostulations and commands. He went on, keeping

GENERAL RICHARD MONTGOMERY (*After the painting by C. W. Peale in the Philadelphia Museum*)

to the unfrequented lanes; a strategy that his intimate familiarity with the town made possible. The noise about the cottage arose to a hue and cry; he knew that the streets and lanes would shortly be swarming with soldiers looking for him. He broke into a run in those portions of his

157

way that were sufficiently obscured by darkness to make it safe.

As he ran he laid his plans to get out of the city. It would be impossible to cross Boston Neck; he must go to the American lines by water. He knew that except at those points where the British had erected batteries the waterfront was not thoroughly patroled. From the northwestern edge of Boston it was only a mile across the bay to the opposite shore, where General Putnam was posted in a redoubt. Making a wide circle, he swung around toward this direction and made his way to the water's edge.

He looked about for a boat; there was none in sight. He stripped off his clothes, rolled them into a bundle, fastened them to his shoulders with his belt, and plunged into the water just as a squad of searchers came running toward him. He was fifty yards from shore before the pursuers caught sight of him. They hallooed; he dived and swam beneath the surface. Coming to the top and glancing back over his shoulder, he saw his pursuers running up and down looking for a boat. The danger was not yet passed. The starlight on the water made him visible at a distance; concealment was impossible; if they found a boat they would surely take him.

The water was warm, the surface placid, the tide slack, and he had no currents to contend against. He was a trained swimmer; he had spent many boyhood hours in these same waters. There was a fighting chance; and he was a good fighter. A hundred yards, a hundred and fifty he proceeded. Still they had found no boat. Two hundred, three hundred, and there were no pursuers.

He was a quarter of the way across, swimming easily, watching the receding shore over his shoulder, when he discovered a craft putting out at a distance below. The advantage was with him; the boat took the water so far

from his point of departure that he was nearly three-quarters
of a mile ahead of it.   When he was in mid-stream the boat
had covered half the distance between them.   He heard
shouts on the shore he approached; the American pickets,
ever alert, had heard the firing and were at the water's
edge to see what it was all about.

He was three-quarters of the way across.   The following
boat was 200 yards behind.   The soldiers in it fired a volley
that sprinkled about him.   From the shore ahead were
answering shots.   A few more strokes, and he dived.
Coming to the top, the pursuers fired again; again his friends
ashore answered the fire, this time in greater volume, for
their number had increased.   He was going more slowly
now.   It became a question of the tenacity with which the
British pressed the pursuit, of how close they would be willing to go to the hostile shore.

CHATEAU DE RAMEZAY, MONTREAL, HEADQUARTERS OF THE CONTINENTAL
ARMY DURING THE AMERICAN OCCUPATION

He was within two hundred yards of the sheltering beach; the boat was not fifty yards behind. Out of the night ahead flashed a solid volley, heavier than any; the swimmer could hear it chattering against the planks of the craft; could hear groans and cries and curses, as some of the shot went home. The pursuers stopped; put about; returned. He was safe.

Morning was astir when he presented himself, wet as he was, at the mansion where Washington had headquarters. Early though it was, the commanding general sent to have him admitted. Washington sat at the table, as he had been sitting two days before, when John was last there. Those about him were fewer; there was one who had not been there on the other occasion; a young man with a brilliant eye, and a manner full of nervous enthusiasm, who took John's fancy in the fleeting glimpse he had of him.

GENERAL SIR GUY CARLETON (*From an engraving by A. H. Ritchie*)

Modestly, but with dignity, John reported what he had learned. Washington thanked him warmly, and he left. As he went, General Knox arose from the table and followed him, to take him by the hand. As they stood there, John muttering something in return, the one who was a stranger to him, the man of fiery eye, spoke for the first time.

"I am likely to borrow this Captain Stevens of you, General Washington," John heard him say.

Whereupon the young patriot went away in a glow, with a mist of gladness before his eyes that quite kept him from seeing Fontaine, entering the house as he left it.

The man of fire whom John had seen with the commander of the army was Colonel Benedict Arnold; what they
discussed was a plan to lead an expedition against Quebec,
proposed and fervently fostered by Arnold.

But the time was not ripe. From the beginning it had
been the policy of the colonies to exhaust every peaceful
resource in an attempt to obtain their rights before resorting
to force. Until the present the colonists had been acting
only on the defensive; it was not yet consistent with statesmanship to assume the offensive; the attention of the world
was fixed on them. Congress, actuated by this policy,
once more prepared with extreme caution and care a petition
from the colonies to George III, setting forth their grievances
and praying for their rights. Until an answer was returned,
no offensive operations should begin.

The petition was carried to court by Richard Penn, a
descendant of William Penn and an ardent loyalist. It was
signed by the delegates as individuals and not as members
of the Continental Congress, as a concession to the King of
England, who maintained that the Congress was an illegal
body, having no right to convene. George III would
neither receive the petition nor acknowledge it in any way.

QUEBEC IN 1775 (*From an old print*)

In spite of the fact that the document was signed by the delegates in their individual capacities, the monarch chose to consider it as an expression of the idea of a united America; an idea that, according to his view, was unknown to law or reason. He responded to it with a proclamation declaring the colonies in rebellion and calling upon all loyal subjects to assist in subduing them. He asked for 20,000 volunteers to send against the Americans.

But the people of England were not inclined toward the war. The enlistments failed. Conscription was considered, but the thought of it was so distasteful to British subjects that the plan was abandoned as too hazardous. Failing to recruit an army from his own subjects, the English King hired 20,000 mercenaries from Brunswick and Hesse, after a futile attempt to obtain them from Catherine of Russia. The troops were under Riedesel of Brunswick, and Knyphausen, Von Heister, and Donop, of Hesse. This hiring of foreign troops not only aroused the bitterest anger in America, but the disgusted indignation of Europeans as well. Frederick the Great of Prussia expressed himself strongly against it, and ordered that the soldiers be taxed in their passage through his kingdom, "like cattle going to foreign shambles."

Before news of the hiring of the Hessians had reached America, Congress, learning how their petition had been received and despairing of obtaining their ends peacefully, consented to the invasion of Canada. The plan was not only a military expedient, but had also its political aspect. It was believed that the Canadians could be won as allies by a successful campaign against Montreal and Quebec. The expedition was hastened by the news that Sir Guy Carleton, the British general commanding in Canada, contemplated a descent upon Ticonderoga.

Late in August General Richard Montgomery of New

VASSALL HOUSE, CAMBRIDGE, MASSACHUSETTS, OCCUPIED BY WASHINGTON 1775-76; KNOWN ALSO AS THE HOME OF LONGFELLOW 1837-82

York, with 2000 men, set out from Ticonderoga for Canada, intending to take Montreal and proceed thence to Quebec. General Philip Schuyler, commander of the army in New York, was prevented by illness from leading the expedition. On September 12 Montgomery laid siege to Saint Johns, which controlled Montreal. Carleton could gather only 900 defenders; after a siege of fifty days the place surrendered. November 12 Montgomery entered Montreal in triumph. A proclamation was issued immediately, urging the Canadians to lose no time in choosing delegates for the Continental Congress, but the citizens resisted all attempts to persuade them to join the Revolution against the mother country.

To coöperate with Montgomery, Benedict Arnold left the vicinity of Boston in September at the head of 1000 New England militia, with two companies of Pennsylvania riflemen and Morgan's Virginia sharpshooters. He had had his way concerning John Stevens, who was in command of one of the New England companies. The army passed in boats up the Kennebec River of Maine. The journey was difficult; as they ascended the river it became nearly impassable from tangled trees and frequent rapids. There were many portages; much of their provision was lost in the river; cold weather came on, and food ran short. Before the force penetrated to the Claudière, which empties into the Saint Lawrence, 200 of their number had succumbed to cold and hunger. Another 200 returned to New England, sick and disabled. In spite of the hardships, the fiery and impetuous Arnold brought 1000 men through to the river, and on November 13 led them out upon the Plains of Abraham.

But the task had only begun. The town had been forewarned; an immediate assault was impossible, and Arnold was forced to wait for Montgomery. Carleton, passing down the river from Montreal disguised as a countryman, entered Quebec and prepared for defence. Montgomery arriving on December 3, Arnold issued a challenge to the British to come out and fight, or surrender the town. Carleton would do neither. The Americans, suffering pitiably from cold and hunger, sat down to await developments. At the last Arnold and Montgomery decided upon the chivalrous, almost foolhardy, alternative of an assault.

The last night of the year came on bitterly cold; a blinding snow drove before the piercing wind. The American forces were divided into four columns. Two of them, fewer in numbers than the others, were to make a feint against the Upper Town, in front of the Plains of Abraham. Of the others, one under General Montgomery was to attack the Lower Town along the Saint Lawrence and assault Prescott Gate in the Upper Town

FREDERICK THE GREAT OF PRUSSIA

from the rear. Arnold, at the head of the fourth, was to attack along the Saint Charles, on the opposite side of Lower Town, and join Montgomery in the final assault on the gate.

In the dead of night the troops were marshaled in their respective positions. The signal was given. "Men of New York," said the brave Montgomery, "you will not fear to follow where your general leads. Forward!"

Through the bitter night the men swept on. A battery opened on them at close quarters, firing grape. In the first discharge Montgomery fell dead. His loss struck at the hearts of his followers; they struggled valiantly for a while, but fell back in confusion.

John Stevens, moving forward with his company on the opposite side of the town, heard the firing. He was weak with hunger and exposure; excitement played havoc with his nerves, and his limbs trembled. In front was Morgan with his riflemen. In the fore-

DEATH OF GENERAL MONTGOMERY (*From the painting by Trumbull*)

front of all dashed Benedict Arnold, shouting victoriously and waving his sword.

They pressed forward. The driving snow blinded them; the cold numbed. From the front burst the din of combat; the smell of burnt powder came with the stinging snow; their blood warmed. Step by step they fought onward.

There was a cry ahead. Some soldiers passed John, going to the rear. Between them they bore a wounded man. In the flash of musket-fire John saw that it was Arnold; Arnold, whom he had come to revere as all that was heroic; Arnold, the brave, the indomitable, the idol of his dreams of glory.

"Is he killed?" cried John, pausing for a moment in the fight as they bore him past.

"Nay, I am not killed!" made answer Arnold himself,

in feeble voice. "Forward! Forward! The town is ours!"

"Forward! Forward!" echoed John, his whole being stirred by the sight of his hero wounded.

He was at the front now, fighting madly. Above the dark mass of struggling men loomed the shadow of a huge figure: Daniel Morgan, now in command of the column. Through the streets, past barriers, against a murderous fire that swirled about them with the pelting snow, beset on all sides by the enemy, they fought on, even up to the gate of the Upper Town.

In the fight John, surrounded by a small squad of soldiers, became separated from the column and could get

THE TOMB OF MONTGOMERY IN SAINT PAUL'S CHURCH, NEW YORK CITY

no farther against the odds that opposed them. In spite of rash bravery, he and his small band were forced back, until his companions, to avoid capture, gave way and retreated, dragging him with them.

Bitterly did he lament the misfortune as they made their way along the streets over which they had come, deserted now that the combat had swept past. In the distance they heard the roar of battle; shots and cries, cheers and shrieks. Farther and farther into the heart of the city the noise penetrated.

Suddenly it ceased for a moment, and turned at last to glad cheers of victory. The party of fugitives, staring at each other in wonder at the change, listened long to distinguish the cries; listened for the call of the Virginia woodsmen who were with Morgan; for the yell of the New England militia. They heard only the huzzas of the British, and knew that Morgan was taken.

FREDERICK THE GREAT (*From the engraving by E. Hartmann*)

With heavy hearts they made their way in silence back to the Plains of Abraham, where the shattered American forces were gathering from the vain assault. All their labor, all their suffering, had been in vain; many of their comrades lay dead along the cruel streets of the town, and Montgomery, the well beloved, was no more.

Upon this scene of disappointment broke the great year of 1776, and on its first day General Washington spread to the heavens the first distinctive American standard. It was known as the Grand Union, or Cambridge Flag. Like the ensign permanently adopted as our national symbol, it is believed to have been the invention of Washington himself. It gave America the Stripes; the Stars were soon to come.

CHAPTER X

DORCHESTER HEIGHTS

"THIS talk of not being ready to fight is well enough, but when shall we be ready to fight, at the speed we are making? For my part, I believe this man Washington is no such great warrior as fame would have him, and I could wish we had a man of energy instead. Here he has been sitting down before Boston for eight precious months, and nothing has been done except much work with pick and shovel. We are fourteen thousand strong; we have a store of powder and ball; Henry Knox has dragged siege guns from Ticonderoga and Heaven knows where; the soldiers are impatient and eating their heads off; all this time the good people of Boston have been ground down by British soldiers; yet nothing is done! If Washington intends to fight, let him fight; if he does not, let him make place for one who will. There are plenty; there is Hancock, and Putnam, and Lee, and Artemas Ward, ready for the task; let them have a chance, say I!"

Lieutenant Culver, loitering with a group of officers about the yard of Harvard College on a day in spring, 1776, delivered himself in this fashion concerning the way matters had been

MARTHA WASHINGTON

conducted in the siege of Boston. Lieutenant Culver, be it said, had been recently found to be of no further service in connection with the staff of the general commanding. A murmur of mingled endorsement and dissent greeted the speech, some agreeing with the disgruntled lieutenant, and others supporting their commander-in-chief with more or less vehemence. One there was who entered the lists with hot fury to champion Washington. It was Fontaine Stevens.

"What you say is folly!" he cried, with flushed face and strident voice. "Instead of supporting Washington as you should in his efforts to make an army out of a motley array of raw recruits and to supply it with the necessities of war, you and the rest of your pack cry at his heels because, forsooth, he is so much wiser than you that you cannot understand him."

" 'Tis well enough for you to say so, for you are one who has been through so many

CUTTER HOUSE, ROXBURY, MASSACHUSETTS, HEADQUARTERS
OF AMERICAN OFFICERS DURING THE BOSTON SIEGE

wars and are of his staff as well," sneered one who had
supported the original speaker, "but I cannot see what he
has gained by dawdling. For my part, I agree with President Hancock, who urged him to set fire to the town of
Boston and burn it to the ground, if needful, to drive out
the cursed English. It is high time that he showed his
mettle."

"Mettle, say you!" returned Fontaine; "I will tell
you what his mettle is! He has had the courage to stand
his ground against the whole pack of you, because he knew
better than you could know; and as for fighting,—you do
not know, do you, that he would have made an assault
last week if his officers had not spoken so strongly against
it? When the time is ripe you will see that he can act!"

Into what acrimonious wrangling the discussion would
have run cannot be told, for before any of the group had
subdued to his own voice the clamor that arose at this point,
an orderly rode up and directed Lieutenant Stevens to
report immediately at headquarters.

The expressions of the young lieutenant are fairly repre-
sentative both of the lack of proper subordination in the
army and of the popular humor of the time. Having no
realization of warfare on the scale which obtained about
Boston, and burning with patriotic ardor, soldiers and
citizens generally had small patience with the cautious
delays of the commander-in-chief. Almost they would
rather have struck a blow and lost than not to have struck
at all. The popular fervor grew to white heat when news
came that the town of Portland, Maine, had been wantonly
assaulted by four British ships under Captain Mowatt on
October 16, 1775, and a large part of it set afire and burned
by shells and grenades. They were still further incensed
by the news that George III was sending hired Hessians
against them. Washington bore their clamorous criticism

with a patient equanimity consistent with his high character and sublime moral courage.

The news of the burning of Portland and of the hiring of Hessians by the English King reached Congress at Philadelphia on the same day, October 31, and threw that body into intense excitement. Those who favored a temporizing policy were driven into a helpless minority. Some of the members were ready to declare independence at once. Congress advised New Hampshire, Virginia, and South Carolina to frame new republican governments as Massachusetts had done; it urged South Carolina to seize the British vessels then in her waters; it appointed committees to correspond with foreign powers, and took steps for the invasion of Canada.

THOMAS PAINE (*From the portrait by Romney*)

The country was further aroused by the publication in January, 1776, of a pamphlet, written by Thomas Paine, called "Common Sense." It made gross charges against the English, and urged that the colonies were already practically severed from England by the course of events. The pamphlet, endorsed by Samuel Adams and Benjamin Franklin, struck a popular chord; the presses could not turn copies out fast enough to supply the demand. At the same time Parliament gave emphasis to Paine's arguments by closing the ports of America to the world, and instructing British sea-captains to impress Americans for service at sea; a measure to which Congress replied by declaring the ports thrown open, and by issuing letters of marque.

The first fruits of the new state of affairs were brought forth in North Carolina. This colony had grown in population until it ranked fourth in America. A proportion of the inhabitants were Highland Scotch who had emigrated on the defeat of the Pretender at Colloden. Hoping for the coöperation of these Scots, who were loyal, Sir Henry Clinton was sent from Boston in January with 2000 troops to subjugate the colony, and Sir Peter Parker was dispatched from Ireland with a fleet of ten ships-of-war and an army of seven regiments to assist in the work.

At the same time Donald Macdonald, after some communication with the royal governor, Martin, who had taken refuge on a British vessel, raised a force of 1600 Scots and started from the mountains for the coast. But North Carolina had its militia. Aroused by the news of Macdonald's advance, they gathered 1000 strong under Colonel Richard Caswell, and made a stand against the Loyalists at Moore's Creek, where, on February 27, 1776, they defeated and routed the Scots, taking 900 prisoners, 2000 stands of arms, and £15,000 in gold. When Clinton arrived he was afraid to land, and cruised about Albemarle Sound waiting for Sir Peter Parker. North Carolina forthwith assembled a legislature, and declared her independency.

SIR HENRY CLINTON

Matters in Virginia were not less significant. Lord Dunmore issued a proclamation in November offering freedom to negro and indented slaves who would join in putting down the rebels. The proclamation had no other effect than to arouse the inhabitants to active hostilities, for the slaves were contented and happy with their masters and sided with them. Learning in the same month that a party of rebels was on the way from North Carolina to take Norfolk, the largest town of Virginia at the time, Dunmore constructed a fort at the Great Bridge across the Elizabeth River, commanding Norfolk, and prepared for them.

The Virginians did not wait for the help coming from North Carolina. On December 9, a party of sharpshooters, in which John Marshall served as lieutenant, posted itself opposite the fort and attacked it. In fifteen minutes fighting the English lost sixty-one men, and Dunmore withdrew. The Virginians did not suffer a single casualty. Dunmore fled to the British ship *Liverpool*, which had just sailed into the harbor. January 1, seeing that he could not hold the town, he vindictively set fire to it. For three days the conflagration raged, added to by shells from the British vessel. Every house in town was destroyed, leaving the inhabitants without shelter in the midst of winter.

Reports of these affairs reaching the American lines about Boston from time to time served to make the impatience of the soldiers and citizens more acute, and to increase the difficulty of Washington's task. But the time had now come when the querulous were to be appeased beyond their highest hopes. A master stroke, long contemplated, was ready to be delivered. To appreciate the excellence of its strategy it is necessary to fully

GEORGE III OF ENGLAND

understand the topography about Boston at the time of the siege.

Boston was situated on a peninsula connected with the mainland through Roxbury by a narrow neck of land. This neck was completely fortified by both belligerents; there the armies were in a deadlock. To the north Boston approached close to Charlestown peninsula, where the heights of Bunker Hill commanded the town and the bay. These heights had been occupied by the English since the battle of Bunker Hill. The only other near approach of the mainland was south of the city. Here Dorchester Heights frowned down on the Bay and town. All winter long Washington had had his attention on this point. He knew it to be the key to the position; he dreaded lest Howe should occupy it before he himself was ready to do so. But Howe, easy-going by nature, neglected his opportunity, and he was guilty of a fatal omission.

At sunset that day there could be heard the bursting roar of heavy guns firing from the works at Somerville, East Cambridge, and Roxbury. Throughout the night detonations shook the air; never had the firing been so fierce and incessant. The ground shook; the night was aglare.

Out toward Dorchester Heights, with stealthy tread and whispered word of command, crept a long column, silent, obscured by the night. Eight hundred men led the way, accompanied by wagons laden with crowbars and spades, hatchets, hammers, and nails. The wheels of the wagons were muffled with wisps of hay; the axles ran with grease; the noise of the harnesses was deadened with wrapped rags. Behind them came 1200 more men, bringing carts that carried timbers and bales of hay; in the rear came the heavy siege-guns that Henry Knox had gathered from far and near. In a mysterious silence the column wound its way up the heights overlooking the town and harbor.

GEORGE WASHINGTON *(From the portrait attributed to John Vanderlyn in the Capitol at Washington)*

All night long, while the British were occupied by the furious cannonading along their front, the men worked like ants, throwing up batteries and redoubts, mounting the heavy guns. In the morning the British, looking across the waters, saw the Heights heavily fortified and swarming with Americans. Astonished, dismayed, the English generals gathered together to decide what should be done. In the afternoon Lord Percy was ordered to take 300 men and storm the Heights. Neither he nor his soldiers had heart for the task; the memory of Bunker Hill was still heavy upon them. Nevertheless the force proceeded in boats as far as Castle Island, where they prepared for the assault.

In the American lines there was eager rejoicing. Six years before, on that very day, British troops had shot down citizens of Boston in the streets; it was a fitting hour for retribution. Washington, passing along the lines to exhort the men, was received with acclaiming cheers; he had won his long, lingering fight against their doubt and impatience. Tears came to the eyes of Fontaine as he rode beside the commander.

But vengeance was not yet. Before Percy was ready to move, a wind-storm arose, becoming so violent that his troops could not embark. During the night and the next day the wind continued; by the time it had subsided sufficiently to permit of the passage the Americans had made their position secure, and Boston was untenable. Howe, realizing it, prepared for evacuation. He let it be understood by Washington that if his troops were fired upon in leaving he would lay the town in ashes. For nine days the work of evacuation went forward. On March 17, the British army sailed away for Halifax, taking with them 900 Tories, who feared to remain among their former fellow-citizens. Thus, with the loss of not more than twenty lives, Washington, with consummate skill, drove the enemy from Boston, whither they were never to return during the long years that lay ahead of the patriots.

Washington, making formal entry March 20, was received with unparalleled rejoicing. For ten months the citizens had been in a beleaguered city; their joy at their liberation knew no bounds. In spite of the deliberate departure of the British, there were signs of haste and confusion throughout the town. They left more than 200 serviceable cannon, ten times more powder and ball than the Continental army had ever seen, and an immense quantity of gun-carriages, muskets, and military stores of every sort.

Ezra Stevens, private of the ranks, and proud of it, finding himself in Boston, availed himself of leave from his captain to search out Catherine, his long and dearly beloved. His own heart, throbbing within his juvenile breast, made the noise of the knocker faint and futile as he let it fall.

Catherine herself opened the door; never had she been so beautiful. He had not seen her since that day when he had braved the British lieutenant in her presence —the lieutenant he had taught himself to consider his rival and

CASTLE ISLAND, BOSTON HARBOR

personal enemy. The anxiety of the siege had added to her beauty a half maturity it had wholly lacked before, setting the first contour of womanhood in her soft cheeks; now the relief felt in the occupation of the patriot army brought a light into her face that was like a halo.

Yet there was something subtly sad and still in her expression; a shadow of a haunting dread or grief that had not been allayed. It was in her eyes when she looked over Ezra's shoulders as he stood on the steps of the house, as though she half hoped some one might be following him; it was in her manner when she welcomed him, preoccupied, without heed of him, failing to see the emotion that the meeting stirred within him.

Farmer's youth though he was, Ezra observed the look and the manner; for the heart of the lover is quick. His spirits fell; the doubt he had felt as he came thither through the streets of the town, that had been with him, indeed, ever since his last visit to the house, grew to certainty. Sorrow and rage possessed him; rage against this other man. For her, for Catherine, there was nothing but love; miserable, but steadfast.

The talk between them ran trivially upon incidents in the town and the army during the siege, and upon matters of import of the day; she attended slightingly what was said, both by herself and him; she could not come to speak closely of anything. At last Ezra, in despair, brought himself to learn the truth he dreaded from her own lips.

"During the

TOM PAINE'S HOMESTEAD, LONG ISLAND, NEW YORK

siege," he said, "or in the battles before it, were any of those hurt who lived with you? The British officers, I mean?"

For a moment she appeared puzzled; his heart died, for it seemed to him that she dissembled. "Oh," she said, with the light of understanding coming abruptly into her face; "oh, you mean Lieutenant and Major Hempstead? They were unhurt. For a long time they were not with us, and I saw little of either of them."

Ezra looked at her in amazement, a new hope bounding within him. This gaudy lieutenant, then, was not his rival! Or, if he would be, he was nothing to Catherine! Words were on his lips; words that had been surging through the months of their separation.

Before he spoke the least one of them, hesitating through sheer awe of what he would say, she broke into his purpose.

"John! John!" she said. "What of him? Why do we hear nothing of him? Know you aught of him, Ezra?"

Whereupon Ezra, private soldier and patriot, understood many things, to the end that he understood practically nothing at all.

GENERAL HOWE EVACUATING BOSTON (*From the engraving by M. A. Wageman*)

CHAPTER XI

THE BIRTH OF THE FLAG

IT was a dull morning, the morning of August 27, 1776.
Nine thousand patriots, under General Israel Putnam,
lay in the fortifications on Brooklyn Heights, and along the
roads to the east and south, in advance of the position.   In
the waters south of Long Island, off Gravesend, lay the
English fleet, under Lord Howe; with it
was a British army, commanded by his
brother, General Sir William Howe,
come to strike a blow, hoping to take
the Americans unawares.

But Washington had outguessed
them.   New York province was the
center of the long line of colonies in
rebellion; New York City was the
key to the center.   For the British
to pierce the center was to
divide the belligerents, and to
hold the province was to sever
the enemy.   The ground was
cogently strategic; moreover, it
was thought by the British that

LIBERTY BELL, INDEPENDENCE HALL,
PHILADELPHIA

New York was half-hearted in its resistance to them.
Knowing all these things, General Washington had assumed, when General Howe left Boston for Halifax, that
he would return to strike here.   He was right; the blow
was about to fall.

The American general could hardly hope to hold the
city; his force was too small; the line of defence was too long,

and too exposed to the seas, of which the British had indisputable control. The best Washington could do with his 18,000 troops was to retard the enemy. To this end the shore of Manhattan was girded with small forts; the streets in the lower end of the city, from the East to the Hudson

BATTLE PASS ROCK, PROSPECT PARK, BROOKLYN

River, were barricaded; a strong line of redoubts ran from river to river below Canal Street; at the upper end of the Island and along the Jersey shore were other fortresses. Among them Washington disposed his force with remarkable judgment. On Brooklyn Heights, which commanded the city as Bunker Hill and Dorchester Heights had commanded Boston, were 9000 men under Putnam; —and now the blow was about to be received.

Meanwhile, much had happened. General Washington had been called to Philadelphia by Congress, arriving there May 22, and remaining until June 5. During this visit, Washington, in company with Robert Morris and George

Ross, delegates to Congress, called at the little upholstery shop in Arch Street kept by the latter's aunt, the widow Elizabeth Ross, in regard to a new national standard, the Stars and Stripes. The visitors produced a roughly drawn design, showing the thirteen red and white stripes of the Grand Union Flag, but with a blue canton in the corner on which were thirteen six-pointed stars. Mrs. Ross showed the three men how a five-pointed star could be cut from a piece of folded paper with a single clip of the scissors. Agreeing with her that five points looked better than six, the design was altered at her suggestion. Soon after, this design, made in color by William Barrett, a painter of reputation, was sent her, and she made the first Stars and Stripes.

LOOKOUT HILL MONUMENT ON THE SITE OF THE BATTLE OF LONG ISLAND

Mrs. Ross, affectionately known as Betsy, always said that Morris and Ross were a committee from Congress. There is no record of their appointment as such, but as the adoption of a national flag implies the assertion of national independence, there was adequate reason for secrecy at the time. But independence was not to be long delayed.

On Fourth of July, 1776, the Continental Congress, under instructions from the colonies, had declared that the provinces were no longer under the authority of Great Britain, but were free and independent; a new Nation had been born, henceforth to be styled "The United States of America." Congress, already desired by North Carolina to make such a declaration, was urged to the step on May 14 by the assembly of Virginia, under the leadership of Mason, Henry, Pendleton, and James Madison. The news of Virginia's position was received with joy throughout the country; Rhode Island immediately instructed Congress that she should support anything that body did; town-meetings held throughout Massachusetts sent similar messages.

Following the suggestion of the Virginia Assembly, Richard Henry Lee introduced before Congress, on June 7, resolutions declaring "that these United Colonies are, and of right ought to be, free and independent States; that they are absolved from allegiance to the British Crown; and that all political connection between them and the State of Great Britain is, and ought to be, totally dissolved; that a plan

BETSY ROSS HOUSE, ARCH
STREET, PHILADELPHIA

of confederation be prepared and transmitted to the respective colonies, for their consideration and approbation."

A lively debate arose over the expediency of such a measure at that time; it was finally decided to postpone action on the resolutions for three weeks, until the several colonies could be heard from. The next day there appeared in a Philadelphia paper, assurances from Boston that her citizens would support the measure "with their lives and the remnants of their fortunes." The other colonies, following the lead of Virginia and Massachusetts, the two most important of the thirteen, fell rapidly into line. Connecticut supported the motion

THOMAS JEFFERSON: AUTHOR OF THE DECLARATION OF INDEPENDENCE (*After the Photogravure by William Sartain*)

on June 14; New Hampshire on the following day. William Franklin, the loyalist governor of New Jersey, having prorogued the assembly of that colony when it met to deliberate on the question, was arrested and sent to Connecticut for safe keeping; the assembly deciding in favor of the resolutions on the twenty-second. In Pennsylvania the proprietary interests and the peace-loving Quakers opposed it, but a series of meetings in the counties of the province supported the plan. Delaware favored it, and Maryland was brought to the same action through the efforts of Samuel Chase and Charles Carroll of Carrollton. By the time debate on the resolutions was resumed, July 1, every colony had been heard from in favor of the motion save only New York.

This colony contained a large number of loyalists, and the patriotic citizens hesitated, foreseeing that the region would be the scene of civil war as well as invasion, and knowing that their one seaport, on which they depended for their prosperity, being a commercial community, would be closed. Howe was already at Staten Island with a large

READING THE DECLARATION OF INDEPENDENCE FROM
THE STATE HOUSE, BOSTON

force. Carleton, having retaken Montreal and driven Arnold into New York, threatened them by way of Ticonderoga, and Sir John Johnson, son of Sir William Johnson of French and Indian War fame, had a large following of Tories and Indians in the northern part of the State. The situation in New York was further complicated by the recent discovery of a plot concocted between Governor Tryon and the Tory party to blow up the magazine and kill or capture General Washington.

Dickinson of Pennsylvania, while admitting the premises and being in complete sympathy with the principles involved, opposed the measure on the ground that the colonies could gain no strength by the step; that they would be assuming a position from which they could not recede; that France and Spain, on whom they depended, would look with jealousy at a Protestant power arising in the West, and would throw their strength to England; and, finally, that the action was premature in that there was no federal government in existence. On the preliminary vote all the colonies voted in favor of the resolutions excepting Pennsylvania, Delaware, South Carolina, and New York. The last was excused from voting, the delegates not yet having received instructions. On the formal vote Lee's motion was unanimously carried.

WILLIAM ALEXANDER, GENERAL LORD STIRLING (*From the engraving by G. R. Hall*)

A committee, composed of Thomas Jefferson, Franklin, John Adams, Roger Sherman, and Robert Livingston, was appointed to draft a Declaration of Independence. The famous document, prepared largely by Jefferson, was submitted to Congress on July 4 and formally adopted that same evening. The joy of the waiting populace of Philadelphia, when they heard the Liberty Bell proclaiming the event, knew no bounds; as the news traveled over the country it was received with tremendous acclaim —with torchlight processions, bonfires, the ringing of bells and firing of cannon.

New York learned of the Declaration of Independence at the same time that its populace had news of a victory of the American arms in South Carolina. Clinton, baffled in his plan to subdue North Carolina, had continued to coast about, waiting for Sir Peter Parker with the fleet from Ireland. Parker was bringing with him Lord Cornwallis. Arriving at last, the combined forces proceeded against Charleston, being led to believe by Governor Campbell of South Carolina that they would have an easy victory there

LORD STIRLING AT THE BATTLE OF LONG ISLAND   (*From the painting by Chappell*)

because of the strong loyalist sentiment among the inhabitants.

They were disappointed; Colonel Moultrie, hearing of their approach, built a fort of palmetto logs and sand on Sullivan's Island, garrisoned it with 800 raw militia, and on June 18 repulsed Parker's fleet, consisting of ten men-of-war, after a terrific artillery duel lasting ten hours. The shots from the fleet, sinking into the spongy palmetto logs, did no harm, while the balls from the fort badly battered the wooden ships. A storming party of British sent against the fort was baffled by the depth of water in a lagoon that they had expected to cross. At the close of the fight only one of the ten British vessels remained seaworthy; Parker's flag-ship was practically a wreck, he himself was wounded, and 210 of the British sailors were slain. The American loss in killed and wounded was thirty-seven. The victory was nearly ruined by the meddling of General Charles Lee, who would have ordered Moultrie to abandon the fort had he not been prevented by Rutledge, president of the provincial Congress. It was in this fight that Sergeant Jasper achieved fame, leaping over the parapet when the flag was shot down, and nailing it to the flagpole.

On July 9, soon after the arrival of the news of this victory was received in New York, that colony became a

RETREAT OF THE AMERICANS ACROSS GOWANUS CREEK AT THE BATTLE OF LONG ISLAND   (*From the painting by Chappell*)

State by adopting the Declaration of Independence, and the patriot soldiers, by way of celebrating, threw down the leaden statue of George III on the Bowling Green and cast it into bullets to be fired at his soldiers.

But before they could be fired, there was a lull. General Howe was forced to suspend the blow to await the arrival of his brother, Richard Lord Howe, who was on the way to assume command of the British operations, and who bore explicit authority from Lord North to negotiate with the Americans. His authority extended to the granting of pardon to all who desisted from armed rebellion and assisted in restoring tranquillity. He issued a proclamation to this effect upon his arrival, which, coming to Congress indirectly, was published and spread broadcast by that body, with grim irony, bringing ridicule upon him and his superiors at home. "We have done nothing to be pardoned for," said the Americans.

Howe desired to treat with Washington. It was impossible to treat with him as the general of the American army; that would be a recognition of the existence of a government under the Continental Congress, a point England could not concede. Therefore a message was sent to him, directed to George Washington, Esquire. Colonel Reed, receiving the messenger, informed him that there was no such person in the American army.

Howe, taking the hint followed with another addressed to "George Washington, Esquire, etc., etc." Colonel Patterson, who brought the message, explained that the etceteras meant everything. "Indeed," returned Washington, with a smile, "they might mean anything." He declined to receive the message, sending the colonel back to Lord Howe with no other word than his very best compliments. Thereafter Washington received his full military title; a dignity for which he contended, not because of empty punctiliousness or personal vanity, but as a point in statesmanship.

Now Howe had abandoned peace measures, and the blow was about to be struck. The Americans, resting on the Heights, were prepared to receive it. From the lower Bay, where the British were to land, one road led along the coast to Brooklyn; this was guarded by an outpost of troops upon a range of hills, under William Alexander of New Jersey, known as Lord Stirling by virtue of being claimant to a lapsed earldom of Scotland. Another led through Flatbush, over the same hills extended; here stood General Sullivan. Farther in, swinging far to the north, was the Jamaica

Fort Moultrie, Sullivan's Island, Charlestown

road, passing at last beyond the hills at their northern end, and so to the rear of the American advance lines. Here was no one to guard; the 9000 men of Putnam were too few.

Lieutenant Fontaine Stevens, assigned to Stirling's staff, stood by the side of his general in the early morning watching for sight of the foe. For four days Howe had reconnoitered the position, being well taught by the experience of Gage at Bunker Hill; now he was moving. Word of the advance had come to Stirling at 2 o'clock.

Anon the shock came. Long lines, flaming red, wheeled into sight; up burst the blast of musketry and bellow of cannon. All along the wooded hill where the patriots stood spoke an answer; first like the tapping of dull small bells, rising to an anthem, to a pæan of clamorous throated chimes, hoarse and heavy.

"Hah! They be Scots!" quoth my Lord of Stirling, making out the dress of the enemy through the gathering light. It was the Highlanders who attacked; 6000 of them, under General Grant.

Fontaine, running his eye over the field, drew a quivering breath. "Where are they who say we will not fight!" he exclaimed, with youthful emotion. "See how we stand, 1600 against an host! Behold the men of Maryland speaking for liberty."

Stirling, old soldier that he was, said nothing, compressing his lips grimly; but in his eye was a light that was eloquent. For the first time since time was, the Americans met regulars in open field —and they held. 'Fore God, they held!

Hark! What was that? That dull booming roar far to the left? For an hour the sound of Sullivan, engaged with De Heister's Hessians, had come to the ears of those with Stirling; but this sound was farther to the left, and in the rear. They who heard grew pale; the fight was behind them. Cornwallis, Clinton, Percy, under Howe in person, marching all night, had passed the end of the American line by the Jamaica road, where was no guard; the 9000 were all too few!

"Sullivan is attacked in rear," came word. Still the men under Stirling fought; the men of Maryland, of Rhode Island, of Pennsylvania, holding the foe in check, though it was the first open field on which Americans had met the British; though it was a struggle against odds of nearly four to one. Until the dread noise of fighting in their rear was upon them; until singing shot stung from behind, they stood. Then, and then only, they gave way, dissolving into a seething mass.

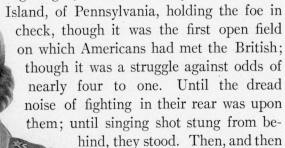

It was not panic that seized them. It was confusion, uncertainty, the impossibility of taking stand to meet the foe face to face,

COLONEL WILLIAM MOULTRIE (*From the engraving by A. H. Ritchie*)

that crumpled them. Crowding, twisting, jostling each other, unable to fire because of their own friends mingled with the enemy, they tumbled back against the base of the Heights, Lord Stirling making such order as was possible out of the confusion, and saving what he could from the wreck.

Most he saved, but he himself was taken. Fontaine, borne along against his will in the hurly-burly, saw him laid hold of by the Scots who surrounded him, men of his own land.

Now those who had stood through four valiant hours, streaming heightward, were mingling with fugitives from Sullivan's command; not fugitives through fear, but through disaster, through the mechanics of battle. Sullivan him-

self, striving heroically to save the line, casting himself
against an implacable fate, had been taken.

The red-coats pressed close against the mingled mass,
shooting, stabbing with bayonets. The Hessians were
there, too, killing; but not, as has been told, in lust of blood,

SIEGE OF CHARLESTOWN   (*From the Painting by Chappell*)

in savage butchery. They killed, lest, in the wild struggle,
they be killed; as many of them were.

Uprose above the mingled mass of Americans a man,
bulky, tremendous in valor, fighting back gloriously against
the driving foe. Blood was on his brow; shouting, he
brushed it from his eyes, that he might see better. About
him were a stout few, holding the brunt of battle in check,
stemming the flow of an army. Fontaine looked lovingly,
and with envy, upon him.

As he looked, the man fell; as he fell, Fontaine gave forth
a cry that pierced the din of war; for the brave one, the
magnificent in valor, was John Stevens!

Through the turmoil that set about him Fontaine pressed
toward the spot where he had seen him last, forgetting all
but that he, who once had failed to meet his private foe,

was braver than the many brave who had stood about him. Closer he pressed to the fatal spot, not giving time to consider by what strange chance the other had come there to the thick of death, from the death they believed he had died at Quebec;

DEFENSE OF FORT MOULTRIE, SOUTH CAROLINA (*From the painting by J. A. Oertel*)

for in the many long months since that fight none had heard word of him.

He came upon a gaunt, haggard youth, a slip of a lad, carrying as burden one stricken down. The burden was huge for his bony limbs and his thin back; it was John, wounded beyond consciousness. In battle men do mighty things.

"Save him! Save him!" cried the Southern youth to the other, thinking of nothing but that John was brave and worthy to be cherished.

The lad looked at him who spoke; in his eyes was both immeasurable grief and high determination.

"Get him away!" cried Fontaine. He laid his shoulder

under the burden; between them they bore the wounded man fast to the rear.

"In the city is one will succor him," spoke Lieutenant Stevens, of Virginia, when they had brought him safe away, "Robert Stevens, of New York, his cousin. Bear him thither; he will be known among them. I cannot go; I must stay."

Without a word, the lad lifted John upon his shoulder, making his way toward the waterside, where boats were.

Who was he bearing the great burden? It was Ezra, his cousin; Ezra, whose love dream was shattered by the love Catherine bore for the wounded man he was carrying to safety. And in his breast as he stumbled along, was grief, great grief, and the love of a strong heart for them both!

SERGEANT JASPER'S MONUMENT, CHARLESTON, SOUTH CAROLINA

CHAPTER XII

SOPHRONIA

IT was mid-morning of September 15, nineteen days after the battle of Long Island. Ezra Stevens, ill at ease, conscious of more elbow than he had ever dreamed of and bitterly regretting an interminable length of leg, sat in the drawing-room of the Robert Stevens mansion, in New York City. Opposite him, beautiful, tender, radiant, with no shadow on her soft cheeks, was Catherine, who had come there from Boston, through a pretty childish whim to be near her father, commanding one of the fortresses on the Jersey shore. The two gazed raptly at Lieutenant Fontaine Stevens, hearing wisdom from his full lips.

"The skill of General Washington in escaping from General Howe after our disaster on Long Island has never been paralleled in history!" quoth that young officer, glowing with enthusiasm. "Overwhelmed in front, and with water behind him over which the enemy had complete mastery, he extricated himself without the loss of a man. It was superb. You should have beheld him, standing there through the dreary night, when the hearts of all were stilled in despair, directing Colonel Glover and his fishermen-soldiers of Gloucester and Marblehead! Calm, serene, confident, inspiring hope where there was nothing to hope, he was master of the moment to the least last muffled oar in the hands of his fishermen-soldiers. When the last man was safe, and only then, he took boat and left!"

200

COLONEL JOHN GLOVER (*From a pencil drawing from life by Trumbull*)

"But he is running away, isn't he?" ventured Catherine, timidly. She knew nothing of war; she only knew that the man she worshiped was in a sick-room in that house, and that he must not fall into the hands of the English.

"Nay, he is not running away; he is retreating, a distinction civilians find it deplorably difficult to make," quoth the young marvel of military knowledge from Virginia. "He cannot hope to hold the city now, with Brooklyn Heights in the enemy's hands and the water under their control. General Washington has done the best possible; he has re-formed his lines along the Harlem River, leaving Putnam in New York City to hold the British in check as long as possible. He can only hope to retard them, at best."

"If it is so easy for the British to take New York, why have they not done it?" asked Ezra. In his tone and manner was nothing more than a desire for information.

"Because Howe had hopes of restoring peace without more war," explained Fontaine, who, after all, had much knowledge of the situation, acquired in gossip about headquarters. "At bottom, he is friendly toward us, and opposed to the British policy of oppression. You know, do you not,

BILLOP MANSION, TOTTENVILLE, STATEN ISLAND, WHERE THE PEACE CONFERENCE BETWEEN GENERAL HOWE, FRANKLIN, RUTLEDGE, AND JOHN ADAMS TOOK PLACE AFTER THE BATTLE OF LONG ISLAND

that General Sullivan was sent by him to consult with the Continental Congress, to see what might be done? There are those who complain of him for undertaking the service; for my part, I believe he acted honestly, for the best good.

INTERVIEW AT HOWE'S HEADQUARTERS BETWEEN LORD HOWE AND THE COMMITTEE FROM THE CONGRESS (*From the painting by Chappell*)

Congress received Howe's advances t e m p e r a t e l y, sending Franklin, Rutledge, and John Adams to confer with him at Staten Island. Of course, nothing came of it, except a chance for us to get our breath. And now, if I mistake not, Howe is about to move. Even this morning there is talk of a British man-of-war ascending the Hudson and East Rivers, to cut us off; which reminds me that I must return to headquarters without further delay."

Catherine followed him to the door as he was taking his departure. "Is there no hope?" she whispered, anxious for the man lying hurt above. "Will the English come?"

"Ay, girl; I fear they will," returned Fontaine, gently. "If you will breathe no word of it," he went on, impulsively, "I will tell you that even now I am returning from bearing an order to Putnam to withdraw."

With that he left, and Catherine returned to the drawing-room, where Ezra, more ill at ease than ever now he was alone with her, fumbled about for words.

"He is growing strong, you say?" he asked, at last. "You are certain he is growing strong?"

"Oh, yes, yes," answered the girl, understanding that he spoke of John, and showing in speech and manner what happiness she had in his recovery. "Why have you not been to see him, Ezra?" she went on, in her old friendly way.

"I have been many times, as often as I could find leave, to inquire," the boy replied. "I did not come in; I did not wish to intrude."

"Nonsense," said the girl; whereat his heart leapt, for he was only a lad.

"How came he to be there, at the battle?" he asked. "I have not learned that."

Catherine's face glowed with joyful pride. "He was with Arnold until spring," she answered, "while that brave man was striving to accomplish the capture of the city against which he had marched. Then, when Carleton was reinforced and the Americans retreated into New York, leaving Montreal to be retaken by the British, John stayed with them —they were afraid, all the time, that Carleton would advance on Ticonderoga —until Arnold wanted some one to take messages to Washington. He knew what manner of man John is, and sent him. That is how he came upon the field; for he arrived the night before the battle."

The joy in her face lighted it into a new beauty. Ezra, perceiving it, was utterly downcast; though he joyed, too, in his cousin's valor.

"Pray Heaven he may not fall into their hands!" exclaimed the girl, fervently, after a pause, in which each had been absorbed in thought.

"You are like to have to do more than pray for that,"

came a voice from the doorway. Looking quickly, the two saw Sophronia entering.

Without more ado, Ezra took himself off, precipitately, aflame with bashfulness.

"Sophronia, what can you mean?" cried Catherine, when the lad was gone, coming to her as the weaker seeks the stronger in time of stress.

"The British will soon be here," said Sophronia, with impressive calm, "and it is likely that Lieutenant and Major Hempstead will spend much time in this house, being, in a manner, of kin. For his very life, he must not fall into their hands. Seal your lips, child."

"I will! I will! But what shall I do?" Catherine was all consternation.

"Do nothing, but be cautious," returned Sophronia, leaning over to kiss her upon the forehead; a cold, studied kiss, as any one might know but the child that received it.

Master Robert Stevens of New York, man of affairs, rich banker, was finding it difficult to interest himself in the message he held before him. There was a vacancy in his gaze; he was thinking of other things. Howbeit the letter told of the occupation of the city that afternoon by the English, including a report of Washington's futile attempt to hinder Howe's landing at Kip's Bay until Putnam had time to evacuate the city. But it was not the insubordination of of Washington's men that disturbed the banker. Neither did he find comfort in the interesting account of how Mrs. Lindley Murray, with intuitive knowledge of Howe's disposition, had lured him and his chief officers to luncheon when they came to cut off Putnam's retreat, and held them there, with their army halted, until the Americans were able to get away, thus accomplishing what the New England brigades failed to do.

Clearly, Robert Stevens was troubled in spirit. He rustled his correspondent's news; he tumbled his white hair with nervous hand; he bit his lip; he cleared his throat frequently, as though he felt restriction there; he even frowned, which was a thing the man of affairs rarely did, even when alone. In the midst of such demonstrations of annoyance, Mistress Stevens entered the room, resplendent, beautiful.

"Shall I disturb you, Mr. Stevens?" she said.

"Indeed, that can hardly be, my dear," returned her husband, as he placed a chair for her.

"What news have you had to-night?" she asked, indifferently, as she seated herself, as though with nothing more than a civil intention to make conversation.

Robert Stevens looked closely at her before replying. "It can scarcely be that you have failed to hear the news," he ventured; there was an air of timidity about the man as he addressed his wife.

"You refer to the occupation of the city by General Howe?" She made her brows suit the carelessness of her tone, but her eyes searched his face narrowly.

"Melissa," he said, solemnly, pacing the floor before her chair, "I regret to observe that I fear you do not appreciate the full import of the event, and its bearing upon us."

WASHINGTON AT KIP'S BAY (*From the drawing by H. L. Stephens*)

"I believe that I do," —half bored.

"My position is delicate."

"Precisely so," —smiling slightly.

"I hope, if I may be permitted to mention the matter, that you will not embarrass me by ostensible friendliness with the — " he hesitated for a word —"the new occupants of the city.

"Because of my early views of this war, which I had the courage to express," went on Robert Stevens, gaining more courage for the present expression, "I have been in some shadow among my fellow-citizens; I have been suspected, I fear, of sympathy with the enemy. In fact, Melissa, I have been held a Tory!" Another pause; when he went on, he spoke more rapidly, with some excitement, as one who abandons caution and risks much. "And I regret exceedingly to be obliged to say, Melissa, that your attitude has not been one, to put it mildly, —has not been one conducive to restoring me in the confidence of the community."

She looked surprised, and hurt. "I am sorry my behavior does not please you, Mr. Stevens," she murmured, expressing martyrdom in voice and look.

"And I must beg of you to consider carefully the need for acting with great discretion in the present juncture," he went on, passing over her speech. She made no answer, of word or look. "I must beg of you not to extend the hospitality of my house to any of the British officers who will be in the town. I shall not even wish my son-in-law, Major Hempstead, to be more than an infrequent visitor. He, as a man of delicacy and tact, will understand my position.

"And now that we are pursuing these unpleasant topics, my dear," Robert Stevens continued, ignoring her manner, "I feel constrained to mention another matter. I am obliged to tell you that I am displeased with your treatment of my

Independence Hall, Philadelphia, Pennsylvania

worthy kinsman, John Stevens, who has my respect and admiration."

"I beg of you, do not feel obliged to tell me," returned his helpmate, sardonically.

"I am gratified to learn that I need say no more," the man hastened, glad to read into her words a meaning she did not intend. "I will only remind you, further, that it will be advisable for you to preserve his presence in this house a secret. For his sake, only, Melissa," he added.

"Ah, I perceive. You desire me to help you shield a traitor and a rebel." There was open defiance now in the woman.

Robert Stevens, deeply pained, paused before he spoke. "I will leave you to reconsider those hard words, Melissa," he said, and left the room.

Mistress Stevens, following him with a look of amusement mingled with a trace of contempt, beheld her daughter Sophronia standing close beside her. For a moment the two fixed each other with level glances, in which was no warmth. The mother spoke.

"What think you now of our brave patient?" she asked, as though to learn how much the girl might have overheard.

"What should I think?" rejoined Sophronia.

"Do you not know that the British will be here before sundown? That we are more than likely to have Lieutenant Hempstead and his rout at dinner this very day?"

"Then I am soon to be amused again," replied the girl. "But what has this to do with our patient, as you choose to call him?"

"What, Sophronia?" rejoined her mother, with some acerbity. "How shall we seem in the eyes of the English after harboring a rebel who has not only taken up arms against his King, but who, as we learn from the lieutenant's letters, acted the spy in Boston?"

"I purpose concealing his presence here from all who come, at every hazard," returned the girl.

"Are you a rebel, too, that you seek to hide this rebel?" demanded her mother, restraining her resentment; this child of hers overmastered her.

"I care nothing for the war."

"What is your interest, then, in this man?" with a touch of irony.

"I love him." Her tone was casual.

Baffled, direful, the woman held her peace, biting her lip.

"You fully understand that I wish this man to be safe in your house?" resumed the daughter, impassively still.

Mistress Stevens, sometime the Widow Osborne, made no answer by word; only the look of defeat in her eyes told what her course would be.

As they remained thus, there was a great clanking in the hall, and Lieutenant Lucas Hempstead entered.

WASHINGTON'S RETREAT AT LONG ISLAND (*From the engraving by M. A. Wageman*)

CHAPTER XIII

THE SECRET OUT

JOHN STEVENS, pale from long confinement and gaunt from the hardships of the Canada campaign followed so soon by his hurt, paced the floor of the little room where Mistress Stevens had had him taken, much to the displeasure of his admiring kinsman, when they brought him to the house, wounded. As he wheeled forth and back, his hands made quick gestures of impatience; his face showed annoyance, setting from time to time in determination. As he was pacing, Sophronia Osborne came into the room.

ALEXANDER HAMILTON, ARTILLERYMAN
(*From the painting by Chappell*)

"Why have you not told me that the English are in New York?" he asked abruptly, partly rebuking her.

"How do you know they are in New York?"

"Cousin Catherine told me. Nay, do not blame the child," he went on, when Sophronia showed disapproval.

Sophronia shrugged her shoulders. "You would have learned soon," she said. "The child has done no harm."

211

"You speak of doing me harm as though I were a sick child myself," John returned, somewhat petulantly.

"In truth, you have been sick, and men, when they are sick, are ever children, when they be not worse." Sophronia spoke lightly, almost merrily.

"Tell me how they came here?" John went on, reverting to the matter of moment. "Was there more fighting? Is Washington still alive? Is our army broken?"

"They came by ships, up the two rivers," Sophronia answered. "There was no fighting that day, the Americans fleeing; but on the next General Howe attacked the American center at Harlem Heights. Your men fought bravely; the British were repulsed. Now your army is somewhere to the northward, ready to oppose the British. General Washington is still in command."

John, who had stood while he heard this, took his seat when Sophronia finished, sighing with relief.

"How comes it that British officers frequent the house?" he asked, presently, his old misgiving concerning the patriotism of his kinsman reviving. "Does Master Robert Stevens suffer them?"

"Nay," returned Sophronia; "you might better reverse that, and say that they suffer him to remain in his own home, when all other rebels are driven from the city, and their property   turned   over   to   their   Tory
                                                         neighbors."

"He is a Tory, then!" cried John, angry and chagrined.

"Not so," rejoined Sophronia;

THE BEEKMAN HOUSE IN 1860: HEADQUARTERS OF SIR WILLIAM HOWE, SEPTEMBER, 1776 (*From a lithograph by Sarony, Major & Knapp*) "but he hath a wife who steers him through narrow places."

At that John was silenced, feeling himself on treacherous ground when the talk turned to women.

"What British officers are here?" he asked, presently.

"You might conjecture that," suggested Sophronia.

"Lieutenant Hempstead, perhaps?"

Sophronia nodded. John looked darkly out of window, ruminating, before he proceeded. "Is his brother, the major, also here?" he asked.

"Nominally; but for the most part he remains at head-quarters, as a matter of delicacy, having observed that Master Robert Stevens is averse to the entertainment in his house of British officers." Sophronia, busied in trivial things, spoke casually, with little interest in what she said.

"Are there others here?" asked the young kinsman of the host.

"One Isaac Francis," answered the girl, absently. John scowled at that. "And Nancy Hempstead," she added, as though she had at that moment recalled her presence in the house.

A look of livelier interest came into John's face. "What does she do here?" he asked, with an effort to appear unconcerned.

Sophronia, shrugging her shoulders, smiled. "Being a woman, I never feel confidence in telling why a woman does anything," she returned, in a tone that left it to be surmised that she had a theory, nevertheless, to fit the case.

John fell victim to her subtlety. "What inference do you draw from her presence?" he asked, considering himself adroit in piercing her reticence.

"It would be unfair, perhaps, to say." She answered only after a pause, devoted to earnest consideration of some detail of housewifery in the sick-room

LOOKING ACROSS THE CORRIDOR, IN-
DEPENDENCE HALL, PHILADELPHIA

"It is a matter of such small concern to me that you will scarcely injure her, in any event," remarked John, with a quaver in his voice, a flush of excitement that destroyed all the effect of indifference for which he struggled.

The girl, looking at him slyly from the corners of her eyes and looking away again, quickly, pretended not to see the color rushing into his pale cheeks. "For my part," she went on, treating the matter lightly, as though it indeed were something that concerned either of them little, "for my part, I do not find it difficult to account for her being where Master Francis is to be found."

John, stricken dumb for a moment by the implication, looked keenly at her to see whether there might be any purpose of disclosure in it. He could see none; she was wholly absorbed in what she did about the room.

"Is there no danger that Catherine will tell her I am here?" he asked, presently, after a long pause. "They are close friends, I believe," he went on, considering himself shrewd in the form of the question; for what he sought to learn was whether Nancy Hempstead knew of his presence.

Sophronia, absorbed in puttering, did not answer. He asked the question again.

"She has already told," replied Sophronia, slowly, bringing her attention to the subject with some difficulty. "When the English girl first came, your cousin, being, as you say, only a child, told her you were here, and would have had her help with the care of you, thinking, child that she is, that my strength might give out."

John's heart died within him. Nancy, living in that house, and learning that he lay wounded, close to death, had not come to him! The tremendous meaning of it crushed him; he could hardly think.

"Is there no danger that the English girl will tell?" he asked, in hollow voice, starting forward in his chair. It was not fear of what might follow disclosure that appalled him; it was the thought of the possibility that she would betray him.

"That we can only leave to hope," returned his companion, evenly.

John struggled to his feet. "Mistress Sophronia, I must get back to the army! I must leave here! I must go, and at once!" His voice trembled with emotion; his hands twitched. Some might have thought it fear that shook him. Sophronia was not one of those, but she considered it best to meet his words as such an one might have met them.

"Let me be the judge of that, John Stevens!" The assurance of her voice would have inspirited one who suffered from lack of courage; John it only silenced.

At the moment when Sophronia was closing the door of John's room, Isaac Francis and Lieutenant Lucas Hempstead were standing by the buffet in the dining-room —the same that had been the scene of quarrel a year before —helping themselves to glasses of toddy.

"By the Lord Harry!" Francis was exclaiming, half in

PRESIDENT'S CHAIR AND DESK IN
INDEPENDENCE HALL

pique and half in mirth, "By the Lord Harry! If you fare no better with this thin-hipped slip of a Yankee girl than I with your sister, we are both likely to pass the rest of our days as melancholy types of celibacy; for, believe me, I can no more win a gentle look from Nan than Howe can win a battle." This, in allusion to many long and tedious manœuvers in which the British general had lately been engaged, endeavoring to dislodge General Washington from his front.

"Belike I might tell you the reason of that," observed Lieutenant Lucas, deeply, tossing off his toddy.

"Belike you will do me a kindness, if you will." Francis persisted in being half droll and half angry.

"Have you memory of one John Stevens, of Boston, with whom we had words here at a certain ball last year, who failed to meet me on the field of honor?" Lucas assumed an air of importance, and mystery, as one having much superior knowledge.

"Ay, and an insolent braggart he was," commented Francis, concocting another brace of toddies. "But what of him?"

"Much of him. My sister, I believe, fancies him!" with the air of importance and mystery intensified.

"My word!" Francis, ceasing his operations, stared at Lieutenant Lucas to make sure he was not being made a butt. Perceiving his companion to be in dead earnest, he gave a long, low whistle and fell to his mixing again.

Sophronia Osborne, coming down the stairs from John Stevens's room, heard the whistle. She stopped, mid-step, to listen. Recognizing the voices, she crept silently to the dining-room door and took position, hidden among the hangings there.

"Never tell me, my dear fellow, that a man like that will take my love away from me," she heard Francis saying.

"I will tell you that, and I will tell you more than that!" returned Lieutenant Lucas.

"Nay, nought that could be more than that!" laughed Francis.

There was a pause; they stood with raised glasses; Sophronia, through the hangings in the doorway, could see Lucas fixing the other with level glance.

"The man is here!" he said.

Francis, setting down his glass untasted, in extremity of surprise, spilled a bit of the contents on his lace cuffs. "In what guise?" he asked, recovering himself at once, and resuming his frivolous manner. "In the guise of the blackamoor who polishes my boots?"

"In the guise of a wounded hero, brought here after the battle on Long Island."

Francis, drying the liquor from his lace, stopped, and looked his astonishment once more. "Now, in Heaven's name, if you have your senses, unravel this to me before I take leave of mine!" he cried.

"Thus it is, then," began Hempstead, sipping his drink as he marshaled the story. "Belike I have fared better with my little lass than you with my sister, for to-day, when I told her of my ardent affection, she was so far impressed by my devotion as to give me her confidence, and to ask me, in sacred secret, to accomplish for her a mighty adventure. And what think you the adventure was?"

"To drive me mad. I have no other guess."

THE NATHAN HALE STATUE, ERECT-
ED BY THE SOCIETY OF THE SONS OF
THE REVOLUTION, CITY HALL PARK,
NEW YORK, NOVEMBER 25, 1893

"It was to rescue this fellow, this hound who insults and runs away, and who would have choked me to my death, like a blackguardly footpad, to rescue him, I say, and save him from this nest of vipers, because, forsooth, she loves him! What think you of that?"

"I think the fellow has his fill of lovers, forsooth," returned Francis. Whereat Sophronia, standing concealed from them behind the hangings in the door, smiled deeply. "But now, why tell you this to me, and what shall you do in the matter?" he went on, first pausing to drink off his toddy, with greater success this time.

"I tell you this that I may have to do nothing," returned Lucas, with a significant leer at the other. "Are you alert?"

"You would have the fellow come to grief, I make no doubt, through me?" Francis returned the leer.

"Is he not of the enemy, and within our lines, under concealment?"

"A spy?" asked Francis, catching the other's meaning.

"Twice a spy!" returned Lucas, with emphasis. "For my part, I have not forgot the night he visited Boston!"

"I believe I owe it to the fellow," quoth Francis, growing whimsical again. "But what is the move?"

"You have only to inform headquarters, keeping the matter strictly from my hearing, mind you, and let matters take their own course."

"When would be timely?"

"In war, there is no time so fit as the immediate time."

Stopping only to drink another toddy, Master Isaac Francis left the stately mansion of Robert Stevens to pass leisurely up the street in the direction of British headquarters.

The savage severity with which Howe had hanged Nathan Hale the day after his capture without trial gave Francis every reason to believe that his rival would go to a fate as swift and terrible.

INTERIOR OF INDEPENDENCE HALL, PHILADELPHIA, SHOWING PORTRAITS OF THE SIGNERS

John Stevens was pacing his narrow room, disturbed beyond restraint by an impatience to be back in the ranks of the patriots. He had fretted to go since his strength began to return; now the thought that Nancy Hempstead was under the same roof with him; that, knowing him to be there, she cared too little to come and see him; and the belief that her indifference arose from her concern for another, made him desire to go with an earnestness that was almost fierce.

Until now he had not known how much he cared. Even that night in Boston, when, death dogging at his heels, he stopped to press a kiss upon her cold forehead, he had never known so well, now that the dreams he dared were shattered and dispersed. But he did not repine; he did not grow heavy in spirit, nor make complaint. He only knew that for the good of his soul he must be away from that house, must go back to his first love, his true love, that would never fail him; his country and its cause.

Turning as he paced the floor with tumbled thoughts, he was aware that Sophronia Osborne was in the room. Something in her face and manner gripped his attention.

"A moment ago I told you that when the time came, you should go safely away from here," she said, evenly and low, without preface. "That time is now. Your presence here is known to those who should have known nothing."

"To whom is it known?"

"To Lieutenant Lucas and Master Francis; they plot to harm you."

"They can do nothing with me," said John, misliking a course that smacked of running away.

"You were once a spy; so much they know," returned the girl, indifferently. "You are now concealed within the British lines. Lieutenant Lucas hates you. Master Francis is a fellow of cunning, who would work against you from sheer love of intrigue, even were not he to gain credit by it among the English officers. This Francis has even now left the house to make the matter known at headquarters. And if you are captured what assurance have you that you will not meet the same fate as your late comrade Captain Hale? If you care to go, I can make it possible, but it must be done at once."

THE BATTLE OF HARLEM   (*From the painting by Chappell*)

"I will go," said the man, quickly. Without further word, and as calmly as though she planned nothing more than an appearance on the avenue, Sophronia turned to a chest of drawers in a corner of the room, from which she proceeded to take certain articles, leisurely and deliberately.

John, pacing the room again, giving no heed to what she did, paused abruptly in his stride, as though something had at that moment occurred to him. "How know you all this?" he asked.

"I overheard the two talking in a room below, a moment since," returned Sophronia, busy about the chest.

"How came they to know that I am here?" John, standing rigid in the center of the room, his eyes fixed upon space, asked the question; with eyes fixed vacantly, stiff and straight, he awaited the answer.

When Sophronia answered, it was without interest in what she said, with thoughts only upon her employment. "From that part of their talk that I came upon, I should take it that the sweetheart of one of them disclosed the secret," she said.

The eyes of the man, fixed on vacancy, shut over the swift look of grief that came into them. When they opened, the grief was gone, and his gaze had returned to earth.

"But that is small odds," went on Sophronia, more briskly, "for here we have the means of undoing all the harm that has been done. Come. I am ready."

He turned toward her. In his face was no sign; he had conquered; his sorrow lay buried beyond reach.

In her arms she held a livery of green, such as coachmen of the period wore. In one hand was a jar of dark stain. John understood and took the chair to which she directed him with a look. Silently she proceeded, with deft hand, to darken the skin of his face, his neck, and hands; solemn and serious he was, without a thought of the grotesque, as she transformed him into a blackamoor; sober as a clown who decks himself for the part he is to play.

Only when she was leaving the room, having finished her task and bidden him don the livery, did he speak. Then, out of curiosity, he asked her what this would avail?

"It is not for nothing that my mother fetes the British officers," she answered. " 'T was a small matter for the daughter of Mistress Stevens to obtain passports permitting herself and retinue to cross the lines."

A moment after she was out of the room John Stevens was in coachman's livery, making no mirth of it. Ten minutes later Isaac Francis, sauntering up the street toward the Stevens mansion, accompanied by half a dozen British officers and followed by a squad of soldiers, paused for a moment to blow a kiss to Mistress Sophronia Osborne, riding forth in her coach.

"Egad!" exclaimed one of the English officers, staring after the departing equipage, " 't is a likely looking black-amoor the fair Sophronia hath to drive her!" To which Master Francis, engrossed in other matters, gave no heed.

In the latter part of October, the Continental army rested on White Plains. Its being there was the result of excellent generalship on the part of Washington. He had a force inferior in every point to that under Howe excepting the one point of the individual bravery of the soldiers. At that, the personnel of the Continental army was racked. The men were downcast. Enlisted for short periods, and only as the militia of the several states from which they came, many of them were returning home at the expiration of their terms of service. Rations were low; money was scarcely to be had. Nevertheless, Washington, with con-- summate skill and sublime courage, continued to maintain a front against Howe, blocking him in his attempt to control the Hudson.

After the battle at Harlem Heights, the day following the British occupation of New York City, Howe's problem was somewhat complicated. Washington, at the head of Manhattan Island, had a country spread behind him; to surround him would be difficult. The Hudson River was guarded by Fort Washington, at the upper end of Manhattan, and Fort Lee, on the Palisades opposite. Fort Washington had been laid out by Alexander Hamilton, then twenty years of age. The work was done with such skill that Washington's attention was drawn to the young engineer, he forthwith attached him to his own staff. A friendship sprang up between them that was to endure throughout their joint lives.

It was hoped by the Americans that the two forts would bar the British fleet from ascending the Hudson; but October 9, two frigates passed up, demonstrating the ability of Howe to reach Washington's rear by water. Ascertaining this, Howe planned to surprise Washington's left by a movement up Long Island Sound, believing that the American general would be expect-

First Meeting of Washington and Hamilton
(*From the painting by Chappell*)

ing him along the Hudson. Leaving Percy in command before Harlem Heights, he moved the greater part of his army nine miles up the sound to Throgg's Neck, a peninsula whence the only egress to land was over a bridge or through a swamp.

Washington outguessed him. When Howe reached the peninsula, he found the bridge destroyed, and the Americans in sufficient force on shore to prevent him from fording the marsh. For six days he hung his hopes on the peninsula.

During that time, Washington, realizing the impossibility of holding his advance line with both ends permanently exposed to the water, withdrew his army to White Plains, leaving only a garrison at Fort Washington, under Putnam, and another at Fort Lee, under Greene.

On the morning of October 20, Lieutenant Fontaine Stevens, riding between outposts before White Plains with dispatches, was made aware, through much dust and noise behind him, of the progress of a coach along the road he followed. It was an elegant equipage, such as he might expect to encounter in a city of size. The sight of it here, dusty and draggled, making its cumbrous way over the rough roads between two belligerent armies, aroused his poignant curiosity. He stopped to await it.

As it came nearer, his gaze, attempting to make something of the strange sight, was arrested by the figure of the negro   coachmen that drove it. There was something   bafflingly familiar about the air of the

VIEW OF WHITE PLAINS FROM MOUNT MISERY RAMPARTS

man. Staring and puzzling, the coach came nearer. Still staring, the young lieutenant from Virginia gave a shout of astonishment and joy, and spurred swiftly to the side of the box, signaling the driver to stop as he came up.

"John Stevens! For the love of Heaven, what do you here?" he cried.

The driver made no answer, merely looking down upon him. Fontaine, taken aback by the reception, was at a moment's loss, when the coach door opened, and Sophronia Osborne stepped forth. Confounded, Fontaine dismounted from his horse, saluted her elaborately, and stood staring, first at one and then the other.

The girl gave him no more than a look and a smile, but went at once to the front of the coach. "I have brought you thus far," she said, looking up at her coachman. "You will have no further need of me." She smiled, plaintively, as she spoke. What might not the man have seen in that smile; what might not he have learned from the quaver of her voice, had there not been before him the memory of another to occupy the whole horizon of his heart? Let time answer.

Still silent, John Stevens dismounted from the box, and gave over whip and reins to a footman whom Sophronia beckoned from the rumble. "I owe you much," he said, giving no glance to Fontaine,

WASHINGTON'S HEADQUARTERS AT WHITE PLAINS

who stood mutely by, an astonished spectator. "Perhaps I shall be able to repay you in kind."

In Sophronia's face as she answered him was what no man had seen before, and which no man saw now; for so the fates intended. "Think you I have done this thing for hire?" she said.

She held forth her hand. He pressed it to his lips, gratefully; that which was in her face as he did so, which

RUINS OF OLD FORT WASHINGTON, BUILT IN 1777

no man had seen there before, was beheld of man now. Fontaine saw it, for so the fates ordained. Seeing it, his wonder grew.

With no further word, she entered the coach, bidding the driver return to New York City.

Left alone, the two kinsman stood silent for a space, Fontaine gazing wistfully at John; John ignoring him with native dignity and pride, remembering only the other's manner toward him when they were together, in front of Boston. Fontaine spoke first.

"John!" he said, holding out his hand impulsively.

"Cousin John! I crave your forgiveness, being much in the wrong. I have injured you, in thought and deed; I have not understood, fool that I was. Until I saw you, magnificent, superb, in the fight where you got your wound, I did not understand. Now, knowing my fault, I crave your forgiveness, believing you to be so noble that I may hope for pardon."

The set face of the New England man relaxed as he grasped the extended hand warmly. "You might well have believed me a coward when I failed to appear at my engagement," he said. "I bore you no malice for that. Indeed, I have borne you no malice at any time; yet you might have learned the truth later, when we met before Boston, had you seen fit to request it of me."

"I should have known well enough without word from you, or any man," returned Fontaine, fervently.

John smiled quietly. "Shall I tell you now?" he asked.

"No, no!" cried the other. "There is no need of that!"

TABLET ON ENGINEERING BUILDING, COLUMBIA UNIVERSITY, NEW YORK CITY, COMMEMORATING THE BATTLE OF HARLEM HEIGHTS

CHAPTER XIV

THE TABLES TURNED

GENERAL HOWE attacked the American outpost on Chatterton Hills on October 28. The engagement is known to history as the battle of White Plains, which is an inaccuracy. The attack succeeded, the Americans being driven back upon their position at White Plains; but the victory was fruitless. The English lost 229 men, the Americans 140, and Washington was as firmly lodged as ever. Remembering Bunker Hill, Howe forbore to press an assault.

What deeds of mighty valor were done on that day at Chatterton Hills by a captain of Continentals dressed in green livery, and with fading dark stains on hands and face, need not be told. Like one courting death, he raged along the line of the company he commanded, heedless of danger and mighty in battle.

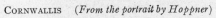

CORNWALLIS   (*From the portrait by Hoppner*)

Howe, discouraged, waited in front of White Plains for three days. On the last night of October Washington withdrew to North Castle, a stronger position, and one better protected in rear. Howe moved over to Dobb's Ferry. Thence he could attack Fort Washington or move upon Philadelphia, the "rebel capital." Washington countered

230

by sending 5000 under Putnam into New Jersey. Heath
was sent to Peekskill to guard the Hudson with 3000;
Charles Lee was left at North Castle with 7000, to await
further orders.

Forts Washington and Lee absorbed many men in
garrison. They had lost their value; unable to prevent
British vessels from ascending the Hudson, they were in
danger of capture. Washington ordered them evacuated.
Meanwhile, he went with Heath to lay out fortifications at
West Point, against a descent of Carleton from Canada.

But Congress, learning early the ways of a popular
government in time of war, sent messages
to Greene, who commanded both forts,
urging him to hold them. Washington's
order of evacuation had been conditional;
Greene shrank from the responsibility of ignoring the
wishes of Congress. More-
over, he believed the forts
could be held. Wherefore,
and being allowed latitude
for discretion under the
form of Washington's order,
he reinforced Fort Washington, that being the most exposed to attack, bringing the

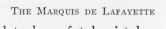

THE MARQUIS DE LAFAYETTE

garrison to 3000 men. It proved to be a fatal mistake.

Washington returned from West Point on November 14,
and learned what had been done. It was too late to undo
it, for that very night British vessels passed between the two
forts, and in the morning Howe was in front of Fort Washington with preponderating force. November 16, Howe
stormed the place, taking it after desperate resistance by
Colonel Magaw, commanding. The British lost 500 men

killed and wounded; the Americans, 3000 captured. Washington, from the opposite bank of the river, witnessed the tragedy with iron composure; when the Hessians, angered by the resistance of the Americans, began to massacre the prisoners, he wept. British officers promptly put a stop to the butchery.

Washington, on the Jersey side of the river with 6000 men, sent orders to Charles Lee to join him. Lee, pretending the orders left him discretion, failed to obey, at the same time endeavoring to poison the mind of Congress against the commander-in-chief, hoping to succeed him. It was an act of deliberate and treacherous villainy, but the prejudice in favor of Charles Lee, to which he had added by arrogating to himself all the credit for the recent victory at Fort Moultrie, was sufficient to blind the American people to his character, and maintain him in their favor.

Washington could not wait for him. Being joined by Greene, who barely succeeded in saving the garrison of Fort Lee from the fate that had overtaken Fort Washington, he began his retreat across New Jersey. He crossed the Delaware on December 8, Cornwallis at his heels. There for the time he was safe, having taken the precaution to seize all the boats within seventy miles. Cornwallis had either to collect other boats, build a bridge, or wait until the river froze over.

There was promise of much mirth in New York during the holiday season. Howe, for his victories over the Americans, had been made a knight commander of the Order of the Bath; festivities in celebration were at hand. The rebellion was extinguished, thought Cornwallis, the British general; another time would suit for striking the last blow. The Christmas cheer at New York gave promise of much pleasure, after the field. So he returned to New York. He even packed his portmanteau, ready to sail

WASHINGTON CROSSING THE DELAWARE (From the painting by Emanuel Leutze in the Metropolitan Museum of Art, New York

for England as soon as the triumph was over; for another could complete his work now. The Hessians under Donop and Rall, the Scotch under Grant, posted along the Delaware, would be sufficient, as soon as the river froze.

It was Christmas. The soldiers of the victorious army in New York City reveled in barrack and grog shop; their officers the while engaged in fetes and balls and grand occasions.

Along the west bank of the Delaware, dispirited, shivering, in want of food, huddled a handful, 6000 men all told. They, and only they, stood between the troops of England and the liberties of America. Washington, Cornwallis close at his heels, crossed with 3000. Sullivan and Gates, arriving with the troops lately under Lee, had brought the total to 7000. Charles Lee himself, moving tardily from North Castle, had been captured when dining at a distance from his command. The affair was fortunate for the patriots, although it resulted in deliberate treachery on the part of the captured general; but at that time the character of Charles Lee was not known, and his capture added to the general gloom.

Now the 7000 had dwindled to 6000; soldiers whose terms were expiring were leaving daily; January 1 there would not be 3000 left. The country was in utter despair; since Moultrie there had been no victory; the declaration that the colonies were free and independent, made so proudly a short six months ago, was worn to a grim joke. Many patriots, taking advantage of a proclamation promising pardon for those who would take the oath of allegiance to King George, abandoned the struggle, seeking shelter under the gracious forgiveness of their outraged Sovereign. It was a time that tried men's souls.

And 6000 lay shivering, despairing, on the farther bank of the Delaware. When the river should freeze .   .   .

THE BATTLE OF TRENTON

It was not frozen yet, though the day was cold, and masses of ice churned their way down the turgid flood. But when it should freeze!

General Washington stood, wrapped in his cloak against the cold, on the west bank of the Delaware, nine miles above Trenton. The sun, setting on Christmas day, was a dull blur in the cold grey west. Across the river, nine miles below, Colonel Rall drank deep of Christmas cheer, with many a Hessian jest. His thousand compatriots made a mad festival of it. Farther below, at Burlington, Donop and his men did honor to the day in pot and bowl. British officers in New York raised many a glass, as the sun was setting, in honor of the red ribbon conferred on General Howe for vanquishing the Americans. And General Washington, his back toward the setting sun, looked out across the ragged waters of the tumbling river! Twenty-five hundred soldiers at his back, without cloaks, shivering, gazing at the ground in moody silence, heard the ice grind down the river.

To the commander came Fontaine Stevens, saluting; his heart was heavy within him; gloom was in his cheeks.

"Cadwalader and Ewing have given it up; they cannot cross," he reported. Cadwalader was to have crossed against Donop at Burlington, substituting for Gates in the command of that detachment; Gates preferred to run off to Congress, intriguing, thinking only of himself. Ewing was expected to cross directly upon Trenton.

Hearing the news, a fire of loftier enthusiasm burned in the eyes of the commander. Treachery, defeat, despair, wrought not upon the mighty heart that beat within his bosom. His will arose to the purpose he had in mind; on him was the weight of fate; towering giant of strength that he was, he bore it upon the wings of his soul, with gaze turned eastward, across the ice-laden waves.

Three o'clock in the morning. Out of the black night came blasts of sleet and snow, chilling, insufferable. Black, shivering shadows gathered into line and rank on the eastern shore. In two columns, they moved southward through the driving cold and snow. The tiny army was across the river. For ten hours Colonel Glover and his fishermen

SURRENDER OF COLONEL RALL AT THE BATTLE OF TRENTON   (*From the painting by Chappell*)

from Gloucester and Marblehead, had been struggling through the ice.

Sunrise! A pallor in the east, making ghostly the town of Trenton, white with snow. Belated roisterers, those whose heads were stronger than their fellows', quaffed their last draughts in the Christmas revelry, to do honor to the Prince of Peace. In New York, British officers, dreary with much punch, crept vagrantly to bed, their red uniforms awry.

Out of the pale dawn, crinkling through the soft plush of falling snow, whining across the whining of the wind, came the sound of a shot. Another shot; others; many more. Colonel Rall, stumbling from a swaying bed, pulled on his clothes and rushed into the streets of Trenton. Guns were there, planted, sweeping the way; cannon of the Americans. Ragged soldiers, limping on frosted feet, rushed forward; in their chill throats was a shout of triumph. Colonel Rall fell dead, before the web of wine was out of his brain. In the city of New York, British officers lay dreaming of red ribbons, and pink cheeks; British soldiers groveled in grog-shop corners.

The thing was done. A thousand men surrendered; of the Americans two were frozen to death on the march and two killed in the assault. Before night Washington returned safely to the other side of the Delaware with his prisoners.

The thing was done! Victory had come to the American arms at last. Hope lived once more. The genius of Washington flashed forth through the obscure gloom of the time that tried mens' souls; his fame ran from lip to lip; faith in him as the savior of America grew; militia hurried to join his ranks; soldiers whose terms expired reënlisted; a mad joy ran through the country. When news of Trenton reached Europe the fame of Washington as a general came to rival that of the warriors of history; the prestige of the United States grew in a bound.

Three days later, Washington returned again to Trenton. Donop had left Burlington December 26, just before Cadwalader finally succeeded in crossing to attack him, and all the outposts were gathered at Princeton. Cornwallis, hearing the news of Trenton, mounted a horse and hurried to Princeton, without waiting to get the portmanteau that had been carried aboard ship; the festivities at New York came to an abrupt end.

WASHINGTON ON THE BATTLEFIELD AT TRENTON (*From the painting by Trumbull*)

January 2 Cornwallis advanced with 8000 men upon Trenton. Washington withdrew his force to a position south of the Assunpink River, which enters the Delaware a short distance below Trenton. Cornwallis was retarded in his march by the continuous galling fire poured into his columns from the woods along the way; and by Greene, who, with 600 men and two cannon, constantly made him stop and form for battle, and slipped away before a blow could be delivered. When Cornwallis reached Trenton late in the afternoon Washington had placed his army in a strongly intrenched position and commanded all the fords and the bridge across the Assunpink with artillery.

It was too late for Cornwallis to attack. He went into camp, planning to turn Washington's left flank in the morning, fold him back on the Delaware, and compel his surrender. "At last we have run down the old fox, and we will bag him in the morning," he said, in high spirits, as he retired.

Washington's situation was critical. In his front was an army outnumbering his own and much better equipped; behind him a river that could not be crossed without great time and labor. But he was not dismayed. He planned a coup that for cool daring and keen strategy has few rivals in military annals. The greater part of the British army was in front of him; he learned that more troops, still at Princeton, would move to reinforce Cornwallis in the morning. At Princeton and New Brunswick were large quantities of British stores; to seize them and break the British line would compel Cornwallis to fall back upon New York.

All night long the campfires in the American lines burned brightly; all night long the British sentinels heard the American soldiers across the Assunpink working with pick and spade, throwing up trenches; but all night long the Continental army was nevertheless slipping like a monster serpent from the trenches of the camp and crawling silently to the eastward, crossing the Assunpink above, and stretching away for the Princeton road.

In the grey morning Colonel Mawhood, moving along the road from Princeton, bringing up a force to join Cornwallis, encountered the advance of the American army, under General Mercer, who had been dispatched to break down the Stony Creek bridge on the main road to Trenton. Believing them to be fugitives, Mawhood hastened toward them. He was speedily undeceived. There was a sharp engagement;

The Trenton Battle Monument

Mercer was killed and the Americans were beginning to waver, when Washington, riding upon the field, stiffened them again. The entire forces from both sides arrived and joined battle, and the engagement became general. It did not last long; in fifteen minutes the British line was cut in two, part of it fleeing to join Cornwallis and part of it retreating to New Brunswick. The British lost 200 killed and wounded and 300 prisoners; the Americans lost a hundred in killed and wounded.

Cornwallis, awakening in the morning ready to "bag the fox," could scarcely believe his eyes when he looked across the Assunpink and saw the enemy's deserted trenches. He could

WASHINGTON AT THE BATTLE OF PRINCETON
(*From the painting by Chappell*)

make nothing of it; the fires still burned, having been kept up to the last moment; there was no trace of an army in the distance; the pickets had heard nothing all night but the work of entrenching. He was completely at a loss.

In the height of his confusion, when he was sputtering about among his staff demanding where the fox had gone, his ears caught the sound of the firing near Princeton. His face blanched; the blood left his lips. With crying haste he set his army in motion, racing for New Brunswick to save the stores there. The road lay through Princeton.

They met Mawhood's fugitives, and learned the story. The road was heavy with thaw; it was a weary way. Cornwallis, utterly downcast and humiliated, was half frantic with apprehension for his stores at New Brunswick; indeed, for his own safety, for Washington lay between him and New York. He thought of his portmanteaux, now probably rolling on their way to England, and wished in the bottom of his heart that the vessel had sailed soon enough to take him before the news of Trenton reached New York.

Washington could not press his advantage to a conclusion. His soldiers were weary and still ill-shod; bloody footprints marked their trail; he would not ask them to march to New Brunswick, and he dared not risk a general engagement at present. Turning northward therefore from Princeton, he went to the heights behind Morristown, where he took a position in which the British would not dare attack him, and from which he could threaten their lines of communication if they should attempt to maintain their hold upon the Delaware River points.

Cornwallis, appreciating the situation, moved on to New Brunswick. A few days later Putnam, who had been with the force in Philadelphia, moved forward and occupied Princeton, forming the right wing of the army; Heath, commanding on the Hudson, formed the left, with Washington

QUAKER MEETING-HOUSE ON THE BATTLEFIELD OF PRINCETON

at Morristown in the center. The British were driven from Hackensack by George Clinton, descending from Peekskill; a body of Hessians was expelled from Springfield; Elizabethtown was taken by General Maxwell, and the British retired from Newark. The enemy now retained only New Brunswick, Amboy, and Paulus Hook in the entire State of New Jersey; a month before they had held it all.

In a campaign of three weeks Washington had rallied a broken army, fought two successful battles, taken 2000 prisoners, and wrenched New Jersey from the enemy. But he had done much more than this. He had restored hope to a despairing country; he had infused enthusiasm into the hearts of patriots; he had rebuilt in them a faith in their own arms. The British generals were afraid of him. Americans, even those who had been lukewarm, made haste to Morristown to join the army. The inhabitants of New Jersey had suffered bitterly from the British who had plundered and pillaged, murdered and outraged everywhere; now the time had come when they, no longer defenseless, could strike back.

We of a later day should like to think that part, at least, of the inspiration which carried our soldiers on to victory at this time came from the Stars and Stripes, then first given to the world on the battlefield. The celebrated portrait of Washington painted by Charles Willson Peale only two years after the event, was not only the work of an artist scrupulously exact regarding details, but of a soldier who commanded a company through this campaign, and his picture shows the new national flag. And, in

GENERAL HUGH MERCER (*From the pencil drawing by Trumbull*)

further confirmation, John Trumbull, who was Washington's aide-de-camp at Trenton and Princeton, also painted a portrait of the commander-in-chief which shows the flag of thirteen stars and thirteen stripes, and Trumbull himself says that the accessories of this painting, "down to the

STONY CREEK BRIDGE

buttons and spurs, were carefully painted from the different objects."

General Howe considering it best to wait until spring before attempting to dislodge the Americans, Washington went on to organize his army. There had been almost no organization; the troops were militia-men recruited in the various States for terms of three or six months; their officers were unused to war; there was no discipline such as is necessary to the larger operations of an army, and there were bitter jealousies and quarrels between the militia of the

respective States. Prejudices, local, social, political, and
religious, were exceedingly violent, affecting even the de-
liberations of Congress.

For a long time Washington had sought to remove or
remedy these defects. As he was retreating through New
Jersey, he told Congress that the "short enlistments and

DEATH OF MERCER AT THE BATTLE OF PRINCETON   (*From the painting by
Trumbull*)

a mistaken dependence upon militia have been the origin
of all our misfortunes," at the same time recommending
that a certain number of battalions should be raised directly
by the United States. The advice was followed by Congress,
and at the same time Washington was given almost dicta-
torial power.

An increase of the State militia to 66,000 troops was
authorized, and Washington was given the power to enlist
12,000 infantry, three regiments of artillery, 3000 light
cavalry, and an engineer corps in the service of the United
States, all the new levy to serve during the war. The

officers in the regular army were to be appointed by Washington, who was furthermore empowered to fill all vacancies and remove any officer below the rank of brigadier-general in any department of the army. He was authorized to take any private property needed for the army, allowing a fair compensation to the owners; and he was instructed to arrest on his own discretion and hold for trial by the civil

TREE UNDER WHICH GENERAL MERCER WAS SHOT, PRINCETON

courts any person who refused to accept Continental paper money or otherwise manifested want of sympathy with the American cause.

The clause about Continental money is significant. The finances of the country were deplorable; Washington himself kept the credit alive for a time by pledging his private fortune. John Stark followed his example, but these sacrifices would have availed nothing had it not been for Robert Morris of Philadelphia, who not only pledged his own funds but financed the expenses of the government.

Congress had assistance from France, as well. Vergennes, the French minister of foreign affairs, saw in the uprising of the Americans a chance to strike back at England for the loss of Canada. He played upon his King's resentment, and guided the popular feeling of kindly interest in America which had ripened and burst under the broad teaching of Voltaire, Rousseau, and the French philosophers. These thinkers had taught the French the theory of liberty; they found an object-lesson in the struggling colonies across the seas.

VIEW OF THE PRINCETON BATTLEFIELD TO-DAY

Vergennes was not ready to brave England openly in his assistance of America; he would wait until they had proved themselves trustworthy allies. But meanwhile he sent them money in secret, furnished them with provisions and arms, and permitted American privateers to fit out in French ports. Congress, having great hopes of an alliance with France, had sent Silas Deane and Arthur Lee, the brother of Richard Henry Lee, to Paris; in October, 1776, the astute Franklin went to join them.

Franklin became the rage of the hour in the French capital. No one except Voltaire had ever been so popular. His pictures were placed in shop windows, the style of his hat was affected by Parisian dandies; ladies had their gloves dyed Franklin hue, dishes of French cookery were named

after him; every honor was done him. He seemed to the
French to sum up the virtues of the American cause: justice,
good sense, and moderation. The first-fruits of his mission
was an agreement on the part of France to furnish 2,000,000
livres a year. Three ships were at once fitted out and despatched for America, and the commission was paid 1,000,000
livres for tobacco that they promised to deliver. Further
than this the government was not yet ready to go.

But there were individuals ready to go much farther.
Foremost of these in fame was Gilbert Motier, marquis
de Lafayette, a youth of nineteen years. Hearing the news
from America at a dinner-party at Metz, he instantly resolved to go and offer his services to Washington. Fitting
out a ship at his own expense, leaving his beautiful young
wife to weep and wait for him, defying the King, who for-
bade his going, he set sail from Bordeaux on April 26, taking with him DeKalb and eleven other officers. America
had already received two   valuable
recruits in the Polish   officers, Pulaski and
Kosciusko.

HOUSE IN WHICH GENERAL MERCER
DIED, PRINCETON, NEW JERSEY

CHAPTER XV

A MILITARY MYSTERY

IN all his military career, brilliant as it was throughout, George Washington never displayed more consummate generalship than during the three weeks in June, 1777, when, by a series of well-chosen manœuvers, he held Howe in the city of New York and prevented his march across New Jersey upon the capital at Philadelphia. Beside some of his more spectacular achievements his operations in these three weeks are not popularly conspicuous; they lack the glamour of war, there being no battles fought; his operations were largely academic, so to speak; but from a military point of view they are a marvel of precise strategical wisdom.

LORD GEORGE GERMAINE   (*From the portrait by Reynolds*)

It was Howe's intention, in the spring of 1777, to push across New Jersey and take Philadelphia, the importance of which, as the "rebel capital," was exaggerated in the

British mind.   To carry out this purpose he moved from New York with a large army on June 12.   Washington, divining his purpose with that perception which never failed him, came down from the heights behind Morristown and occupied a strong position with 8000 men at Middlebrook, eight miles from New Brunswick, on the British line of march.   Howe could not pass on toward the Delaware and leave the enemy on his flank; neither could he attack him, because of the strength of the position, although his army numbered 18,000 men.

In the hope of luring Washington from his impregnable position, he made a feint to cross New Jersey.   The American general would not be beguiled.   For eighteen days Howe tried either to get safely by him, or to dislodge him. In the end he gave it up, and returned to New York.   With the exception of one slight engagement near Bound Brook, there was no fighting in the campaign; Washington, without a blow, had completely baffled every attempt of a largely superior force to march through the State of New Jersey.

Howe's situation now gave him much anxious thought. He could not rid himself of the idea of taking Philadelphia; at the same time General Burgoyne, on his way south from Canada, was likely to stand in need of assistance.   Burgoyne's advance through the valley of the upper Hudson was part of an elaborate plan to divide the new States in two.   Lord North and Lord George Germaine contrived it during the winter, with the help of Burgoyne, who returned to England in the fall of 1776.   Burgoyne was to move up Lake Champlain and Lake George, take Crown Point and Ticonderoga, and proceed to Albany; Saint-Leger, with a lesser force, was to ascend the Saint Lawrence, cross Lake Ontario to Oswego, join a force of Tories and Indians there under Sir John Johnson, take Fort Stanwix, and meet Burgoyne at Albany.   Sir William Howe, at his discretion, was to sail up the Hudson to join the other two forces.

Burgoyne's part in the programme was already under way. He reached Canada in March, and at once began organizing his arms. June 1 he set out with 7902 men, —4135 British regulars, 3116 Hessians, 305 Indians, and 148 Canadians. There was a belief that the inhabitants of northern New York were loyal, and would welcome the English as friends; the march was looked forward to as a pleasant summer's journey; many officers brought their wives and children. The Baroness von Riedesel, wife of the commander of the Hessians, was one of those who went with the invading army.

June 16 the British occupied Crown Point, which had been abandoned; July 1 the army appeared before Ticonderoga, held by General Saint Clair with a garrison of 3000 Americans. Ticonderoga was supposed to be impregnable, but a mile to the south of it was a cliff 600 feet high which completely commanded the works. Saint Clair had not overlooked the threatening possibilities of this height, but, believing it inaccessible, neglected to hold it. On the morning of July 5 the Americans in the fort saw with dismay a British force on top of the hill, and caught sight of brass cannon gleaming in the sun. General Phillips, on the principle that "where a goat can go a man can go, and where a man can go he can drag a gun," had worked for four days and nights in clearing a path and now held the fort at his mercy. The British named the height Mount Defiance.

There was nothing for Saint Clair to do but get his men away, if he could. In the dead of night, July 5, the march began. As the last of the rear-guard was moving out of the fort, a building caught fire and the British saw what was going on. General Fraser at once set out in pursuit.

July 7 he came up with the rear-guard, about 1000 strong, near Hubbardtown, in Vermont. He attacked at once, but the Continentals under Colonels Seth Warner and Francis made so stubborn a fight that Fraser was about to retreat from the field in disorder when Riedesel came up with heavy reinforcements and drove back the Americans, who left one-third their number on the field. But the delay gave Saint Clair his chance to join Schuyler at Fort Edward. The British destroyed some stores at Skenesborough, now Whitehall, at the head of Lake Champlain, and were ready to move against Fort Edward, twenty miles away.

It is here that the Stars and Stripes finds itself recorded for the first time. Lieutenant William Digby, an officer under Burgoyne, notes the capture of an American battle-flag in the action of July 8, 1777, in his diary, saying of the colors: "They were very handsome, a Flag of the United States, thirteen Stripes, alternate red and white, in (with) a blue field representing a new constellation." This was only three weeks after Congress had passed the official resolution by which the Stars and Stripes became our national standard.

BURGOYNE

The loss of Ticonderoga was considered a tragedy by the Americans. Saint Clair and even Schuyler were bitterly charged with negligence and incompetence; the country was torn with grief and dismay; while the English King and the ministry were exultant. "I have whipped them; I have whipped all the Americans!" cried King George, when news came of the taking of the fortress. Events proved that the tragedy of Ticonderoga was reversed; that it was more of a disaster to Burgoyne than to the Americans, for there he was obliged to leave a garrison of 1000 men whom he could ill afford to spare.

In mid July preparations for a military expedition on a scale never before beheld in America were under way in New York City. Two hundred and twenty-eight ships lay at anchor in the harbor; 18,000 men were embarked on them, or embarking. Surely Howe had something of moment in hand.

What he intended was known to two only beside the Howes: Cornwallis and Grant. For the others there were conjecture, surmise, guess, argument, concerning the destination of the fleet and army, but no certainty. One day a squadron raised anchor, sailed a score of miles into Long Island Sound, and returned. Another day, vessels passed through the Hook, for a night, or a half-dozen nights; another, they floated up the Hudson on the tide. All was secret and mysterious. The English army knew as little what the display portended as the Americans, who watched their movements with tense interest.

It was well into the middle of the month. The city was in a fever of excitement; orders had gone forth instructing officers and men to be ready to sail at a moment's notice. Conjecture and surmise concerning the purpose of the expedition rose anew; talk ran fast and foolish.

A number of British officers were grouped

RUINS OF FORT TICONDEROGA

about the sideboard in Robert Stevens's mansion, for a farewell among themselves before their several duties separated them. A friendly group they were, habituated to coming there for the smiles of the women of the house, or the wine of the host, according to their temperaments and ages. Sir Henry Clinton was one of them; Cornwallis another. Major Hempstead was there, and Lieutenant Lucas. Isaac Francis, secure in his place among military men by reason of an impertinent audacity that stopped at nothing, was in the thick of their talk.

"For my part," quoth Sir Henry, in deep thought, setting down his glass, "for my part, and between ourselves, I cannot but think that my lord and Sir William would blunder heavily in setting off on an expedition against Philadelphia, as some surmise they do, and leaving General Burgoyne on his own resources at this juncture. 'T is true, Ticonderoga has fallen, but our colleague has a long way still to march, and the future holds many uncertainties. I deeply doubt if he will not stand sore in need of assistance before the summer is out, and I humbly hope it is not the intention of our commanders to withdraw their assistance from him."

"It is truly to be regretted that the business of taking the rebel capital is not already finished," observed Cornwallis, circumspectly, "so that we might turn at once to the north."

"I know nothing of your military affairs, gentlemen," interposed Francis, "but for the life of me I cannot see why so much importance is attached to the capture of Philadelphia, for all it is the rebel capital, as you say."

"The capital of a country, sir, is the heart of a country," rejoined a brigadier, crushingly. "To take the capital is to destroy the life of a nation."

"Undoubtedly that is true in Europe, to a great extent,"

WASHINGTON'S HEADQUARTERS AT MORRISTOWN, NEW JERSEY

returned Francis, "but it seems to me to be different with America. While Philadelphia is the headquarters of the business of government, it is not the heart of the government; Congress has once before adjourned to another town when Philadelphia was threatened, without seriously impairing the affairs of the country; and may easily do so again, I think."

"There is one circumstance that makes me doubt the wisdom of this move, if there is no other," observed Major Hempstead. "That is the fact that it is being made largely on the suggestion of Charles Lee, the captured American general. Without intending to do the gentleman an injustice, I should be inclined to look with suspicion on any plan of campaign instigated by a general in the army I wished to annihilate."

"Nay, you are wrong there," returned Cornwallis, "for the fellow is in deadly earnest. He feared for his neck, and gave his advice in all sincerity, to save his life, as he thought. But I wish that Lord George had sent positive orders to General Howe to join Burgoyne, instead of leaving him discretion in the matter; it would have removed the responsibility from our arms, and brought the plan to better fruit. Howe, I am convinced, does not understand the importance of acting in unison with the force from Canada." Lord George Germaine had written such an order, but left it in a pigeon-hole in his desk when he went on a holiday, and there it remained undiscovered until after the disaster of Saratoga.

The day following the final order went forth; the expedition was ready to sail. Lieutenant Lucas Hempstead, in full service uniform, sword clanking at his side, entered the drawing-room of the Stevens mansion to make his farewells. Mistress Stevens, perusing a volume in elegant repose, made him welcome with a look closing the book over a

finger as a further sign. Nancy, parrying the wit of Francis —for the fellow would make merry, even when he made
love —came to him, solicitous for his safety in the campaign
about to begin, and glad of an escape from her suitor. At
a window, giving no heed, beyond one slight nod of rec-

INTERIOR OF WASHINGTON'S HEADQUARTERS AT MORRISTOWN, NEW JERSEY

ognition, Sophronia busied herself with her embroidery.
Catherine was not there.

The group shifted. Nancy went to fetch something
she had prepared for her brother's comfort in the field.
Francis, deprived of present interest, sauntered into the
hall and so to the dining-room, where presently was heard
the clink of glasses as he mixed a toddy. Mistress Stevens,
finding Lieutenant Lucas preoccupied and therefore tire-
some, returned to her book. Sophronia continued to em-
broider by the window, unmindful. Into the room, then,
came Catherine.

Shadows had spread over her face again. Since the

day John left she had known no content. Ever at her soul there gnawed a sense of guilt for having revealed his presence to this Englishman who professed love for her, howbeit he had many times protested his innocence in the matter. But worse than that was the thought that John's life had been saved by this dark, inscrutable woman by the window.

"I am off to the war, little child," said Lucas, approaching to meet her while she was still at the edge of the room, so that they might be more nearly alone, and speaking in a low voice.

She made no voluntary response, but in her eyes was a sign that she was not sorry to be rid of him, even though he went against her countrymen.

"Do you not bid me godspeed?" he went on, tauntingly.

"I cannot wish you that when you go to fight mine own people," she replied; "but in all charity I ought to say a kind farewell to you, for we are not like to meet again."

"In sooth, you have a cool assurance that I am about to die," laughed Lucas. "It would almost seem that you wish as much."

"Nay, not that," returned the girl, quickly; for she could not bear to give hurt, even to him. "But I shall soon return to Boston, having newly got passports thither."

Lucas permitted an exclamation of annoyance and chagrin to pass his lips. It had been his one care, involving much intrigue at headquarters, to prevent this very thing.

Sophronia, whose quick ear had overheard what the girl told, and the exclamation, looked blandly over at

WASHINGTON'S HEADQUARTERS AT SOMERVILLE, NEW JERSEY

the two, from her embroidery. None might have known
either from the light in her eye or the smile that suggested
itself about the corners of her lips, that it was she who had
procured Catherine's passports, thwarting him out of sheer
charity for this child, whom she did not wish to see suffer at the hands of any man.   Strange, inscrutable, was
this Sophronia.

"Who knows that we English shall not be again in Boston?" quoth the young lieutenant. Let me warn you,"
he went on, laughing, and seeking to take her hand playfully, "let me warn you, little rebel, that I shall surely make
you captive before I leave your land!"

All in a tumult, Catherine was seeking some reply, when
the return of Nancy and Francis broke into the dialogue,
and permitted her to make her escape. In short space
Lieutenant Hempstead was gone, on his way to fight the foe.

CHAPTER XVI

BAFFLEMENT

ONE pleasant afternoon late in August, John Stevens was riding through the woods near Albany to join the army under Gates, confronting General Burgoyne. John Stevens was now a major in the Continental army, having enlisted in that service as soon as it was established by Congress. He had marched through the snow and sleet on Christmas night when Washington awoke the country and aroused the world with the sound of his guns in the Trenton daybreak; he had kept fires kindled in the trenches beside the Assunpink River that other night when Cornwallis waited to bag the fox; he had done valiant things at Princeton; he had been with the army through the winter at Morristown Heights, and through the campaign of June, when Washington out-manœuvered Howe. Now he was on his way to join General Gates.

The situation of the invading army on the pleasant afternoon when John Stevens went a-riding through the woods had grown precarious. Burgoyne was practically at bay; his plans were falling fast into ruin. The Americans were swarming about him in ever increasing numbers; the promised rising of the

261

GENERAL PHILIP SCHUYLER (*From the engraving by H. B. Hall*)

royalists had failed him; he had a long line of communications to maintain through broken and hostile country; his
supplies were running low; no word came from the south,
promising help; the country behind him was sucked dry
of reinforcements.

At the same time, his Indian allies began to desert him.
From the first their presence with his force was of doubtful
value; in the end it proved disastrous. The
settlers were aroused to vengeance when redskins were sent against them, and
rallied in greater numbers to the
defense of their homes and fire-
sides. Burgoyne had been having
trouble with his savage allies; at
last a crisis came that culminated
in driving the Indians from the
British standard and bringing the
yeomen beneath the American.
This was the murder of Jennie
McCrea by the Wyandot brave
Panther. Jennie McCrea was the
daughter of a clergyman at Paulus

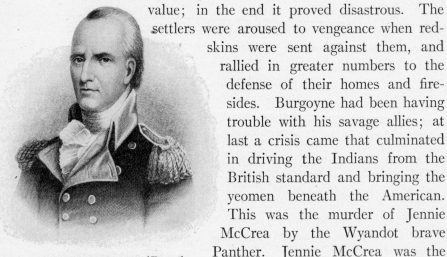

GENERAL JOHN STARK (*From the
painting by H. B. Hall*)

Hook, who was visiting with Mrs. McNeil at Fort Edward.
She was betrothed to one David Jones, a loyalist serving
as a lieutenant in Burgoyne's army; tradition has it that
Jones sent Indians to bring her to the army so that they
might be married; that the Indians fell to quarreling on the
way, and that one of them killed the girl.

It is only known that she was slain, and that the Panther
appeared in the English camp with her scalp. Burgoyne,
who had made an honest effort to control the savages, at
once issued stringent orders against their forming marauding
parties. For a day or two the Indians sulked about the
camp; in the end they left abruptly, in a body. They

took — and left — the vengeance of the outraged settlers, to whom the name of Jennie McCrea became a war-cry.

Burgoyne's army was encamped along the east bank of the Hudson, from Fort Edward south to Battenkill. The Americans were thirty miles below, on the west bank, from Stillwater down to the mouth of the Mohawk. After the fall of Ticonderoga, General Schuyler made no attempt to hold Fort Edward, it being untenable; but he retarded the advance of the British by destroying all the bridges on the line of march and by felling trees along the way, with the result that Burgoyne made only a mile a day. The delay was of inestimable value to the Americans, for

while the invading army was writhing its way through the intricacies of the woodland path, the militia of New England and New York was rising swiftly and assembling at various points, ready to make formidable dispute of their country.

August 13 Burgoyne sent Lieutenant-Colonel Baum with 500 of Riedesel's Hessians to seize

STARK MONUMENT ON THE BATTLEFIELD OF BENNINGTON

stores the patriots had gathered at Bennington, at the foot of the Green Mountains. The expedition was accompanied by Major Skene, a loyalist big with promises that the Green Mountains swarmed with ardent Tories, eager to serve their King. The Green Mountains were swarming, but with quite a different sort of bee. The swarm was

ON THE BANK OF THE OLD WALLOOMSACK, BENNINGTON, VERMONT

lead by John Stark, who had served with distinction at Bunker Hill, Trenton, and Princeton, but had returned home disgusted with the snubs of Congress. Now, however, he took arms again, fighting for New Hampshire.

Baum, advancing into the Green Mountain country, with one eye open for loyalists and the other on the weather, which was threatening, got as far as the Walloomsack River, a small, fordable stream. There his expectations were in part realized, for it began raining abominably; so hard, in fact, that the German determined to go no farther until the weather abated.

The morning of August 14 being clear, Baum was preparing to move when he learned, both by observation and report, that large numbers of countrymen were gathering in his rear. Beguiled by the sanguine Skene, he concluded at once that these were the loyalists come to serve their King. Wherefore he complacently composed himself to wait until they accumulated.

All through the forenoon the countrymen continued to sift through to his rear, loitering and straggling past his lines in small groups, in pairs, sometimes singly. Seeing their numbers, and that all were armed, Lieu-

GENERAL STARK AT BENNINGTON (*From the painting by J. R. Chapin*)

tenant-Colonel Baum was well pleased; for he had lately learned that a body of rebels under Stark was ready to oppose the passage of the stream in his front, and that another regiment, under Seth Warner, for whom Stark had sent, was on the way from Lincoln's camp at Manchester, where the militia was gathering to oppose Burgoyne.

It was not until afternoon that Baum discovered his error. The straggling countrymen, from whom he had extracted such sweet comfort, suddenly opened a blasting fire upon his rear, at the same time that Stark attacked in front. The entire body of Hessians was killed or captured. Just as the Americans were scattering to loot the camp, reinforcements to the number of 500 arrived to succor Baum. The day might have been lost had not Warner

come up at the moment with 500 fresh troops, and served
the reinforcements as Stark had the original body. The
Hessians lost 207 in killed and wounded, and more than
700 of them were made prisoners; Burgoyne's army was
reduced by one-sixth of its strength, and the affair awoke
a hope in the American mind that the entire invading army
might be captured as the detachment had been. The
American loss was fourteen killed and forty-two wounded.

Saint Leger was faring little better at Fort Stanwix,
meanwhile. Landing at Oswego about the middle of July,
he was joined by Sir John Johnson with his Tory regiment,
called the Royal Greens; Colonel John Butler, with a
regiment of Tory rangers, and a number of Iroquois
under Joseph Brant, chief of the Mohawks. August 3 this
motley force, amounting to
1700 men, closed about Fort
Stanwix, defended by a
garrison of 300 under Colonel Gansevoort.

General Nicholas Her-
kimer, a veteran of the
French and Indian War,
hearing of the invasion of
the British army, set out
with 800 militia from Tryon
county and reached the
Oriskany, eight miles from
the fort, on August 6. He
sent messengers ahead to arrange for concerted action
between the garrison and
the rescuers, but the messengers were delayed so long
in reaching the fort that

BENNINGTON BATTLE MONUMENT

Herkimer, unable to restrain the impatience of his men, was obliged to advance before he heard the signal he had suggested.

There followed the fiercest fight of the Revolution. At the crossing of the Oriskany the road leads through a semi-circular ravine; here Brant held his Indians in ambush, and when the Americans were in the bottom of the ravine the Indians attacked. At the same time Johnson's Greens charged the roadway. The conflict at once became terrific. Herkimer, badly wounded in the leg at the first fire, sat down on his saddle beside a tree, lighted his pipe, and calmly directed the proceedings. The militia were equal to the emergency; they were familiar with the Indian methods of fighting, and met the redskins evenly; after a desperate hand-to-hand struggle the Tories and Indians became discouraged and withdrew.

At the same time the garrison, hearing the firing at Oriskany, made a sortie under Colonel Willett, drove Sir John Johnson and his Tories across the river, and did not return until they had despoiled the British camp of ammunition, food, blankets, clothes, and five British standards, to say nothing of all Johnson's private papers, including the

JOSEPH BRANT-THAYENDANEGEA, THE GREAT CAPTAIN OF THE SIX NA-TIONS (*From the portrait by G. Romney*)

plans and orders of the campaign. One of the British standards was swiftly hoisted over the fort, surmounted by a rudely temporized ensign of stars and stripes, after the design adopted by Congress in June. Contrived from an old white shirt it was, and a blue jacket, and some strips of red cloth cut from the petticoat of a soldier's wife. Crude

THE BATTLEFIELD AT ORISKANY, NEW YORK. IN THE HOLLOW THE AM-BUSH WAS FORMED

and rude it was, but glorious; for it was one of the first times that the Stars and Stripes ever took the breeze.

Major John Stevens, posting through the woods near Albany one afternoon late in August, knew all these things, having heard them from gossip by the way, and from messengers he met passing southward with news. But the knowledge could not stir his spirits from the depression that held them. For, though his country prospered in the struggle there; though the invaders were held in check, and threatened with capture, there was a grief mingled with events in the North that made him sad at heart.

Benedict Arnold, his hero, was in tribulation. It all

came about through the base intriguing of General Gates,
working upon local prejudices and political exigencies.
The beginning of it was the hatred of New Englanders for
New York. Philip Schuyler was the pivot of the imbroglio.
He was of New York; that in itself was enough to turn
against him the jealousy of some New England politicians
and military officers, them-
selves political appointees.
More than that, he had always taken an active part in
the attempts of New York to
obtain possession of Ver-
mont, their right to which
was claimed as an inherit-
ance from old Dutch times.
Moreover, he was in a com-

PANEL AT THE BASE OF THE HERKI-
MER MONUMENT, SHOWING THE
WOUNDED GENERAL DIRECT-
ING HIS MEN

mand that Gates desired for himself. That was the crux
of the situation.

The workings of guile were many and malicious. Schuyler was blamed for the failure of the Canada expedition.
He was charged with cowardice in abandoning Fort Ed-
wards; the fall of Ticonderoga was attributed to his negligence and incompetency. He was attacked covertly, on
many sides; his reputation was undermined. Behind all
the attacks was the directing hand of Horatio Gates, who
spent much of his time plotting in Congress, stopping at
nothing to injure the man he sought to supersede. At last,
on August 2, Congress issued an order removing Schuyler
and placing Gates in command.

Arnold, for his friendship with Schuyler, of which he
made no secret, suffered with him at the hands of these
New England politicians, and incurred the resentment of
Gates. The animosity against him had found many expressions; the most trying and annoying was in the preced-

ing autumn, when Congress appointed five junior brigadiers to major-generalcies, ignoring him, who ranked them all. The snub was the more poignant from the circumstance that the appointments of the others followed immediately one of the most daring and skilful exploits in the career of this conspicuously brave and able man.

In the fall of 1776 Carleton ascended Lake Champlain in a fleet of vessels of great combined power.   Three of them were large ships brought from England, taken to pieces on the Saint Lawrence, and rebuilt on Lake Champlain. With a few crazy craft fashioned of green timber cut from the wooded shores of the lake and manned by such sailors as he could find, Arnold, guarding

VALCOUR'S ISLAND, LAKE CHAMPLAIN

the north, gave this fleet battle at Valcour's Island on October 11.

It was one of the most picturesque and amazing contests ever waged on water.   Throughout a long and terrible day, Arnold, with his absurd vessels, manned for the most part by farmers and frontiersmen, withstood the preponderating enemy, in well-equipped ships worked by sea-fighters. On the following night Arnold slipped through the British lines, eluding Carleton's vigilance, and got his fleet away. When the English gave pursuit two days later, he held them for four hours with his own vessel, until the others

escaped. When they were safe, and only then, he turned
tail, running his boat into a shallow creek and, setting it
afire, made a successful retreat through the woods.

For Congress to pass him over in appointing major-
generals after that fight was a calculated affront. Only
the persuasions of Washington, who admired and sym-
pathized with him, and a sincere interest in the cause of
the colonies, induced him to continue with the armies. It
was some consolation to him to be sent by Washington to
help Schuyler, after the fall of Ticonderoga. But his
reception by Gates awoke the old wound.

Almost his first experience, after Arnold arrived at the
front, was in a council of war, held by Schuyler in August
to determine what should be done for the relief of Fort
Stanwix. Colonel Willett and another had just come a
perilous journey with word that the garrison was in need
of succor. Although Gates had been appointed to supersede Schuyler, he had not yet taken over the command.
Schuyler, realizing the importance of holding Stanwix,
wished to send assistance, but his officers opposed him.

"He wishes only to weaken his army," whispered one.

General Schuyler, hearing the whisper, set his teeth so
hard that the stem of the pipe he was smoking was bitten
in two. "Enough!" he cried. "I assume the whole responsibility. Where is the brigadier who will go?"

Arnold was the brigadier who would go, and go he did,
burning with resentment at the imputations against his
friend, and the mutterings of the officers against himself
for his supporting Schuyler. On the same afternoon he
set out for the relief of the fort, with 1200 men, who, be it
said, did not share the political prejudice against him, but
followed him enthusiastically.

Arnold, ever resourceful, accomplished his errand without a blow. It so happened that a half-witted Tory, Yan

Yost Cuyler, was brought to the American camp with a number of others, charged with spying. Him Arnold sent, under promise of pardon, to the Tory and Indian camp with tales of the tremendous force the Americans were bringing with them. The man played his part well. Entering the camp in a fright which his half-wit made real to him, he displayed a hat and coat shot full of bullet holes, with a story so convincing that the Indians scattered precipitately, in terror. Saint Leger himself was not slow to seek safety by retreating to Oswego, leaving Fort Stanwix cleared of threat.

August came. Howe's army of 18,000 men, embarked on 228 vessels, had disappeared, vanishing as completely as a morning mist. The uncertainty concerning his destination, which had given the American generals so much uneasiness since he sailed from New York in July, had grown to anxiety. The obscurity of his movements baffled more and more those pitted against him.

When Howe set sail, Washington was at Morristown Heights, watching. To the American general it seemed certain that the British army would proceed up the Hudson to the succor of Burgoyne. That was the logical move. The departure of the fleet to sea was looked upon as a feint. To prepare against surprise, accordingly, Washington sent Sullivan to Pompton, remaining himself at Morristown, ready to move either toward the Hudson or toward Philadelphia.

Presently, came news of the fall of Ticonderoga. Hearing it, Washington was more firmly convinced than ever that Howe intended to go up the Hudson. Wherefore he moved to Ramapo Cove, a rugged defile in the Highlands near Haverstraw, sending Sullivan and Stirling across the river to Peekskill. At Ramapo there fell into Washington's hands a letter from Howe to Burgoyne, in which the British

GEORGE WASHINGTON   (*From the portrait by Colonel John Trumbull*)

commander stated that he was bound for Boston. The manner in which the letter was intercepted aroused suspicions against it; the suspicions grew to a certainty that Howe was on his way south.

The American general accordingly marched toward Philadelphia, ordering Sullivan to follow as far as Morristown, where he could be in readiness to return quickly to the Hudson in case the movement of the fleet should prove to be a feint after all. "Howe's abandoning Burgoyne in a manner is so unaccountable that, till I am fully assured of it, I cannot help casting my eyes continually behind me," wrote Washington on July 30.

The next day the fleet appeared and was reported at the Capes of the Delaware. That could only mean that Howe was proceeding against Philadelphia. Sending orders to Sullivan to come up, Washington marched rapidly to Germantown, where he established headquarters.

But the fleet did not attempt to pass up the Delaware. Instead, it put to sea once more. The thing was inexplicable. Once more Washington decided that Howe was feinting, and ordered Sullivan to countermarch, preparing to return himself to the Hudson.

Still he could not understand, and delayed departure. Uncertainty, confusion, were in the councils of war. Few had positive opinions concerning the British manœuvers; or, having them, could support them with logic or reason. At last, on August 21, a council concluded that Howe was sailing for Charlestown. To intercept him there was beyond hope; the place was 700 miles away. There was much deliberation; in the end Washington and his generals decided to return to New York.

On the morning of August 22 preparations were under way for breaking camp and putting the army in motion. Washington, at his headquarters, was hearing reports and issuing orders; everywhere was bustle and expectancy. In the midst of it came Fontaine Stevens, draggled, dusty with much riding, wide-eyed with wakeful watching.

"The fleet is at the head of the Chesapeake!" he said to Washington. "Howe has landed at Elkton!"

"What leads you to such a belief?" asked Washington, astonished. Twenty-four days before, Howe had been within thirteen miles of Elkton, on the Delaware.

"I have seen two hundred sail, and more, with my own eyes," returned the young lieutenant.

Through the camp ran a turmoil of orders; couriers posted off to bring up Sullivan. Now there could be but one conclusion: Howe surely aimed at Philadelphia.

Washington had with him 11,000 men, well generaled, but insufficient in discipline and military knowledge. His soldiers were ready and eager to fight, but did not fully know how. The enemy numbered 18,000, well drilled,

WASHINGTON'S HEADQUARTERS, CHADD'S FORD, PENNSYLVANIA

fully equipped. To oppose them in pitched battle was hazardous; to defeat them almost beyond hope. Nevertheless, Washington decided to risk a battle. He could not suffer the capital to fall without a blow. Already the people, knowing little enough of war, were weary of a Fabian policy; the moral effect of a defeat would be better than that of non-resistance, however desperate hope of success might be.

Between the British army at Elkton and Philadelphia, in a rough and wooded country, flowing southeasterly into the Delaware is Brandywine Creek, a stream of size, fordable at some few places, but for the most part quite impassable to troops. Washington, recognizing the natural strength of the position, posted his army along the eastern banks of this river and awaited the coming of the enemy.

At the point where Howe's path toward the rebel capital crossed the stream were several fords. The American center, under Greene, was drawn up at Chadd's Ford, Anthony Wayne in advance, with Greene in reserve. The left was guarded by militia under Armstrong; in front of them the river was impassable. A mile above, on the right, behind Brinton's Ford, was Sullivan, posted in thick woods. The principal road to Philadelphia, branching a mile west of the creek, crossed these two fords. Several miles

LAFAYETTE'S HEADQUARTERS
AT THE BATTLE OF THE BRANDYWINE

west of the creek, the Lancaster road left the turnpike, crossing the Brandywine above the forks by Trimble's and Jeffrey's Fords, whence it swung back into the main road at Dilworth and Chester, after a detour of some eighteen miles.

The day after the American army was in position, Knyphausen advanced with his division to within seven miles of Chadd's Ford, where he rested. At intervals during the two days following, the German moved closer to the ford, as though Howe intended to strike there.

The morning of September 11 came, serene and beautiful; light clouds lay rosy along the horizon; dew sparkled on grass and foliage; the river laughed and danced between the two belligerents. Out across the morning burst the blare of battle; Knyphausen was advancing. Wayne met him with his artillery; Maxwell's light infantry struck him back from the ford, driving him, and following after, through the shallow water. Fontaine Stevens, exultant, rode to headquarters with reports from Wayne.

Washington stood among his aides, alert and serious. About him was turmoil and excitement; the noise of fighting at the ford came to his ears, fainter and more distant. Knyphausen was not accepting battle.

"We are driving them!" cried one. "Listen! The fight goes farther away."

Scouts of Sullivan brought word that a detachment of English was marching along the Lancaster road to cross at Trimble's and Jeffrey's Fords, and take Sullivan in flank. Scouts came following to tell that no English marched there; there was a confusion of information.

In Washington's mind was a daring project, if it should prove that the British made a flank movement. He contemplated advancing across Brinton's and Chadd's Fords, crushing Knyphausen, and breaking the British army to pieces before the flank movement could be driven home. Only the lack of drill and training among his troops, and uncertainty concerning the British army, deterred him.

In the midst of his meditation, word came that Cornwallis had crossed, beyond doubt, and was marching down toward the Birmingham meeting-house, on Sullivan's right. Without a tremor, with no sign of emotion, Washington made out an order, gave it to Fontaine, and bade him bear it with speed to Sullivan. It was an order to change front so as to intercept the flanking movement at the meeting-house.

Slowly, cumbrously, lacking training, Sullivan's troops wheeled into the new position. Before the line was set the red-coats were upon them; the battle broke about the meeting-house. The two armies grappled instantly.

Fontaine, watching breathlessly, saw the lines of the Continentals yield, slowly but certainly. They did not crumble; they did not break; they did not pull apart under the ponderous pressure of the British attack. They bent, and stretched, like things plastic, clinging here and there where the topography gave defense a natural advantage, and looping back in thin lines between.

Spurring toward headquarters, Fontaine left the scene, heavy of heart, fearing for the safety of the entire army; Cornwallis was pushing to the rear, with nothing but a drifting mass of men to oppose him. But his fears were unfounded. As he rode, he beheld Greene's Virginians and Pennsylvanians coming up from Dilworth; old neighbors and companions of his, many of them.

So rapid was their march that Weedon's brigade, in the lead, covered four miles in forty minutes. Meeting the Americans, now going to pieces beneath their burden of fighting, Greene's ranks opened to admit the fugitives, closing again against the British, and receiving them with vicious fire.

The lines of red-coats faltered, not expecting any such resistance. At the moment, Greene charged, sending the British advance back upon itself. Beyond that point, where Greene met them, the British did not obtain. Until night the fight hung there, dogged and brutal.

Meanwhile, taking advantage of the diversion resulting from Cornwallis's advance, Knyphausen crossed the ford and fell upon Wayne and Armstrong, driving them from the field after a close contest. But the stability of Greene's division enabled them to re-form, so that in the end the entire army retired through Dilworth to Chester in good order.

Although the battle was lost, the affair on the Brandywine did not dispirit either officers or men. The morale of the army was as efficient as it had been the day Howe landed at Elkton; the brilliant flanking march of Cornwallis had been neutralized; instead of destroying the army, it had simply accomplished its dislodgment. Washington still stood between Howe and Philadelphia, the rebel capital, which it behooved the British general to take without great delay if he hoped to be of aid to General Burgoyne, struggling among the wilds of northern New York. The American army retired to Germantown.

MEETING-HOUSE, BIRMINGHAM, PENNSYLVANIA

Their loss in the battle at the Brandywine was 1200 men; the British lost over 1000. Howe's force now outnumbered Washington's by nearly two to one; the fall of the capital was inevitable. But neither Congress nor the people were greatly disturbed in mind. Congress, investing Washington with the same extraordinary powers they had given him

THE OLD CAPITOL, YORK, PENNSYLVANIA (*From the etching by Horace Bonham*)

after the affair at Trenton, quietly slipped away to York, where they continued to misadminister their affairs.

Washington knew that he could not hope to hold Philadelphia. But there was one thing, vastly important, that he could hope to do. He could hope to keep Howe so busily engaged that he could not get away from Pennsylvania to help Burgoyne. Word had recently come of Bennington, and of Saint Leger's flight; to Washington the annihilation of Burgoyne's army seemed to be only a question of time and opportunity. He himself could promote opportunity by withholding Howe's help.

That he did.   For fifteen days he manœuvered, never letting a day pass without some hostile demonstration, harassing and keeping Howe on the *qui vive* with skirmishings and feints.   Once he crossed the Schuylkill and offered battle; only a violent rainstorm prevented a desperate struggle.   But Howe was held.   Wayne was defeated in a serious engagement; but Howe was held.   Once more

HOWE'S HEADQUARTERS IN PHILADEL-
PHIA

Washington crossed the Schuylkill, hoping to dispute Howe's passage of the stream.   The British general slipped by him, giving a day to the strategy — and great things were happening in day-breadths in northern New York.

At last, on September 26, while Howe was establishing headquarters at Germantown, Cornwallis marched into the rebel capital.   The victorious army had accomplished a march of twenty-six miles in fifteen days; in the North Burgoyne was grappling with the young giant that he had aroused.

But what must Howe do with the rebel capital, now that he had it?   Plainly, he must hold it, or lose his labor.   But to hold it demanded the use of his entire army.   And to hold it would require the capture of Forts Mifflin and Mercer, the watchdogs of the Delaware River, below Philadelphia.   With those fortresses in the hands of the Americans, the fleet could not come to Philadelphia; without the fleet, the army would starve, for the victorious army was as completely and desperately hemmed in by land as though it had never won a battle.

Howe must take the forts.   Moreover, he must hasten.

Haste was not now needful only for the safety of Burgoyne, but for the salvation of the British army of victory, possessed of the enemy's capital. Burgoyne must now look after his welfare, for Howe had work of his own to do. This work, to make a beginning, was to take the two forts guarding the

THE BATTLE OF GERMANTOWN. ATTACK ON JUDGE CHEW'S HOUSE (*From the painting by Chappell*)

Delaware with guns and great chains stretched across the river from shore to shore.

Now there came before the view of the world perhaps the most dramatic and spectacular battle in the Revolutionary War; certainly one which shows as clearly as any the superb daring of George Washington, and his mighty grasp. Howe sent a portion of his army across the river to help the fleet with the forts; the main army remained in Germantown. Here Washington, with his inferior army, attacked them early on the morning of October 4, much as he had assailed the sleeping Hessians at Trenton on the preceding Christmas; and here, but for an accident, he

would have annihilated Howe, as Burgoyne was shortly
to be disposed of.

The attack was brilliant in conception and execution.
The Americans moved in three columns, from three direc-
tions, to converge in the center of the town. In spite of
the warning given the enemy through the attack on Judge
Chew's house on the outskirts of the town, they were

CHEW MANSION, GERMANTOWN, PENNSYLVANIA

making a success of it; victory was almost theirs, and the
British army of victory was close to utter destruction, when
an accident intervened, to prolong the heartbreaking struggle
of the colonies through four more years.

Just at the psychological moment, when fate hung in
the balance, when the two armies were in the death-grapple,
Stephen, of Greene's division, misled by sound of the heavy
firing on Judge Chew's stone mansion, and unable to see
because of the dense fog that lasted throughout the fight,
fell upon Wayne's brigade, the keystone of the entire
structure. In a moment the American army was shaken
loose from its grip on the British; in a moment more,

bewildered, not knowing what had happened, or why, it was in full retreat.

But though the attack failed of its purpose, which was no less than the destruction of Howe's entire force, its moral effect, both in America and abroad, was scarcely less than that of Trenton. For a defeated army to turn and strike a blow at their conquerors which failed only through sheer accident, showed a genius for war in its commander and a spirit in its men that did much to convince the world that the American colonies could never be subjugated. If the audacious plan had succeeded, the end would have been then. Although it did not succeed, it might another time; and there still remained the officers and men who had so nearly executed their purpose against their enemy.

Far in the North, neglected and unaided, Burgoyne grappled alone with the giant he had aroused.

Wych Mansion, Germantown, Pennsylvania. Here Washington and Lafayette made their Headquarters during the Battles in and
about Germantown

CHAPTER XVII

THE LION IN THE TOILS

BURGOYNE'S situation was growing more and more critical day by day. His army was in danger of being crushed by the very numbers of the troops gathering to oppose him; his rations were short, and instead of being friendly the inhabitants were flocking to his enemy. If he advanced he would be obliged to give up his line of communications with Ticonderoga and Canada, for the Americans were ready to fall upon his rear. If he fell back on Ticonderoga he exposed himself to attack and left Gates's army to operate against General Howe, whom he still supposed was on the way north from New York. Refusing to abandon Howe, on September 13 he crossed the Hudson on a bridge of boats and advanced toward Bemis Heights, where the Americans occupied a position strongly fortified by Kosciusko.

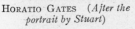

HORATIO GATES   (*After the portrait by Stuart*)

Burgoyne determined to dislodge them. With part of the army he intended to pass to the west of Bemis Heights on the Quaker road, which ran behind the American camp. There Fraser, who was directed to take a more circuitous route, was to meet him; they were to attack the camp in the rear while Riedesel and Phillips, with the left wing and the artillery, were to attack in front. To the execution of these plans the army moved on the morning of September 19.

The American left wing was under General Benedict Arnold. Attached to his command was Morgan, with his riflemen. Major John Stevens, with a detachment of Major Dearborn's New England troops, was in advance at an outpost. Ten o'clock came; the day was warm and bright; the soldiers were in exuberant mood. Their hopes were high. They had learned that Burgoyne had passed over the river; they knew he could never return; it remained for them to prevent him from going farther.

Morgan passed by with a squad of riflemen. "Send some of your men into the trees," he said to John, as he passed; "there are rumors that the British are advancing through the woods."

A score of soldiers clambered into the highest branches of the tall trees. "There they are! There they are!" an excited voice called down from the treetops. "By the river road; and there, by Freeman's farm. Great God!" added the man, beside himself with excitement, "there are a million of them circling around to our left!"

John sprang into a tree, dispatching one of the soldiers to Arnold with the news as he struggled upward. He was a product of the town, was John, and the ascent was not easy. Reaching at last the man who had spread the alarm he looked abroad over the waving treetops and saw a sight both beautiful and awful. Far to the left and

RAPIDS AT SCHUYLERVILLE, WHERE BURGOYNE'S ARMY CROSSED

the right, and in front, scarlet coats glimpsed between the
green trees; the occasional flash of bayonets came from
the cool depths of the forests. Descending to make fuller
report to his superior, he found Morgan returning hastily
from his reconnoissance.

"Is it the whole army?" he asked.

"Yes!" returned the other; "the Hessians are moving
along the river road; Burgoyne it is, I think, who moves in

MIDDLE RAVINE, SARATOGA BATTLEFIELD

the center, and Fraser on the extreme right; though what
they have in mind is more than I can guess."

It was noon before the intentions of Burgoyne were
understood. Arnold, learning what they were from the
men in front, hastened to Gates's headquarters.

"The British are trying to gain our rear by the left
flank!" he said. "Let me have men and I can check the
movement."

"I cannot let you take any men from the works," Gates
said, coldly. "I must not weaken the lines; we are strongly
intrenched here. Let them attack us here."

"But they are gaining our rear!" cried Arnold, in a fever
of impatience.

Gates made no reply.

"They will turn our position; in two hours we shall be helpless," Arnold went on.

"When they arrive we can make dispositions to meet them," returned the other indifferently.

"But if we strike them now we shall have an immense advantage," Arnold persisted.

"I cannot weaken my force," was the dogged rejoinder.

Arnold was not to be put off. He urged, he pleaded. In the end, Gates sullenly consented to allow him to take Morgan's Rifles and Dearborn's Massachusetts troops and attack. In an instant Arnold was on his charger, the gift of Congress, and was tearing down the Quaker road.

Major John Stevens, fretting at the sight of the British advancing unopposed across the left flank, was talking with Morgan and Dearborn when there was a thunder of hoofs, and Arnold rode up to them, raging with the fervor of battle.

"Forward, Colonel Morgan, with your riflemen!" he cried. "Advance, Major Dearborn, and drive me off these impudent Canadians and redmen on our left flank!"

The American troops moved swiftly to the front, attacked the enemy, and pushed their charge so fast and furiously that the latter fled for their lives. Being reinforced, however, they turned upon the patriots and so overlapped them by mere numbers that it seemed as if the rifle corps was doomed to destruction. Morgan sounded his turkey call, and the riflemen rallied at the sound of the woodman's whistle. Aided by the Massachusetts and New Hampshire regiments, they checked Burgoyne's advance near Freeman's farm.

There was only a moment's pause; for Burgoyne by a rapid movement attempted to fall heavily on Arnold's right, while Fraser, who had been drawn thither by the sound of

the conflict, tried to turn the American left. Arnold, however, leading the van of his men, fell upon the enemy with
the fury and the impetuosity of a tiger, and endeavored to
cut Fraser off from Burgoyne. Desperate fighting ensued
in the ravine west of the farm. Arnold was forced back by
a Hessian force sent in by Fraser; but making a rapid

BATTLE OF SARATOGA. GENERAL ARNOLD WOUNDED IN THE ATTACK ON THE
HESSIAN REDOUBT (*From the painting by Chappell*)

countermarch, he fell like a thunderbolt upon that general's
flank, and heavy fighting took place along the line of battle,
Dearborn and Hull with the New England troops winning
fresh fame and glory every minute. Arnold had sent to
Gates, begging that he be reinforced, and now appealed
to him again, only to be refused.

"By God, I 'll soon put an end to it!" cried Arnold, and
plunging into the desperate fray, he soon shook the British
lines so that, here and there, they began to waver before the
deadly fire of the Americans. Victory was hovering over
the patriot banners when Phillips, on the enemy's left,

heard the din of battle resounding through the woods and hastened over the hills with fresh troops, followed by the Hessians under Riedesel. Just at the crucial moment they appeared upon the field, and turned the scale. Riedesel by a furious attack pressed back the American left, and saved the British there from utter ruin; but the American main line, though opposed by the overwhelming numbers of the entire British army, clung like bulldogs to their position. For two terrible hours Arnold's 3000 men fought to a standstill 4000 regulars of the foe, in a combat so fierce that both sides lost from a quarter to a fifth of their numbers.

"By the great Jehovah! to think Gates has lain idle in his works, with eleven thousand men idly watching us few fight the whole British army — what kind of a general is that?" cried an angry Massachusetts major, covered with blood and dust, shaking his clenched fist toward Bemis Heights, as darkness came down upon the scene. "Had Gates reinforced us, Arnold would have crushed them like eggs, eh, Stevens?"

"We could certainly have ended it here and now," returned John, ruefully, his thoughts full of the hero of the day.

The British held the field, but they had utterly failed in the object of their attack. Shattered

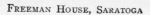

FREEMAN HOUSE, SARATOGA

and dispirited, they bivouacked on Freeman's farm. If Gates had attacked them the following morning, as Arnold begged him to do, he must undoubtedly have compelled the surrender of the entire British army.

That night, in a tent within the guarded camp, Colonel Livingston wrote to Philip Schuyler, the man who had prepared the glorious moment, "Believe me, sir, to him (Arnold) is due the honor of the victory."

But Gates, in his report to Congress, took to himself all the credit of the affair, not even mentioning the name of Arnold. When he learned of the deliberate slight, Arnold was beside himself with rage. He blamed Gates freely for not coming to his support. Gates resented his aspersions, and resented as well the praise that the army universally bestowed upon Arnold, for he could not bear to hear any one but himself well

THE BEMIS HEIGHTS BATTLE WELL: HERE SCORES OF WOUNDED SOLDIERS CRAWLED TO QUENCH THEIR DEATH-THIRST, AND WERE FOUND, A WALL OF BODIES, ABOUT IT

spoken of. In a spirit of petty, spiteful revenge, he withdrew Morgan's riflemen and Dearborn's light infantry from Arnold's division, virtually leaving him without a command.

A fierce quarrel ensued, in which Gates told Arnold that as soon as Lincoln arrived he would have no further use for him. Arnold would have left at once, but the other generals in the army wrote him a letter, signed by all but Lincoln,— who refrained from a public expression out of tact,—begging him to remain. The circumstance did not conduce to more cordial relations between him and his superior, but Arnold, out of deference to them and out of regard for Washington, consented to stay and do what he could. He remained in his quarters, awaiting the day of battle, chafing and indignant. Gates took no more notice of him than as though he were a dog about camp.

For eighteen days nothing more was done. Burgoyne's predicament became hourly more desperate. September 31 news came that a detachment of Lincoln's men had laid siege to Ticonderoga, and had captured three vessels laden with supplies; two days later the unhappy commander learned that New England men, cruising in Lake

MAJOR–GENERAL BENJAMIN LINCOLN (*Painted by J. Herring from the original by Colonel Sargeant in the collection of the Massachusetts Historical Society*)

George with the captured vessels, had cut off his last source of supplies. And now, when even on the shortest rations there remained scarcely food enough for three weeks, Lincoln appeared on his front, swelling the American force to 16,000 determined patriots.

But desperate as was his case, Burgoyne was not the man to despair. On the morning of October 7, taking with him 1500 picked men and his best generals,—Fraser, Riedesel, Phillips, Balcarras, and Ackland,—he marched forth once more to turn the American left. There was a chance; Sir Henry Clinton had sent word that he would soon start from New York; he had learned that Arnold had been deprived of his command, and built hopes upon the circumstance. In any event, the movement would cover a foraging party he had sent out, which was no small matter.

BRIGADIER–GENERAL DANIEL MORGAN

Through the still hours of the night before, John Stevens's men had detected a stir and a bustle in the British camp; early on the morning of October 7 John went in person to report the signs of activity to General Gates. Returning from headquarters, his impulse led him to the tent of

Arnold. An orderly, taking a message to Arnold, returned and bade John enter. Colonel Morgan was with him; they sat conversing in low tones, clearly avoiding that which was uppermost in the hearts of each.

John made a circumstantial report of what he and his men had observed. Morgan, listening attentively through-out, arose in haste when he had finished and departed for his command, scarcely stopping to bid the others farewell.

"Great God!" groaned Arnold, when he had gone; "this is the bitterness of it! The battle is at hand; the hour is come; the pride of England will this day be trailed through the dust, and I must wait here in my tent like a naughty child suffering punish-ment, when the noise of the great and glorious game fills the air! God, 't is too much to be borne!"

His face was tense with pain; his frame trembled with emotion. John, full of grief for him, could only look on in silence. As they stood thus, the sound of a shot came from Free-man's farm, followed by another, and others until the noise rose to a clattering rattle, to die out again presently.

Site of the British Camp at Saratoga, October 15, 1777

John did not stay to hear it die; he mounted his horse and spurred with hot haste in the direction of his command. As he rode the sound of a bugle pierced the air. Its notes were taken up from camp to camp as it called the men to arms. On every side men were assembling, excited and eager; regiments were forming; generals and aides were mounting and galloping to the front of their battle-lines massing in the woody aisles of the forest.

Suddenly there was the roar of cannon near the river, on the extreme right. Poor, advancing in silence up the slopes near the Hudson, had pressed on through the woods, and bursting out into an open glade had made a desperate attack upon the British batteries, whose shot flew harmlessly over the heads of his men. The Americans poured in a fierce fire upon the British left, charged them with their guns, and a sanguinary struggle took place. One of the guns was taken and retaken four times, until Colonel Cilley, leaping astride of it, turned it around and discharged it with fatal effect upon the British; with the consequence that the latter soon took to flight in that part of the field.

Meanwhile, at the other end of the line, in the hills, Morgan assailed Fraser's flanking party in advance of the British right with such a storm of rifle-balls that Fraser was driven back. Immediately Morgan wheeled and fell on their right flank with a fierceness so appalling that their ranks were badly broken; and being now also assailed in front by the New England Continentals aided by 5000 New York militia, a short sharp fight ensued, which terminated in the British giving way before overwhelming numbers. Fraser endeavored now to form a second line west of Freeman's farm, but their organization had dissolved, their guns had been lost, and their lines reeled to and fro under the attacks of the Americans. Arnold, chafing at his own forced inaction, had been watching the battle from his aery on the

Heights, and now saw that one strong, well-aimed blow would both finish Fraser and defeat the entire British army.

The sight of that magnificent opportunity was too much for the splendid generalship of the fiery American on the hilltop. Quick as a flash, he vaulted into his saddle.

"No man," he exclaimed to his aide, "shall keep me in my tent to-day. If I am without command, I will fight in the ranks. But the soldiers, God bless them, will follow my lead. Come on" he cried. "Victory or death!" And turning his black charger around he galloped off to the scene of action and plunged into the thickest of the fighting.

"BLOODY HILL," FREEMAN'S FARM. TAKEN AND RETAKEN SEVEN TIMES DURING THE BATTLE OF SARATOGA

"Call back that fellow," cried Gates to his aide, Major Armstrong, "call him back, or he will do something rash." But Arnold was far beyond the reach of recall; and Armstrong dared not follow him into the terrible dangers into which Arnold rode headlong.

Suddenly, amid all the uproar of the battle, John Stevens heard a wild cry from the left of his corps, and turning swiftly he saw Arnold riding fast and hard to the fighting front, his great black thoroughbred fairly flying along the ground, the long black mane and tail streaming in the breeze as the big charger leapt like a deer over ditches and obstacles.

Arnold was a perfect horseman, and now, erect as a figure of iron, his broadsword flashing in the air, his proud face ablaze with the fury of a berserker, he galloped to the head of his old brigade. The men received their beloved general with cheers, fairly leaping in the air and shaking their gleaming muskets over their heads in wild delight. In a perfect frenzy of joy and courage, they rushed upon Fraser's disordered line, while Arnold, mad with the rage of battle, charged furiously up to and through the British ranks.

Fraser, mounted on a big grey gelding, was the very soul of the British defense; Arnold perceiving it, directed Morgan to have him slain. Calling several of his sharpshooters aside, Morgan pointed Fraser out to them.

A moment or two afterward, Fraser rode down toward the rifle corps; several rifles cracked, and he fell, to rise no more, at the same instant that Arnold charged the British center. Balcarras was posted there behind intrenchments, however. Finding the position too strong, Arnold swept swiftly off to the left and fell like lightning upon the Canadians to the north of Balcarras. All along the lines the battle was now raging with fury, but amid all the uproar and the tumult, John could hear Arnold's "voice ringing over the battlefield amid the smoke and flame like a trumpet," as an officer described it. Leading charges, issuing orders, cheering his men on in clarion tones, brandishing his sword, galloping amid a hail of bullets with a smiling face, he broke the Canadians, who fled in utter rout, leaving Breymann on the extreme British right quite isolated. Morgan, wheeling again like lightning, fell upon Breymann on one side just as Arnold at the head of Brooks's regiment assaulted the German works on the other. The incarnate genius of battle, a thunderbolt of war, Arnold swooped down upon the terrified Hessians.

"He is the devil!" cried the frightened mercenaries, as

SURRENDER OF BURGOYNE AT SARATOGA   (*From Trumbull's painting in the Rotunda of the Capitol at Washington*)

they fired a volley and fled, leaving their commander, Breymann, slain upon the field. The whole right wing of the British was utterly crushed; their line was crumpled up and taken in reverse. At this moment a wounded German fired at Arnold, killed his horse, and pierced Arnold's leg with the ball from his musket. It was the same leg that had been wounded at Quebec and the pain was intense; still, as Stevens ran up to avenge his chief, Arnold called to him from where he lay, "For God's sake, don't hurt him —he's a fine fellow." The poor German's life was saved by the man he had shot.

Arnold's fall and the growing twilight put an end to the battle; but the victory was complete, nevertheless; and Arnold was carried off the field, rejoicing in the splendid and glorious part he had played in obtaining it. In all the camps of the patriots, there was nought but gaiety and rejoicing that night.

The next day Burgoyne drew his army off to the north, ascending the Hudson to Saratoga, but doing no damage beyond the burning of General Schuyler's magnificent house and granaries by some of the British officers. Gates, who knew how to follow up a victory occasionally, though fighting was not in his line, kept close on the heels of the retreating enemy, with his force now increased to 20,000 by the militia that poured into the American army by hundreds every day. When Burgoyne reached the place where he had formerly crossed the river he found its passage impossible in the face of the 3000 militia and batteries of cannon posted on the other side of the stream. A council of war was held by Burgoyne; it advised that the artillery and baggage be abandoned, and that the troops should make their way by night to the ford near Fort Edward and cross there. News, however, came to them that the Americans were guarding the fords, and that a force had taken up a strong position between Fort Edward and Fort George. The British were surrounded; but Burgoyne still hoped for some news or assistance from Clinton.

The hope was vain. Clinton, waiting in New York until 3000 expected troops arrived from England, had started up the Hudson October 5. Landing near Putnam's headquarters at Peekskill, he completely outwitted that

SITE OF GATE'S HEADQUARTERS AT BEMIS HEIGHTS

general in three days' manœuvering, taking Forts Clinton and Montgomery by storm, with a loss to the Americans of 100 killed and wounded and 200 captured. Governor Clinton, fighting with the militia composing the defending force, was wounded by a bayonet thrust. Putnam abandoned Peekskill, as well as Forts Independence and Constitution, leaving the Hudson open to Albany. Clinton sent 500 troops ahead, who stopped to burn Kingston on the way. At the same time he dispatched a message to General Burgoyne telling him of the approach of assistance. The message was contained in a silver bullet. The messenger was captured; he swallowed the bullet, but his captors gave him an emetic and recovered it.

A few days later, Burgoyne, despairing of hearing from Clinton, finding his camp swept by cannon fire from the east and south and harassed by Morgan's riflemen on the west, sent a flag of truce to Gates asking what terms would be granted; to which the latter replied, unconditional surrender, a proposal indignantly rejected by Burgoyne. Gates, who knew what Clinton was doing, even if Burgoyne did not, consented to make terms; and in a few days they were agreed to. Burgoyne was about to sign them, when a Tory messenger brought the news that Clinton was approaching Albany. To the honor of British arms, a council there decided that their word was pledged beyond recall and that it was now too late to draw back. The articles were signed on October 17, and the British marched out with the honors of war, piled their arms near the ruins of old Fort Hardy, and were prisoners of war. The Americans, with great delicacy, remained in their own works, not wishing to humiliate their gallant foe; and when Burgoyne advanced and gave his sword to Gates, saying, "General Gates, the fortune of war has made me your prisoner"; Gates immediately returned it to him with the words, "I shall always be ready to testify that it has not been through the fault of your Excellency."

Thus did Gates reap the honors sown by the noble Schuyler, the heroic Morgan, the stout Herkimer, the bold Stark, and that thunderbolt of war of whom a British historian wrote: "Arnold displayed more military genius than all the generals put together on both sides engaged in that war, with the most undaunted personal courage." His heroic figure, thundering over the plains of Saratoga upon his great black charger, must ever fascinate the mind of the soldier, thrill the heart of the patriot, and inspire the imagination of poet and painter. One cannot follow Arnold's life to its close without a feeling of regret that he was not carried from the field at Saratoga mortally wounded. That he lived to experience the same regret there can be no doubt.

THE VACANT NICHE

"Let me die," sighed Arnold on his death-bed, "in this old uniform in which I fought my battles. May God forgive me for ever putting on any other!" And in the Continental buff-and-blue he had worn away on the lamentable morning of his treason, he passed from earth. Nothing bespeaks more strongly the consummate tragedy of Benedict Arnold's career than the Battle Monument which rises on the banks of the Hudson to commemorate the victory of Saratoga. In the square shaft are four high Gothic arches, and in these are placed heroic statues of the generals who won the victory. Horatio Gates, unworthy though he was, stands there in bronze. The gallant Schuyler, the intrepid Morgan, honor the other two.

But where is he whose valor turned back the advancing Saint-Leger? whose prompt decision saved the Continental position at Bemis Heights? whose military genius truly gained the day? A vacant niche — empty as England's rewards, void as his own life — speaks more eloquently than words, more strongly than condemnation, more pitifully than tears, of a mighty career blasted

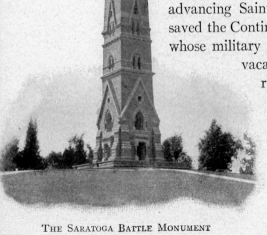

THE SARATOGA BATTLE MONUMENT

by the lightnings of Heaven, a great life hurled into the abyss.
This is America's way of honoring Arnold in his dishonor.

Gates is shown with his spy-glass,   t h a t
being the only weapon he used
while Arnold was engaged in leading his exultant men into the
very heart of the British line.
Through the thick of the battle
the commanding general sat in
his tent, discussing the principles behind the Revolutionary
c a u s e   with an
Eng-   l i s h
offi-

PHILIP SCHUYLER

cer of rank, who had been
brought there to die.

Mortally wounded as the
Englishman was, he held his
own with the wordy Horatio,
and provoked him into some
heartless   abuse,
f o r   lack
of a

HORATIO GATES

better rejoinder. Burgoyne received from Arnold the light-
ning-stroke that forced his
surrender; Gates saw a little
of the battle from a safe distance. The spy-glass in his
hand is no badge of courage
or honor. But for political influence, Gates would have had
no share in the Saratoga victory.

DANIEL MORGAN

When General Schuyler appeared upon the scene of that memorable surrender, John and many other officers came to pay their respects to the man who had made that surrender possible; yet so great and lofty was the spirit and the mind of the man and so far from envy was he, that nought but calm happiness radiated from his heart and features. It was he who took unto himself the care not only of the Baroness Riedesel and her children, but also that of Burgoyne, whose embarrassment over the destruction of Schuyler's lordly mansion was chivalrously dissipated at their meeting by the generous behavior and courtesy of the latter. In the House of Commons Burgoyne later told of his reception by Schuyler.

"I expressed to General Schuyler," he said, "my regret at the event which had happened, and the reasons which had occasioned it. He desired me to think no more of it, saying that the occasion justified it, according to the rules of war. . . . He did more; he sent an aide-de-camp to conduct me to Albany, in order, as he expressed it, to procure me better quarters than a stranger might be able to find. This gentlemen conducted me to a very elegant house, and, to my great surprise, presented me to Mrs. Schuyler and her family; and in this general's house I remained during my whole stay in Albany, with a table of more than twenty covers for me and my friends, and every other possible demonstration of hospitality."

In comparison with the generosity displayed by the American army and its chiefs, it is sad to recall the bad faith exhibited by Congress in its actions concerning Burgoyne's captured army, which the nation was in honor bound, according to the terms of the surrender, to permit to return to Britain, with the understanding that the troops thereof should not again serve in America during the war. Washington himself seems to have suggested causes for delaying their departure, stating openly that if these troops were returned to Britain, they could replace troops over there, thus releasing other forces which could then be used as a heavy reinforcement to General Howe.

Congress, anxious to impose obstructions, ordered that descriptive lists must be made of all the men, an insulting proposal not required by the surrender-articles, and one that led Burgoyne to say rightly that "the publick faith is broke." Congress, having learned this from that perennial mischief-maker, Gates, resolved on January 8 that "the embarkation of Lieutenant-General Burgoyne and the troops under his command be suspended till a distinct and explicit ratification of the convention of Saratoga shall be properly ratified by the court of Great Britain to Congress." Pretending that Burgoyne wished to repudiate the convention, Congress thus achieved its own fell purpose, as it knew well that the obstinate ministry would never ratify the convention for fear lest its so doing would imply recognition of the independence of the United States.

This evil sacrificing of principle to policy, and a mistaken policy at that, cannot be righteously condoned, even by gross expediency; for, as has been said, "to a people struggling for political life, the moral support derivable for the maintenance of honor and good faith, was worth a dozen material victories."

Thus the tremendous drama played out amid the stirring scenes and wild and historic background of the upper

THE SPOT WHERE BURGOYNE SUR-
RENDERED HIS SWORD TO GATES

Hudson, found its *dénouement* in as sorry a tragedy as ever attended a violation of comity between nations. It was, to Great Britain, a lost army; for it never returned again, but, immured amid the semi-wilderness of western Virginia, gradually dissolved away by death, desertion, exchange, and the allowing of those who so desired to enter the American army, or to escape. Burgoyne was permitted to return to England in the spring; and taking his seat in Parliament, he ably defended himself from his critics and became, perhaps out of personal gratitude aided by personal acquaintance with the patriot chiefs and the resources of the country, one of the foremost defenders of

THOMAS JEFFERSON'S STATUE IN THE JEFFERSON HOTEL AT RICHMOND, VIRGINIA (*Edward Valentine, Sculptor*)

the United States in the House of Commons. Some of the officers were exchanged; others resigned from the British service. But near Charlottesville, Virginia, the great bulk of that lost army remained in its cantonments, watched over by sympathetic warders and aided by the kindness of Thomas Jefferson, until the British raids in that State compelled their removal to Maryland and Pennsylvania, where the remnant gradually disappeared from official view, the Germans especially preferring to stay in America and become, as many of them did, useful citizens of the young republic.

Wisely has Creasy named Saratoga as among the fifteen decisive battles of the world's history; for there followed from it consequences so far-reaching that he who loves his country may well pause and review that glorious triumph of our arms. What if Gates won the fame, while Arnold, the real victor, lay prostrate, his heroism unrecognized save by the fighting men who then and there did that great deed for all posterity? The banners that strove with the Stars and Stripes that day have long since moldered into dust; the bright steel and burnished rifle that sung over that deathless field a deadly requiem to many, are long sunk into a rusted pile; but the glory and the fame, the mighty consequences and the ever-increasing issue of that famous field should always be precious to those patriots who appreciate the past, revere their hardy ancestors who did these deeds, and understand the illimitable debt they owe to the men of Saratoga.

MARSHALL HOUSE, WHERE THE BARONESS RIEDESEL AND HER CHILDREN
FOUND REFUGE

CHAPTER XVIII

VALLEY FORGE

EZRA STEVENS lay on the bare ground beneath a squat hut of twisted boughs. His blue coat was in tatters, out at elbow, lacking buttons. One of his shoulder sashes was twisted about his throat against the cold. His shoes were burst out along the soles; one of the soles itself was gone; his naked feet, thrusting through, were torn. Black blood caked on the blue flesh. Over him was a scant blanket, hard and thin. Through the chinks between the twisted boughs that formed the little hut the snow-wind snarled, snapping deep into the flinching flesh of the boy. Thin little drifted tracks of snow stretched behind the chinks, across the bare ground where he lay, climbing his blanket, creeping toward his throat as if to feed on his wasted body.

It was in the hospital of the winter camp at Valley Forge that Ezra lay shivering, one of many American soldiers. The building of huts for the sick could not keep pace with the

MAJOR-GENERAL FREDERICK BARON VON STEUBEN

need of them. Lines and rows of huts similar to his, made of logs for the most part, or of boughs, lay across the waste of white; black paths of beaten snow were between. Round about it all were trenches and breastworks, redoubts and fortifications for defense against a possible attack from Howe, luxuriating in Philadelphia, twenty miles away. And

310

woe to those half-fed soldiers whose shift it was to stand guard in the wind-swept trenches through the black hours of night, with little to warm their blood except a fiery determination to die of cold, hunger, or British bullets, rather than give up the fight for their country.

Since December 17 the army had been in quarters at Valley Forge. Forts Mifflin and Mercer had fallen, and Howe was secure for the present in the rebel capital. But for Gates he need not have been secure. Gates, puffed up after the surrender of Burgoyne, for which he saw to it he got the credit, waxed insubordinate to the commander-in-chief, and made such a clamor to Congress that that body refused to allow Washington to take any troops from the

LAFAYETTE'S HEADQUARTERS AT VALLEY FORGE

northern army without the express permission of Gates and Governor Clinton. For lack of this aid, Washington was obliged to permit the watchdogs on the Delaware to fall into the hands of the British. Now that it was too late, the troops from the North, for the most part, were with Washington and in camp at Valley Forge.

That is how it chanced that Ezra Stevens, half naked, half starved, lay shivering on the frozen ground beneath a shelter that was no shelter from the winter. He had been at Chatterton Hills, had Ezra; he had fought in the ranks that Arnold hurled like a thunderbolt against Fraser at Freeman's farm; he had seen the pride of the English army wither and fade before the yeomanry of America. Bullets had laden his ears with their whinings, but none had come near, though he had more than once bared his thin breast to them in the madness of battle. Now he was come here.

There was much noise out on the parade ground; some one was shouting in choleric excitement. For a while he heard it without heeding. Now a voice was raised above any other voice; the words it spoke were in an unknown tongue. "*Sacrebleu!* Gott-vertam de gaucherie of dese badauts. Je ne puis plus! I can curse them no more!" Gott-vertam! He had heard a Hessian say that once; one whom he had struck down with a blow of his musket-butt, who lived to gasp that much and die. Were the Hessians in camp, them? Well, that would be better than to die of cold, and hunger, lying out on the frozen ground.

Some one, stooping low, entered the rude hut, and came toward him, past the other sick, still crouching, for there was little room to stand upright within, and the visitor was a man of size. Ezra could not see who it was. There was only a half-light in the close space; his eyes were poor at best. Besides, he did not greatly care who it might be, even though it should prove a Hessian. If only —he shuddered —if only it were not the Hessian he had struck down, crushing him to death with his musket-butt! How strange that he had been able to strike such a blow! Now he could not so much as raise such a weapon; he had tried yesterday, before they brought him here to lie on the bare ground, with not even straw between himself and the earth.

"Well, Ezra, my lad, how do you fare to-day?"

It was the voice of John, his hero! The lad's eyes opened; when he had closed them he knew not. He smiled. Smiling, his teeth fell chattering and a shiver shook him, till he fairly squirmed on the hard ground.

"God, lad!" muttered John, compassionately, stooping yet more to lay hand on the jerking shoulder. He stripped his ragged, threadbare coat from his shoulders and spread it on the boy. He could do no more than that, there in that winter camp. Even the men in the hospital died for lack of food and warmth; died by day and by night, silently, with tight lips and eyes that stared death out of countenance;

WASHINGTON AND LAFAYETTE AT VALLEY FORGE (*From the painting by Alonzo Chappell*)

perished from hunger and cold while hogsheads and bales of stores lay spoiling by the wayside for lack of transportation through the mismanagement of the quartermaster-general, Mifflin.

"Who is that on the parade?" asked Ezra, falling quiet; for the touch of the other did that much. Nevertheless, he spoke with clenched teeth, guarding against another tremor.

"Drilling the men?" returned John, uncertain what the boy meant.

"Cursing them in German," explained Ezra, sparing of words.

"That is Baron von Steuben," answered John with sudden animation. "He comes from Germany to drill our army. He was made to love our cause by the great Franklin, whom he met in Paris. He is a warrior of experience and repute, a profound military scholar, having studied and served much at war. It is wonderful what he does with our men. They are becoming proficient in arms; they will

PANORAMA OF THE OLD BARRACKS AND WINTER QUA

be a fighting machine before he is done with them, that nothing can resist. The men all love him. You must gain strength so that you may learn tactics as well." John's voice fell as he finished; the sight of the meager, pale lad who had once carried him wounded off the field of battle, lying on the ground, shivering, took the heart from his words. War is not all glory; and many a man earns the title of hero by silent and patient suffering far from the trumpets and the shouting.

Ezra made no answer, other than a pathetic smile. The

eyes of the other grew moist, beholding it; biting his lips to hold back the tears, he remained silent, casting about for some word of comfort. In the silence came another to the opening of the shelter, stooping to enter.

"Is Major John Stevens within?" asked the newcomer, unable to see, having come so newly from the glare of the snow without. There was a movement of welcome in the hut.

CONTINENTAL ARMY AT VALLEY FORGE, PENNSYLVANIA

"Is it Fontaine asks?" inquired John quietly, not able to distinguish the features of the other, in silhouette against the white background of the camp without; but he knew the voice.

"Ay, that it is," returned the other, "and right glad I am to find you at last, having been much put to it to obtain opportunity since you came from the North; for I have been little but a messenger between camp and Congress, at York, these weeks past, spending most of my time betwixt and between. I saw you come here and followed." Becoming more accustomed to the gloom, Fontaine's eyes made out the figure lying prone on the ground, and he stopped abruptly, looking a question at John.

"'T is Ezra, my cousin," whispered John, interpreting the question.

"Nay, our cousin, then," returned Fontaine. "How goes the day, my lad?"

"Slowly," murmured Ezra, "and yet too fast, for I fear me it is my last, and I do not wish to go, believing there is somewhat still that I might do."

"Ay, that there is, a-plenty, lad," returned Fontaine, cheerfully, "and you shall live to do it. Why, we shall have you a general yet!"

"If all were generals, there would be no soldiers to be led, and for my part, I believe that I would do better with a musket than a sword; but I am little like to have the use of the one as the other." The answer, droned in a low tone, overtaxed the boy; he fell shivering when he was through; his teeth chattered with a loud, horrid rattle, which ceased only after John had briskly rubbed the thin flesh at the wrists.

"Come, lad, have new courage," cried Fontaine, simulating merriment, when Ezra was still again; "for I have great news for you, and all patriots."

"Is your news that Gates has been made our general?" said John.

"God forbid!" cried Fontaine, looking hotly at his cousin.

"I did but mock," explained John. "I have heard much of his plots to overthrow Washington, and have seen how they served General Schuyler."

"You make a grim jest of it," retorted Fontaine, to whom the name of Gates was utterly repugnant. Then bending still closer to the prostrate form, "I really have great news

Washington's Headquarters at Valley Forge, Pennsylvania, Looking South

for you. Franklin has at last persuaded France to make an open alliance with us; we shall shortly have the aid of France by sea and land."

"What can that avail?" returned the lad. "For very lack of straw whereon to lie, I die." In his tone was no complaint; he was resigned; he only told what was true, because it was true.

"Come, talk not of dying!" urged John, laying tender hand upon his shaking shoulder. "You are in low spirits today; to-morrow you will mend."

"Ay, to-morrow I shall mend; for to-morrow I shall be in the promised land," made answer Ezra, with much labor. "I should have been glad to die on the field of battle; to die thus is horrible. But I am content, since it must be so!"

The two, kneeling now beside him, could speak no word.

"God bless our general, and our cause!" The sound of his whispering was scarcely articulate.

"Come, Ezra, arouse yourself!" cried John, hopelessly. "Think of your mother, — your sisters, — all those who cherish you. For them, if not for yourself, make the struggle to live."

"If I cannot live for my country's sake, how shall I for theirs?"

Fontaine, taking sudden thought, bent his head closer to the prostrate lad, whispering in his ear one word. Hearing the word, Ezra's eyes rekindled, having lately closed. He reached up a feeble hand. They grasped it, both.

"Catherine!" he whispered, smiling. "Catherine! Tell her how I died, and be good to her!"

The lids dropped; the hand went limp; the smile died on his lips, which still held the form of a smile, as he lay on the stark ground dead!

Vergennes, the French minister, had long been giving

REAR VIEW OF WASHINGTON'S HEADQUARTERS AT VALLEY FORGE

secret assistance to the colonies, as a blow against E n g l a n d . After the fall of Burgoyne, and Washington's masterly operations in New Jersey and Pennsylvania, the statesmen of France considered it safe to declare their intention and recognize the independence of the United States. In February, 1778, the French alliance was perfected and announced.

The alliance was not wholly popular in America. It was suffered only because the Americans saw in it a possibility of winning the war. In New England friendship with a Catholic power was peculiarly objectionable; moreover, there was fear that France would demand Canada as the price of her aid.

England, learning of France's action, declared war on her, March 13, 1778. Britain's situation at the time was critical. After the loss of Burgoyne's army, she receded from every one of the principles which had brought on the war. Lord North turned a political somersault. There was talk of abandoning the colonies entirely. North proposed a commission to treat with Congress, with power to negotiate peace, grant amnesty, and suspend the laws of Parliament concerning America. In the midst of the political turmoil of the day, George III summoned William Pitt, earl of Chatham, to take charge of the government, much against his will. Whether Chatham, who was universally loved in America, might even now have succeeded in holding the colonies, can never be known, for he had scarcely assumed office when he was stricken by the disease that had already worn him down, and died, May 11, 1778. Lord North remaining in power after the death of Pitt, the commissioners were sent to treat with the Americans. They were everywhere received with such contempt and ridicule that they soon abandoned all hope of effecting anything.

Having discovered that the colonies were not to be subjugated by military operations on a large scale, and being stirred to resentment by the treatment of the comissioners, Lord George Germaine now hit upon the plan of wearing down the endurance of the colonies by desultory warfare along the borders, — a policy which thenceforth governed the war.

Sir William Howe spent a merry winter at Philadelphia, with Washington shivering in the trenches at Valley Forge. But hearing, in the spring, that he was being blamed for bungling the campaigns of 1777, he sent in his resignation. His departure, May 18, was signalized by a grand farewell banquet and pageant, called the Mischianza.

A month later, the British evacuated Philadelphia, finding no advantage in remaining there, and learning that Count d'Estaing, with a powerful French fleet,

HALLWAY IN WASHINGTON'S HEADQUARTERS AT VALLEY FORGE

was approaching the coast. The rebel capital would be untenable if naval control of the Delaware River should be lost.

Sir Henry Clinton, who succeeded Howe in command, found it necessary to march across New Jersey with the army, the fleet being required to take away some 3000 Tories

DINING-ROOM AND SECRET PASSAGE IN WASHINGTON'S HEADQUARTERS AT VALLEY FORGE

who could not be left behind in Philadelphia. On the morning of June 18, 1778, the rear-guard of the British army moved out of the city; before night the advance of the Americans marched through the streets.

Washington, leaving Valley Forge, set out in pursuit of Clinton, determined to strike a heavy blow at the retreating army. From this purpose Charles Lee sought to dissuade him. Lee had recently been exchanged for General Prescott, of the British army, who had been captured by an adventurous band of patriots in Rhode Island, where he was in command of the troops at Newport, then held by

the English. Failing to turn Washington from his intention, Lee endeavored to make him believe that Clinton did
not intend to march across New Jersey. When Washington
persisted, Lee grew sulky, and would have nothing to do
with the plans.

On the night of June 27, the left wing of the British
army, 8000 strong, commanded by Lord Cornwallis, was

PARLOR AND SECRET PASSAGE IN WASHINGTON'S HEADQUARTERS AT VALLEY
FORGE

near Monmouth Court-House, on the road from Allentown.
The right wing, of about equal strength, under Knyphausen,
lay beyond the court-house on the road to Middletown.
Washington, marching to the north of the British route,
and more rapidly, by a road converging upon their line of
retreat, had turned Clinton toward Sandy Hook, the British
general not caring to give battle.

It was Washington's plan to strike the left flank first
with an advance of 5000 men, following with an attack by
the main army, so as to envelop Cornwallis. He had
offered Lee command of the advance, Lee being senior
major-general in the army. Lee at first had sullenly refused,

whereupon Washington had entrusted the attack to Lafayette. Subsequently, Lee changed his mind, and accepted
the command.

The morning of Sunday, June 18, came on intensely
hot; the thermometer registered 96 degrees in the shade.
Knyphausen, proceeding in the British line of march, was
already under way, and Cornwallis, with whom went Clin-

PANORAMA OF THE HILLS SURROUNDING THE WINTER QU*

ton in person, had passed the court-house following him,
when Lee began the advance ordered by Washington.
Grayson, Jackson, Scott, Varnum, Wayne, and Maxwell
was their order of going; behind, at a distance, came Lafayette, with Greene and Stirling. John Stevens was in
Wayne's brigade; Fontaine was attached for the day to the
staff of the young French marquis.

Out across the fields, reeling with heat, they marched,
exuberant, foreseeing victory; over a deep ravine on a causeway where swamps steamed in the hot sun; on for a mile,
and over another ravine, and then out upon the plain,
where Cornwallis, perceiving them, had hastened to give

battle. The American lines were beginning to fold him in; already Lee was to the north of him, and Lafayette, coming up by another road, was hurrying to the southward, to encompass him there.

Wayne —"Mad Anthony," his soldiers called him, with love in their hearts —was advancing, eager to strike. "God willing, we will whip them this day!" muttered

E CONTINENTAL ARMY AT VALLEY FORGE, PENNSYLVANIA

Major John Stevens, casting an eye along his line of soldiers, and turning a gaze upon the field before them, where the enemy was being entwined by the Americans.

"Do not attack; make only a feint," came the order from Lee to Wayne. "The main attack will be delivered elsewhere."

The soldiers, at a loss to understand, disappointed, fretting to be at the red-coats, halted, wiping their brows, cursing.

Now were the men of England moving to come between Wayne and the American right, under Lafayette, that moment entering the field from the court-house. But the Frenchman would surely hold them, boy though he was!

"Fall back! It is useless to try to stand against the regulars of England!" Lafayette, getting the order from Lee at the moment when he was about to assail the enemy, stood for a moment dumfounded, not able to comprehend. In the next moment his eyes flashed.

"Ride for your very life to General Washington," he whispered to Fontaine. "Tell him to hasten, for there is treachery here! Lee betrays us, or I mistake much. We might crush them utterly, but are held off by orders from our superior in the field. Tell the commander that, from me!"

Back along the road flew Fontaine, the sides of his horse reeking, the clatter of the fight falling fainter in his ears as he rode.

Now one of the divisions on the left was falling back, ordered to do so by Lee. Their ground was superb for offense; they outnumbered their foe, and nearly surrounded them; but they must fall back! What could it mean? What sudden and unknown danger forced them from their vantage?

The other troops, perceiving the retrograde movement, withdrew slowly, sullenly, in good order. Through the ranks ran muttered imprecations; victory, within their grasp, was slipping away from them. Back they turned to the high ravine they had so lately crossed, and so proudly. Here they could stand against the sudden danger, whatever it might be.

"Retreat!" The order ran from lip to lip, coming from Lee.

Across the ravine, out upon the fields, hot under the sun, straggled the soldiers of liberty, angry, sweltering; many fell by the side of the way, stricken with the terrible heat. Behind them came the British, making the most of the strange retreat.

So, on to the first ravine they went, falling into disorder. John, silent, wrathful, marched with his men. Before him, approaching across the ravine, he beheld a horseman, riding furiously. It was Washington.

Lee, riding apace away from the fight beheld him too, and reined in, for the sight of the commander was ter-

BATTLE OF MONMOUTH   (*From the painting by Chappell*)

rifying; his face worked with a rage as mighty as his soul; his eyes flashed fire; like an avenging deity he was.

"What is the meaning of all this!" Above the rattle of battle rang the words, spoken in fierce anger. Lee, impertinent egotist though he was, could not answer; could not meet the towering gaze of the other, but looked askance, trembling like a craven.

"I desire to know the meaning of this disorder and confusion!" Louder, more fiercely, accompanied by an oath.

Lee, humilated, flew into an answering rage. His

WASHINGTON'S REBUKE OF LEE (*From the bronze doors of the Capitol at Washington*)

troops had fallen into disorder, he said. There had been mistaken information; he had no mind to beard the entire British army with troops in such a situation.

"I have certain information that it was merely a strong covering party which attacked you," said Washington.

"That may be, but it is stronger than mine, and I did not think proper to run such a risk."

"I am sorry that you undertook the command, unless you intended to fight the enemy." Hot and fast the words flew between them.

"I did not think it prudent to bring on a general engagement."

"Whatever your opinion may have been, I expected my orders would be obeyed."

The fugitives, pouring around them, raised a cheer at sight of Washington. Without further word he set about restoring order from the confusion.

The British were coming, not a quarter of an hour away. Hastily, with great skill, a line was thrown along an eminence behind the ravine, commanding the causeway crossing it. "Thank God for Baron Steuben now, and his training of our men," said John Stevens, as he watched the men deploying into their new positions with mechanical precision, exhausted and demoralized though they were.

Lee, sullen, surly, with gaze on the ground, remained where Washington had met him, awaiting orders. To him came the commanding general, in calmer mood, having made his dispositions. "Will you retain the command on this height, or not?" he asked.

"It is equal to me where I command."

"I expect that you will take proper means for checking the enemy."

"I shall not be the first to leave the ground; your orders shall be obeyed."

In a moment the shock came; fiery red over the quivering fields, the British lines advanced. For a space Lee held; but the impact was too great. He withdrew his men, fainting with heat, across the causeway, whence presently he was sent to the rear by Washington, who cared not to risk him further in the fight.

All through the remainder of the terrible day the English strove to break down the defense of the Americans; all through the day the patriots held. Deeds of valor were done on every hand. Molly Pitcher, wife of an artillery-man, while bringing water to the battery saw her husband shot down beside his gun. Without hesitation she took his place and fought the gun throughout the battle. She was presented by Greene to Washington, who gave her the rank of sergeant. Against such spirit the attack grew hope-

less. When the sun was sinking in the west, the British broke, withdrawing to the ground where Lee had encoun-tered them early in the morning.

MOLLY PITCHER AT THE BATTLE OF MONMOUTH (*From the painting by D. M. Carter*)

On the morning of the next day they were gone, marching in the night toward New York. But for the conduct of Charles Lee who can say what might have been? Clinton surely would have been defeated; perhaps a part of his army captured; perhaps all of it. New York might have been regained; the war might have been ended.

On the day following the fight Lee wrote an impertinent note to Washington, demanding an apology for the lan-

DEATH OF THE EARL OF CHATHAM   (*From the painting by Copley in the National Gallery, London*)

guage used toward him on field of battle. Washington returned a crushing reply, intimating that he would soon have opportunity to explain his conduct to Congress, to the Americans, and to the world. Lee rejoining with further impudence, he was arrested and presently brought before a court-martial, charged with disobeying orders, with misbehavior before the enemy in not attacking, and in conducting an unnecessary, disorderly, and shameful retreat, of which Washington had accused him in his first note; and of gross disrespect to the commander-in-chief, of which he was subsequently guilty.

Although he was convicted on all charges, his punishment was nothing more then suspension from command for a year. Before the year was up, however, he fell into controversy with Congress, and was dismissed the service. Thenceforth he devoted his time to writing scurrilous abuses of Washington and Congress, until his death in a mean public-house in Philadelphia, in 1782. His last wish was that he might not be buried in consecrated ground, because he had kept so much bad company in this world he chose to continue it in the next.

For many years it was the habit to construe his behavior as an eccentricity of waywardness, and to condone it, in part; but eighty years afterward papers were discovered in England, among the effects of the descendants of Sir Henry Strachey, secretary to the Howes in New York, which contained a full plan for the capture of Philadelphia, written in Lee's hand, for the instruction and benefit of the Howes, at the time he was prisoner in New York City. Since then his name has been linked with infamy, second only to that which surrounds the memory of Benedict Arnold.

CHAPTER XIX

A MATTER OF MESSAGES

IT was an evening in late August, 1778. The streets of New York City were beginning to stir again with the life that had deserted them through the insufferable heat of the day. The sky in the west was cooling; the moon, rising across the East River, made those who now went their way through the streets forget the glare of the day.

Clinton still held New York City, though Washington lay at White Plains ready to pounce upon him should he show his head. The armies were in the position occupied in the fall of 1776, save that now the Americans were the aggressors. Only lack of a navy prevented their taking New York. And that lack was fairly made up when D'Estaing arrived on the coast with the French fleet. The vessels of the allies came to the mouth of the Delaware on July 8, too late by a day or two to intercept Lord Howe's squadron, leaving Philadelphia. Thence they sailed to Sandy Hook. Here a council of war was held between D'Estaing and Hamilton and Laurens, Washington's aides. The French fleet outnumbering the British in the harbor of New York, it was

ADMIRAL THE COUNT D'ESTAING (*From the engraving by H. B. Hall*)

determined to destroy it; but when the French were ready
to proceed into the harbor, pilots found that two of the
heaviest of the men-of-war could not cross the bar, and
the project was abandoned.

Instead, and that the English might not rest too securely,
an expedition was organized and sent against Newport.

BENJAMIN FRANKLIN AT THE COURT OF FRANCE

Newport had been seized by Lord Percy in the fall of 1776,
and had been occupied by the British ever since, most of the
time under Major-General Prescott, an unmitigated ruffian.
It was Prescott who was captured by a band of men when
he slept one night in a house a few miles out of the lines;
and it was he who was exchanged for Charles Lee, on the
eve of the Monmouth campaign. Since early summer,
however, the place had been commanded by Sir Robert
Pigott, as amiable and accomplished as his predecessor
was not.

Since April General Sullivan had been stationed with a
small force at Providence. To him Washington sent 1500

men under Greene, who was born thereabouts and knew the country with boyhood lore. With them went Glover, because there was navigation to be considered in the strategy, and Lafayette, a kinsman of Count d'Estaing's, which last was to coöperate with his fleet and the 4000 French soldiers aboard.

D'Estaing arrived during the last of July. Pigott's force was divided, part being stationed on Butt's Hill, at the northern end of the State. To cut off this force, Sullivan landed on one side of it, while D'Estaing disembarked on the other. But Pigott, perceiving their designs, withdrew from Butt's Hill, whereupon Sullivan occupied it. The move was resented by the jealous Frenchman as hasty and over-reaching. While Sullivan was appeasing his outraged honor, Howe arrived outside with the English fleet.

D'Estaing immediately reëmbarked his 4000 men and set out to give battle. For two days the fleets manœuvered for the weather gage; just as the fight was about to open a terrific wind, famous for fifty years afterward as the great storm, drove the combatants apart. When D'Estaing finally reassembled his fleet, much the worse for its adventure with the storm, nothing would do but that he must go to Boston to refit. This he presently did, in spite of the persuasions of the Americans, taking his 4000 troops with him.

After his going, on August 29, Pigott attacked Butt's Hill, endeavoring to take it by storm. The assault was fruitless of anything but great loss of life. Sullivan held out, in spite of his desertion by the French troops and the defection of some 3000 militia from New England, who went home disgusted with the behavior of D'Estaing. Now they were waiting for whatever might happen next. There was a rumor that reinforcements were about to start from New York; Lafayette, mounting his horse, had set off post haste to Boston, seventy miles away, to urge D'Estaing to hasten back.

Thus it was with the armies on an evening of late August, 1778, when the people of New York were beginning to come out beneath the cool rising moon to refresh themselves after the day's heat. Through the softness of the night they walked in groups and pairs, — citizens, soldiers, patriots, Tories; maidens and young men.

The mansion of Robert Stevens, man of affairs, stood dreaming in the moon flood. Massive, dark, it towered into the sky, fretting the night with roof and gable; at its feet, and across the garden about it, lay a heavy shadow. Its customary blaze of illumination had dwindled to a flicker here and there through the great windows, blinking and listless.

In an arbor, where the line of shadow crept inward as  the moon rose, sat Sophronia and Nancy Hempstead. The girl remained in America, held by a fascination she would not acknowledge. Since the night when this inscrutable woman who now sat with her had borne John Stevens to safety and returned to brave the wrath of those who designed against him, she had lost all thought of returning, until — Why had she not known he was there, at that time? Who kept it from her? What trick did it mean? and what

MAJOR-GENERAL JOHN SULLIVAN (*From a family portrait*)

had the trick been that this woman had played upon him?

"Our little Isaac has not been near these many nights," came the voice of Sophronia across the shadows of the evening, carelessly, making talk.

"No." Nancy had no mind to speak of him.

"Perchance he has a fear that the Americans will shortly return," suggested Sophronia, with a little laugh.

"Perchance you do him injustice," returned Nancy, beginning to wonder whither the other was really intending that the talk should drift.

Sophronia only laughed once more. "Belike, you would welcome the American army for more reasons than that it would drive this lover away," she hinted.

Nancy stirred quickly; her gaze sought to pierce the gloom before the other's face; quite as easy a feat as to penetrate beyond that calm, dispassionate, coldly beautiful countenance.

"Belike, that may mean more to you than to me," rejoined the English girl, ill at ease, but making the best show she could.

"What? Their coming back? Nay, 't is equal to me; for have I not lovers o' both sides? Is there not your very brother, now, waxing warm toward me after these many years? And Major André? My faith, I am even like to relieve you of Francis, before we are done."

"Him you are quite welcome to," said Nancy.

"So much I know already," laughed Sophronia, "but more I only guess. Come, tell me, who is this American lover of yours? 'T is a pretty night for such a tale."

Nancy's face grew hot with shame and anger; she could hardly endure to have this woman twit her thus, feigning innocence; keen suspicion whetted itself on her heart. "I know not what you may mean, nor why you should speak

Ruins of Old Stony Point

so securely of my American lover," she returned, calmly, restraining herself.

"If there is aught that Mistress Hempstead would know of those in the patriot army, belike I shall be able to tell her." A voice, the voice of a man, close at their elbows, came out of the shadows.

Nancy, with a stifled scream, half rose from her bench. Sophronia turned in the direction whence the voice had come, where the shadow of a man loomed now in the moonlight. "You do well to come prowling about thus, whoever you may be," she said, rebukingly, "whether you come to eavesdrop, or to frighten two women who take the cool of the evening."

"I acknowledge myself as deserving your censure," returned the interloper, "but it was rather to avoid eavesdropping than to indulge in it that I spoke so abruptly, even at the risk of startling you. For I had only come up, when I heard words passing between you which I feared might lead to some confidence not intended for my ears."

"Civilly said," conceded Sophronia, "though why you are here and who you are is a matter that you have not hit upon. Pray, if you have business in coming, be so good as to state it."

"That is a demand at once unfair and unlikely of being complied with," returned the man. But with his words he lifted his hat from his head, where it had rested close above his eyes, and stood forth in the rays of the moon, so that they might see his features. Looking simultaneously, they beheld Fontaine Stevens.

At sight of him, Nancy half rose to her feet again. "In Heaven's name!" she cried, beneath her breath, awed, "what do you here?"

" 'T is plain enough, in faith, what he does here," interposed Sophronia. "In the first place, he comes to spy upon the British, and in the second he comes to see the fair Nancy; whereby I am answered in my impertinence!" She was merry enough over it, was Sophronia.

"Since you guess so shrewdly, I will confess that you are right," returned Fontaine, with a laugh in which he endeavored to turn aside embarrassment from both Nancy and himself.

" 'T is good for the soul," observed Sophronia.

"But not, perchance, for the neck," rejoined Fontaine, alluding to his employment.

"You need not fear that we shall betray you," Nancy hastened to assure him.

"Nay, more than that," added Sophronia, "we shall help you, belike. Is there aught you came to learn that you have not ascertained? If there is, perchance we can inform you." She spoke as though the matter of revealing military secrets was as trivial as remarking on the state of the weather; as though it was nothing more than a slight civility she intended toward Fontaine.

"Sophronia!" Nancy could not repress an expostulation.

"Am I wrong?" purred Sophronia. "Should I have said only that I will help?" The light of the moon, climbing above the roof, was upon her face; they could see her brows raised in pretty inconsequential questioning.

"You surely will not think I would betray my country," retorted Nancy; "nor can I permit you to do so," she went on, rising to her feet and taking a pace toward Sophronia.

"But you surely can permit me to betray mine, or to befriend it," rejoined Sophronia, "as the case may be. I am not myself certain which would be more accurate in speech," continued Sophronia, easily. "And now, pray, what is it that you would still learn?" to Fontaine.

"In the circumstances, I may not ask you," answered

Fontaine, chivalrously; he had listened to the dialogue between the young women with growing uneasiness.

Perhaps he expected some recognition of his gallant sacrifice from Nancy, for he looked toward her, half unconsciously, as he answered Sophronia. But Nancy was so far from appearing grateful or appreciative that she turned her head to avoid his glance. Sophronia, perceiving the play, smiled to herself, as she proceeded.

"Sir Henry Clinton leaves to-morrow for Newport, with five thousand men, to the succor of Sir Robert Pigott," she began, casually. "He intends, I believe, to bring the English forces away with him, having recently been obliged to send another five thousand men to the war with France in the West Indies, and not feeling strong enough to hold both New York and Newport with his present resources. Beyond that, nothing is contemplated more than expeditions of destruction up and down the coast, at short distances. If this is any news to you, or of value, make free with it; for, be assured, it is my affair that I give it to you. For the rest of your errand," she went on, rising, and passing toward the portal of the arbor, "I may do as much, I hope. Commend me to our kinsfolk with the army," she added, in the same even voice, coming where Fontaine still stood without the arbor, "and extend to them my wishes for whatever measure of

STATUE TO COLONEL JOHN GLOVER AT BOSTON, MASSACHUSETTS

success they may desire. Perchance we shall meet soon again; for the present, good night, and good bye!" With that she swept away toward the house, and was soon lost to their view.

For a moment of silence, Fontaine leaned over the railing about the bower. Nancy, within, averted her face from him; she could think only that this other woman spoke easily of her kinsfolk in the American army, sending them messages; that John would learn of her part in helping the American cause, even by so little as the information she had given to Fontaine. The adroitness of the woman frightened her. What might she not have accomplished during the time John lay wounded in the house?

A hand was on her arm, tender, tentative; the voice of Fontaine was in her ear. "My errand is only half done," he said, softly.

"I am sorry that you came," she said.

"As a spy, or as a lover?"

"I had not thought of you as that," she answered, hesitating to use the word.

"Will you not think of me as that?" he asked her, gently. "When once I told you of my love, you called it the prattling of a boy. I have forgotten neither my love nor what you said of it. I am a man now, Nancy, and still I say, 'I love you.'"

She turned her face toward him; in it was sadness, and pity. "Then I am doubly sorry you have come," she said, placing a hand in sympathy upon his lapel.

He bowed his head. "Be that as it may," he said. "I shall come again. Perchance another time you will at least not be sorry. I have been abrupt; I have been too bold, but love has lain in my heart these many months, and I was fain to tell you of it again even on such a slender opportunity as this. I hope I do not offend."

"It is not that," sne murmured. And then, "I shall always be sorry, if you come to me as a lover; but always glad, if you come as a friend, as a companion."

He raised his eyes to hers; she did not falter before his gaze, though a blush mounted to her cheeks and burned there, hotly, in the light of the moon; though her secret was in the light that lingered at the bottom of her eyes.

"I understand," he said, simply, when they had looked so at each other for a space. There was silence. "Is there any one in the army I serve of whom you would have word?" he went on, taking his glance away now, to spare her.

He felt her hand tremble in his lapel before she answered. When she spoke, it was in a whisper. "John Stevens," were the words she said.

He told her of the honor that had come to him in the service, of his bravery, his loyalty, his devotion, and the love his comrades bore him, in all of which she found glad pride, for all that he fought with the foes of her country.

"Is there a message I shall take?" he asked.

"There is no message I can send," she replied slowly, and smiling softly. "If ever it may be so, the message must come from mine own lips."

He bent to kiss her hand; without another word he was gone into the shadows that lay about the garden.

CHASE HOUSE, NEWPORT, RHODE ISLAND, WHERE GENERAL PRESCOTT WAS
CAPTURED

CHAPTER XX

A LULL

LIEUTENANT FONTAINE STEVENS, making his way out of New York City, was disturbed in mind. Should he or should he not make use of the information given him by Sophronia Osborne, despite the protest of Nancy? It involved a nice point of honor, as he analyzed it. He was still uncertain when he arrived at Washington's headquarters. Once in the presence of the commander, however, his scruples vanished, and he told what he had learned without reservation.

Washington straightway dispatched a message to Sullivan, telling of Clinton's plans, and the Americans withdrew from Rhode Island, ferried across the bay by General Glover, the same who had saved the army at Long Island, and made Trenton possible. Clinton arrived with his reinforcements the next day, and the siege of Newport was over. The expedition against Newport, which failed through the inefficient coöperation of the French allies and the insubordination of the yeomanry, was unfortunate in many ways. For one thing, it created a violent prejudice against the French alliance, D'Estaing being held responsible for the failure because he had taken

Anthony Wayne *(From a sketch by Colonel Trumbull)*

344

his fleet away from Sullivan. Dissatisfaction with the allies was expressed by both people and soldiers; Sullivan himself issued general orders in which he hoped that America would prove "able to procure that by her own arms which her allies refused to assist her in obtaining." On the other hand, the French officers were displeased at the criticisms of the Americans. It was only by the greatest tact that Washington was able to restore a semblance of harmony.

The failure was a bitter disappointment to Washington, who wrote concerning it: "An unfortunate storm, and some measures taken in consequence of it by the French admiral, blasted in one moment the fairest hopes that ever were conceived, and from a moral certainty of success, rendered it a matter of rejoicing to get our own troops safe off the island. If the garrison of that place, consisting of nearly six thousand men, had been captured, as it was, in appearance, at least a hundred to one in favor of it, it would have given the finishing blow to British pretensions to sovereignty over this country, and would, I am persuaded, have hastened the departure of the troops in New York as fast as their canvas wings would carry them away."

The campaign in Newport was the last in the North during the Revolution. From that time forth there were no military operations of either unity or magnitude. Clinton continued to hold New York City, and Washington continued to watch him, forming a cordon about him from Connecticut to New Jersey. If the Americans had had a proper navy the war would have ended then; as it was, the British were free to come and go by water.

But the situation was not without incident. Clinton sent out foraging and marauding parties along the Jersey and Connecticut coast. In the autumn of 1778, Martha's Vineyard was plundered from end to end, the towns of New Bedford and Fair Haven, with all their shipping, were

burned.   There were also surprises and encounters in New
Jersey.

One operation in 1779 gave some promise of develop-
ment.   The Hudson River was held by the powerful fortifications at West Point, primarily; but lower down the
river were smaller fortifications, at Verplanck's Point on
the left bank, and Stony Point on the right.   While the fort
at Stony Point was building, Sir Henry Clinton seized it,
May 31, and reduced that at Verplanck's Point with the
Stony Point batteries.

Clinton proceeded to make the place impregnable, as
he thought.   It had heavy natural advantages: on three
sides swept the Hudson, about the rocky feet of a cliff; on the
fourth, at the bottom of a long slope, was a morass, crossed by a causeway. Clinton's engineers took advantage of all the topographical opportunities; in a little time the place was sufficiently fortified to provide Clinton with a base for operations against West Point.

THE STORMING OF STONY POINT   (*From the picture by
Chappell*)

Thinking to divert Washington from the defense of the river, in July Clinton sent Tryon into Connecticut on an errand of destruction. The man, worthy of his mission, landed at New Haven, burned the shipping and part of the town, slew some of its citizens in the process, and would have destroyed the place utterly had not the yeomanry gathered and driven him back to his ships. Proceeding along the coast, Tryon avenged himself on Fairfield, Green Farms, and Norwalk, and was going on to New London when bad news came from New York, recalling him.

Stony Point had been taken! That was the news. Washington was not to be beguiled away from his main defense by any brutality exercised in Connecticut. Neither would he idly

GENERAL HENRY LEE— "LIGHT-HORSE HARRY"

permit it to go on. The steps he took to prevent it were characteristic of his high strategy. "Mad Anthony" Wayne, in whose fierce valor there was more method than madness, was sent with 1500 men to storm the place.

The adventure was undertaken on the night of July 16, 1779. Not a gun was loaded, for the work was to be the work of the bayonet, done by surprise. Even the dogs of the country-side had been slaughtered to insure against their giving the alarm. The charge up that hill in the darkness of the night was one of the most spectacular in history. Not until the Americans were upon them did the garrison know they were coming. There was much firing for a space on the part of the British, but the Americans, in two columns, swept over the works; at the head of one, wounded, waving his sword, with a bandage about his bleeding head, Mad

Anthony was borne on the shoulders of his exultant men. The Americans lost fifteen killed and eighty-three wounded; the British sixty-three killed, and 533 prisoners.

Clinton, chagrined, called in Tryon, and moved against Stony Point, intending to entice Washington into battle, hoping to defeat him disastrously. But Washington was

MONUMENT TO THE VICTIMS OF THE WYOMING MASSACRE AT WYOMING, PENNSYLVANIA

too shrewd for him; he would risk nothing for the sake of Stony Point that might weaken his hold on West Point. The fortifications were destroyed and the place abandoned, leaving Clinton with an empty victory.

In order to demonstrate to those whom it might concern that the American army was neither asleep nor afraid, another blow was presently struck at an unexpected quarter. The British had a strong fort at Paulus Hook, on a long neck of land extending into the Hudson, joined to the mainland by an isthmus of sand, guarded by a deep ditch. The garrison was 500. They had grown careless, secure in the strength of their works and their remoteness from the American lines.

Major Henry Lee had been apprised of this; "Light Horse Harry," son of that lowland beauty to whom Washington's heart had turned in youth; father of Robert Edward Lee, who was to achieve rank as one of the foremost generals of modern times. On the night of August 18 Lee, with 300 picked men, crossed the creek and rushed the fort, possessing himself of it in brief space. It was little more than a prank, a feat of daring. The Americans could not hold the place; they had scarcely time to take 159 prisoners, when the fleet, alarmed, came up, and Lee withdrew, having lost two killed and three wounded. But it showed the English what unexpected things they might expect from their foes.

Meanwhile, on the thin borders of the country, savage war had been going forward, as part of the inhuman policy of Lord George Germaine to wear away the rebellion. New York and the valley of the Mohawk suffered worst. Here, at the beginning of the war, rose a bitter conflict between the Tories, who were strong, and the patriots, who were stronger. Many Tories, numbers of Highland Scotch among them, were driven out. These gathered at Niagara, under the leadership of the Johnsons and the Butlers. With them was John Brandt,

MASSACRE AT WYOMING (*From the painting by Chappell,*

Thayendanegea, a full-blooded Mohawk, but a missionary of the Church of England,— at once the greatest Indian warrior of his times and a man of civilized culture and education.

On July 3 a band of Tories and Indians, numbering 1500, fell upon the settlements in the Wyoming Valley, in north-eastern Pennsylvania. Most of the valley's fighters were with Washington's army, but Colonel Zebulon Butler, with 300 men, made a stand against the invaders for an hour. The resistance was futile; most of the Americans were killed, either in the fight or by subsequent torture. The next day the fort surrendered, and the valley was laid waste. Though no more lives were wantonly taken, the number who perished in endeavoring to get away from the place filled the country with horror and anger. It is often said that Brandt conducted the raid. He did not; he was not present at the time.

On November 10 there was a massacre at Cherry Valley, in New York; all the houses were burned, and about fifty inhabitants slaughtered, without regard to age, sex, or condition. The valley of the Mohawk was in a state of terror; the country was horrified. In the following summer Washington sent Sullivan with 5000 men to destroy the nest of vipers at Niagara. The punitive expedition laid waste the country of the agricultural Iroquois, after defeating the Tories and Indians on August 29 at the battle of Newtown, on the present site of

WHERE COLONEL ALDEN FELL IN THE CHERRY
VALLEY MASSACRE

Elmira; but the force could not penetrate to Niagara. Although they had suffered heavy damage, and were irretrievably weakened, the Tories and Indians continued their work in the Mohawk Valley

THE CHERRY VALLEY MASSACRE MONUMENT

until the close of the war, filling the land with blood and terror. Farther to the west and southwest along the new frontiers ran the same border warfare. Boone and Harrod were in Kentucky; James Robertson and John Sevier had driven the Cherokees into subjugation on the Wautauga, in Tennessee. Now the movement of the pioneers was carried westward to the territory held in the name of King George by a few isolated British posts, at Natchez, Kaskaskia, and Cahokia on the Mississippi, at Vincennes on the Wabash, and at Detroit.

In the winter of 1777–1778, while Colonel Henry Hamilton, commander at Detroit, was endeavoring to stir up the Indians to attack the isolated and scattered settlements in Kentucky and Tennessee, a young Virginian, tall, massive, ruddy, with deep-set blue eyes beneath yellow brows, was planning a counterstroke that was to bring to the United States all the vast territory lying west of the Alleghenies.

ILLOW HILL, SITE OF THE FIRST SETTLEMENT AND SCENE OF MASSACRE AT CHERRY VALLEY

This man was George Rogers Clark, then twenty-five years of age. He had been a pupil of Donald Robertson; James Madison was one of his fellows in school. He had had hard experience of the frontier on the upper Ohio, where he was a land surveyor; woodcraft and warfare were his intimates. Returning thence in the fall of 1777, Clark heard of the surrender of Burgoyne's army, and at once determined upon a project he had long entertained.

It was nothing less than to go into the Northwest Territory and drive out the English. He had had spies in the country; he knew it could be done. He laid the matter before Governor Patrick Henry when he reached Virginia; they consulted with Jefferson, Wyeth, and Madison. The plan was approved, and Clark was given a commission to raise a force for the expedition.

The thing was done secretly; people supposed the force which he gathered about him at Pittsburg in the winter of 1777 and 1778 was intended for the defense of Kentucky, whence Clark had lately come. It was difficult to get men, but in May, 1778, the tiny army set out, 180 strong, with a few pieces of light artillery, in a flotilla.

One thousand miles they rowed and drifted down the Ohio to the Mississippi, no man knowing of it. Kaskaskia, weakened by the withdrawal of part of the garrison to strengthen Detroit and Niagara, was easily taken; Cahokia and other settlements submitted; Vincennes, summoned by Clark through the Catholic priest Gibault, who bore messages there, surrendered. The inhabitants, mostly French, were complacent enough; especially when they heard of the alliance between the United States and King Louis XVI.

Colonel Hamilton, hearing what had happened, came from Detroit with 500 men and seized Vincennes. There he spent the winter, stirring the Indians to outrage; but Clark did not suffer him to intrigue securely. In the dead of winter, through a country closed by great cold, Clark marched from Kaskaskia with 130 men, sending the stores and artillery by water, down the Mississippi, up the Ohio and Wabash. He arrived on February 23, after a march of sixteen days. The townspeople surrendered, and assisted in an assault on the fort. The fight was long and stubborn; in the end, Hamilton surrendered at discretion, and the hold of England on the Miss- issippi Valley was forever broken.

Although England met with reverses ashore, on the sea her pre- ponderance was over- whelming. With a sufficient and efficient navy, the Americans would have brought the war to a close much sooner than they did. If the Continentals had had ships, Howe never

GEORGE ROGERS CLARK (*From the portrait by Jouett*)

would have got away from Boston, after Concord and Bunker Hill; he would not have taken New York; there would have been no Brandywine. Congress made many attempts to create one, but they proved abortive, for the most part; a navy, more than an army, is the work of time and experience. In the years of the war, only one ship-of-the-line was built — the *America*, a seventy-four, but this was given to the King of France while still on the stocks. Out of thirteen new cruisers laid down in the fall of 1775, only six ever took the water; the others were destroyed by the British. Between 1775 and 1783 there were twenty frigates and twenty-one sloops-of-war in the American service; of these more than half were destroyed or captured.

Nevertheless, the American navy, supplemented by a

veritable fleet of privateers and such craft, did so much lively damage to British shipping, even going so far as to cruise off the English coast, that insurance rates on English vessels advanced to the unheard-of rate of twenty-five per cent; this guerilla warfare on the ocean accomplished the destruction or capture of 600 British vessels, as against 900 taken by the English.

GEORGE ROGERS CLARK (*From the statue by Charles J. Mulligan, at Quincy, Illinois*)

These bold and impudent cruises of American craft under the very paw of the British lion brought forward more than one hero. First of them was Lambert Wickes, in the *Reprisal* of sixteen guns. In the summer of 1777 he sailed about the British Islands, doing all manner of mischief. The vessel foundered off the banks of New-foundland on the way home. That same summer Gustavus Conyngham, with the *Surprise* and the *Revenge*, took so many prizes in the North Sea and British Channel that insurance rates for the little journey from Dover to Calais arose to ten per cent, almost prohibiting commerce.

But the greatest of them all was John Paul Jones, a Scotch sailor, who had been engaged in the Virginia trade from boyhood, and who offered his services to Congress when the war broke out.

At the age of thirty, he sailed from Portsmouth, New Hampshire, November 1, 1777, in command of the *Ranger*, eighteen guns, and on December 14 secured the first

ACTION BETWEEN THE "BONHOMME RICHARD" AND THE "SERAPIS" (*From the painting by J. Rogers*)

recognition of the Stars and Stripes from a foreign power through the salute fired by Admiral Le Motte Piquet in Quiberon Bay, just north of Nantes. Setting off on a cruise in British waters, he thoroughly frightened England, Ireland, and Scotland, sending insurance rates up to nearly prohibitive prices. On April 14, 1778, he captured the British sloop-of-war *Drake* with superior armament, and brought her safely back to France, adding enormously to American prestige thereby. He had lost only eight men, while the enemy lost forty-two.

Returning from that cruise to Brest, he was placed in command of an expedition then being arranged for the following year. This was designed as a demonstration against the British coast; Franklin arranged it, as part of his duties in France. French ports were freely open to American vessels for outfit or refuge, and France herself supplied the vessels for this expedition. The flag-ship was an East India-man, crudely transformed into an engine of war, and called the *Bonhomme Richard*, in honor of the author of Poor Richard's Almanac. She carried the armament of a thirty-two-gun frigate.

Three consorts were added to the fleet; the *Pallas*, a transformed merchantman, thirty-two guns, the *Vengeance*, and the *Cerf*, all French built. To these Franklin contributed the *Alliance*, a new frigate of the American navy, recently built at Salisbury, Massachusetts, and named in honor of the French alliance. As a further compliment to France, a French captain, one Landais, was appointed to command her; a circumstance that almost destroyed her efficiency, for Captain Landais was of no weight as an officer, and his advancement fomented both jealousy and insubordination in the crew.

Cruising about the coast of Scotland with this motley squadron, Jones ran across a merchant fleet of forty sail, under convoy of two British frigates, the *Serapis*, of forty-four guns, and the *Countess of Scarborough*, of twenty. It was past 7 o'clock at night; the weather was dirty, but the sea was remarkably smooth. Jones, in the *Bonhomme Richard*, engaged the *Serapis*. At the first fire, two eighteen-pounders on the American vessel exploded, and the men would not thereafter fire the others of that caliber. This gave the *Serapis* a preponderence of metal, an advantage increased by superior sailing qualities.

After a short period of heavy firing, the *Serapis*, in attempting to cross the bows of her enemy with a purpose of raking her, fouled.

"Have you struck your colors?" cried Captain Pearson, of the *Serapis*.

JOHN PAUL JONES (*From the portrait by C. W. Peale in Independence Hall*)

"I have not yet begun to fight," retorted Captain John Paul Jones.

For a moment the two vessels drifted apart, only to come together again with the bowsprit of the *Serapis* lying across the high poop of the *Bonhomme Richard*, near the mizzenmast. Jones immediately had the bowsprit lashed fast to the mast, and, as the vessels swung together alongside, grappled and held his heavier antagonist.

There followed a scene of horror. Broadsides were poured into each vessel at such close range that the muzzles of the guns sometimes struck together. 'Tween-decks became a shambles. The Americans were driven from their guns, but continued the fight from their upper decks with muskets and hand-grenades. One fellow, climbing out on the mainyard, dropped a grenade into the main hatch of the *Serapis* that set off a row of cartridges. Twenty men were blown into fragments, and forty others injured.

CATHERINE II OF RUSSIA (*After the portrait by Rosselin*)

All the while the *Serapis* was afire, and the *Bonhomme Richard* on the point of sinking. Two-fifths of the British crew was killed; hardly a man on either ship remained scathless. The fight went forward in this case, sullenly, doggedly, until Jones himself aimed the cannon that shot the enemy's mainmast in two, whereupon Pearsons surrendered. The crew of the *Bonhomme Richard* was transferred to the *Serapis*. At 10 o'clock the next morning the American ship sank.

The spectacular fight was insignificant from a strictly military point of view, but it bore results of moment, indirectly. Primarily, it carried an impression of American prowess throughout England and all Europe that became a national asset. More important still, it placed European international politics on a new basis. For a long time England had made herself obnoxious by insisting on the right to search neutral vessels for goods belonging to belligerents. Because of her overwhelming naval superiority, the practice made her obnoxious to the other nations; already she was embroiled with Spain and Holland, largely through the behavior of her vessels at sea.

Catharine of Russia had long had in contemplation the establishment of a new principle in international law, covering the carrying of goods. When Paul Jones captured a British vessel under the lion's paw, Europe was so impressed by the feat that Catharine considered the time propitious for promulgating the new doctrine. Accordingly on March 8, 1780, she issued a proclamation maintaining that goods of a belligerent nation carried in neutral ships should be free from search. Thus the brilliant victory of the redoubtable Scotch captain had its effect in bringing a new order of things into the maritime world, and the gallant little American navy of the Revolution was not in vain.

CHAPTER XXI

AUGUSTUS

"WHY the Almighty permits such men to remain at the head of our affairs as those I have lately left behind me in Philadelphia is more than I can comprehend."

General Benedict Arnold, rising petulantly from the desk where he was engaged with Major John Stevens in overlooking routine papers, limped to the window and gazed out across the waters of the Hudson to where the fortifications of West Point raised their heads on the opposite cliff.

It was September, in the year 1780. Since July Benedict Arnold had held command here, with his headquarters in the Robinson house. John Stevens, detached from his command and appointed aide at the suggestion of Arnold himself, had been with him more than a month.

Arnold applied for the command and was granted it by Washington early in the summer, following the dismal series of difficulties that had involved him in quarrels and affronts for nearly two years.

When Clinton evacuated Philadelphia in June, 1778, Arnold was given command in the capital, his wounded leg rendering him incapable of serving in the field. His situation was trying at best; the city was filled with Tories or Tory sympathizers; there was much property belonging to those who had been disloyal during the

361

BENEDICT ARNOLD (*After an etching by H. B. Hall*)

British occupation that must be confiscated; under the arrangements for its sale and the disbursement of the proceeds it was inevitable that there should arise much bickering and backbiting, requiring a man of tact at the head of affairs. Arnold was not a man of tact; moreover, he was placed in a position where his authority conflicted with the jurisdiction of the Assembly and Council of Pennsylvania, and where he was in close and constant contact with the Continental Congress, a body he despised and abhorred.

When Arnold took command in the city, there reigned there as belle a beautiful and accomplished young woman, Margaret Shippen. She was courted by scores of suitors; during the British occupation she became the center of a very furore. The impulsive Arnold straightway fell victim to her charms. Being Arnold, and having felt her fascination, he set about to win her, regardless of the circumstance that she was of the moderate Tory party which, while not actively supporting the British, desired a return of the colonies to British allegiance under the benefits of Lord North's overtures.

His methods were characteristic of the times and of the man. No one in town had a better stable of horses; no better dinners were spread in the whole town than those which graced his board; his wines were many and rare, and his guests drawn from the élite of the city.

His lavish expenditures at a time when the people and the army were in immediate need of necessities, his partiality toward the Tory friends of Mistress Shippen, his blunt dealings in the adjustment of matters involving citizens and the Council, his accumulation of debts, his financial ventures to recuperate, all stirred up against him sour enmity, and started many a whisper through the town. At last, when his intimate enemy, Joseph Reed, was made president of the Council, Arnold determined to quit the army and retire to a life of quiet and seclusion, intending to found a settlement in western New York with his old soldiers, who persisted in loving him.

Considering this plan, he left Philadelphia for a journey to New York. He had scarcely more than turned his back, being with Washington at Morristown, when he learned that Reed had publicly made formal accusations against him before the Council, and had sent copies of the accusations to each governor with a request that the several legislatures be made aware of them. The charges were that he had granted an improper pass permitting a ship to enter port; that he had used public wagons for the transport of private goods; that he had usurped the prerogative of the Council in permitting individuals to go into the enemy's lines; that he had unlawfully bought up a lawsuit in a prize vessel; that he had "imposed menial service on sons of freemen" serving in the militia, and that he had made purchases for his private benefit at a time when the stores, by his own official order, were closed to the public.

Arnold was in a rage. He returned at once to Philadelphia, and demanded an instant examination into his

ARNOLD'S MANSION, FAIRMOUNT PARK, PHILADELPHIA

conduct, anxious to vindicate himself; anxious, above all things, to be set right before the eyes of Mistress Shippen, who already favored him. That was in January, 1779. In March, a committee of Congress, investigating the charges, reported them groundless. But before Congress adopted the committee report, Reed appeared with alleged further evidence, and prevailed upon that body to resubmit the case to a joint commission, to be composed of members of Congress, and the Assembly and Council of Pennsylvania.

Arnold was more incensed than ever at the failure of Congress to vindicate him through its own committee, after it had found him innocent. He considered it a deliberate affront; he believed himself to be the object of malicious and jealous persecution. His rage grew; his resentment mounted day by day. When the joint commission, seeking to avoid the issue, recommended that he be tried on the charges by court-martial, he was unable to conceal his disgust.

But though they humiliated him, one thing they did not accomplish. They did not deprive him of the affections of Mistress Shippen, whom he took to wife within a week of the day when the commission reached its indecisive decision. One more thing, at least, they did not achieve; they did not destroy the faith of Washington in Arnold. Full of sympathy for the brave man always, the commander-in-chief appointed the court-martial for May 1.

MOUNT PLEASANT MANSION, ARNOLD'S FORMER RESIDENCE

It was December 19, 1779, before the court-martial made a finding, so many and so minute were the delays interposed by Reed and his fellows, who sought continually for more evidence in the hope of bringing about a conviction. But after an unhappy haggling summer and autumn, and an annoying nagging before the court of his fellow-officers, Arnold was found entirely blameless. But, that the Council might be saved its face, it was held that Arnold, while he had had no wrong intent, had been indiscreet in the matter of the pass and the public wagons, and recommended that he be publicly rebuked.

This Washington did, as gently as he might, on January 26, 1780. Against him Arnold held not the least malice, knowing well that he had been obliged to execute the finding of the court, but against Congress he bore the most malignant and rancorous hatred. With this in his heart, he asked for appointment to the command at West Point, which Washington readily gave him, glad to be able to express in that way his unalterable confidence and esteem.

And with this in his heart, he spoke to Major John Stevens, his aide, looking the while through the window across the Hudson to the bristling heights of West Point. John gazed up from his work with a look of compassion; his devotion to this man was the love of one strong man for another. "You take the matter too heavily," he said, presently. " 'T is well known that Congress has little weight with the country, and less since their recent behavior toward you. How little you have been harmed by the miserable affair is shown in your being freely appointed to the command of such an important post as this, and by the favor in which General Washington continues to hold you." Two years before West Point had been a solitude, but under the direction of Kosciusko, a system of defense had been erected which was believed to be impregnable, and here had been stored the magazines of ammunition, not only for the use of the post, but of the whole army. In granting the request for the command, Washington had shown unlimited faith in Arnold. It is not surprising that he, looking moodily through the window, winced at the words, with an expression in his eyes that would have sorely puzzled John had he seen it.

"This is the critical position of the American lines," John went on, believing he had hit upon a consolatory theme, "and you are here as fully in a way to show the country what a brave man may do, as you were that day at Freeman's farm, when you drove Burgoyne to bay."

Arnold turned from the window, his face flushed, full of excitement. "Ay, and I mean to show them what a man may do!" he cried, pacing the room with uneven, hasty step. "Those numskulls in Philadelphia, and the rest of the pack that has hounded me! I mean to show them! I mean to show them well!"

John, perceiving his unusual agitation, considered it best to say no more, and applied himself to his clerical work once more, in silence. After a space, Arnold returned to the chair he had quitted, and fell into abstraction.

"John," he said, impulsively, having thought long and deeply, "John, would

Washington's Headquarters at Tappan, New York

you care to undertake for me an important mission in New York?"

John looked up quickly, astonished at what the other said. "How mean you?" he asked, wide eyed. "If there is aught I can do for you, or the cause, I shall go, right gladly."

"Belike, you may do much, my friend," returned Arnold, with averted gaze.

John, expressing his gratification at the prospects of rendering a service, waited for the other to propound the errand.

"It is a matter of the utmost delicacy," said Arnold, arising and moving toward the window again, as though disturbed and undetermined. "It is a matter of such grave significance that I have refrained from mentioning it, or even intimating it, to any one. Even now I hesitate to speak of it further to you."

"It would be unseemly in me to press you for your confidence," replied John, respectfully. "I — you already know my loyalty to yourself, and to our arms. My discretion, of course, is only human."

Arnold, hastening from the window, placed an arm upon his aide's shoulder. "In faith, John, I trust you in both far beyond most men, or I should not have so far broached this subject. And now I have determined to go on," he continued, briskly, taking his seat again, and facing John with steady gaze. " 'T is a scheme I have had in mind for upward of a year, that I would have your assistance in carrying out. Even as long ago as the summer I was in Philadelphia, when Congress was spending its spare time baiting me, I was tentatively laying the foundation of it. In that summer, — prepare to be astonished, my young friend, at my temerity,— in that summer, I fell into correspondence with Sir Henry Clinton, representing myself as an American general who inclined to change his allegiance and serve with the British army, if all could be arranged. Ay, well you may stare; and you are likely to stare more when you learn the import of what I did.

"The correspondence continued, he writing through the name of John Anderson, and I as Augustus. I found the seed taking root with him. When my misfortunes clouded about me, and the time seemed fit for me to change my command, I asked for and got this crucial post. Thereupon — prepare to be further amazed — thereupon, I let fall to Clinton hints that Augustus was General Arnold, and that he contemplated turning the fortress of West Point over to the English. What think you of that move, John?"

John Stevens, pale, aghast, pushed his chair back from the table with a grating noise, and rose slowly in his seat, fixing the other with a look of horror. "I should say, sir," he said, hoarsely, "that unless what you tell me is a cruel hoax, your behavior is incredible."

Arnold laughed nervously. "Can you see no other interpretation for it?" he asked, coughing behind his hand.

"In God's name, what are you coming at?" cried John, springing to his feet and recoiling from the man, in fear and loathing.

"Why, then, this it was!" cried Arnold, in return, rising also, and gazing with fierce challenge at the other. "I saw a chance to bring an end to the war; I saw a chance to entice Clinton into a trap by a show of treachery, and destroy his army; I saw a chance to overwhelm England in one catastrophe. Of my own responsibility, without word to any man, I undertook this thing. I am ready to take the blame; I am ready to share the glory. My satisfaction will be in ending the war; in doing what all the other generals, backed by the ingenuity of the Continental Congress, have failed to do! 'T is well I have said nought of it, it would seem, since you, who profess to love me above all others, put such an evil face upon my conduct," he concluded, with an angry sneer, and turned to leave the room.

"Sir," said John, firmly, though his head fairly reeled with the thought of it all, "do me the justice to concede that the matter had an evil look, with what you told me in the beginning; and if I was aghast at the thoughts your words stirred you should be neither surprised nor angry." Arnold paused to hear what further he might have to say; the anger had gone from his face. In its stead was a wistful, hungry look; the look, if John had but known it, of an exile that yearns for his childhood home.

Kosciusko

"And at the best, sir," continued John, gaining self-control, "the enterprise is one fraught with danger, both to your reputation and to our arms."

"Reputation! Great God, Stevens, is it not time that I did something worthy to lose my reputation, since it is already gone?" He said it with hot rancor in his heart.

John gave him no heed in that. "Consider, sir," he said, earnestly, "what the consequences might be! Assume, sir, that there should be some fatal fault in the plans, and the fortress should fall? Where, then, would be the cause, for which you have fought so valiantly, and so well? And what would your own wretched condition be?"

"Stevens, I tell you I care nothing for that part of it," returned Arnold, in strange excitement. "I might hang, and my name go down the centuries covered with opprobrium, if the matter was misunderstood; I might merely be censured and deprived of command; or " — with bitter irony — "I might at last succeed in winning the gracious compliments of Congress. But that is nothing, for the thing cannot fail if I can arrange matters as I purpose. I will as surely do what I intend doing, as the sun shall rise to-morrow."

"No degree of certainty can justify you in such a hazard without the permission of General Washington, sir," returned John, adopting another line of argument. "It is insubordination."

"I tell you I will take the risk!" rejoined Arnold. "Washington would not thank me for telling him, for he could not give it his sanction. I know that. His position would inhibit him. But I will take the risk."

"What right have you to assume so much?" There was no disrespect in John's manner of asking the question.

"Right! Right!" cried Arnold. "You speak of my right? Great God, man! This is my right!" He touched his leg, twice broken, with the back of his hand. John, for the moment, could make no answer to that. "I tell you more," Arnold went on, subsiding from his excitement in a moment, and becoming grimly resolute. "I shall do this thing, whether or no! I shall bring it about. The harvest is ripe; I have but to send a man to New York, to a rendezvous already named, when Clinton will send one to me, and the whole will be settled. And that I shall do, whether you are the one to go, or another. I have passports in blank from Sir Henry. Whether I write your name in, or another's, I leave to yourself."

For a space John looked fixedly at him. "I can prevent your doing this," he said, at last.

"Ay, you can, but you will not," rejoined Arnold, stiffly. "You can tattle to Washington and bring ruin to

LOOKING UP THE HUDSON FROM THE TROPHY GARDEN AT WEST POINT, NEW YORK

the plan — and perchance to myself, if all my friends put upon it the face you do — but that I believe you will not do."

John, thrown into deep thought, cast his gaze upon the floor.

"I have broached the matter to you, because you seemed to me, above all others, to be the one whom I could best trust," went on Arnold. "Shall I seek some other in whom to repose my confidence?"

He challenged John's loyalty. The man was in grave danger, from many sides. Perchance, after all, John could best serve his friend by going a little way with him in the project; there would still be time to prevent it, if he could not dissuade the rash man; he could tell Washington on his return from New York, if need be. Perhaps he might find another way to interfere, to prevent the terrible risk to man and nation, if he were to make the journey.

"Will you go, or shall it be another?"

With a sigh of responsibility that shook him, John raised his head and met the look of Benedict Arnold.

"I will go," he said.

The two armies spent the summer of 1780 doggedly watching each other, the British lying within the City of New York, and the Americans, with the commander-in-chief's headquarters near Tappan, in a cordon extending from Connecticut to New Jersey. Wearying of this inaction, Lieutenant Fontaine Stevens bethought him of a device whereby he might render his country more service than by the bearing of messages from post to post along the long line of the army.

As a visible result of this thought he became in July a regular member of the household of Robert Stevens, posing as an avowed apostate to the cause of liberty. As such he was suffered to exist in the midst of the English circle

that gathered there, rather contemned by the British officers and wholly despised by his cousin Robert.

What he really did in his capacity of Tory need not be
a matter of conjecture; and if there is any obloquy attached
to his employment it must be conceded to his credit that what
he did was at once of value to Washington and the Ameri-

LOOKING UP THE HUDSON FROM THE UPPER BATTERY AT WEST POINT

cans, and repugnant to his high spirits, to say nothing of
the imminent hazard.

Two there were who divined his business. Nancy Hempstead from the first had been doubtful of his British sympathies. In course of time he took her into his confidence,
excusing himself with the plea that it was politic to do so,
but really because his soul hungered for some form of
frank companionship in the life of sham and deception that
his business built up about him.

It fell out in this way that they came into an easy friendship. Nancy, after the manner of women, forgot the occu-

pation in the man, whom she regarded highly, the more because of the delicacy with which he refrained from any reversion to his old relation of suitor. If he were a spy, he was a gentleman as well; it would hardly be womanly in her to betray him. Moreover she had begun to feel more than a little sympathy for the Americans. Perhaps, too, Fontaine benefited in the eyes of this young Englishwoman by the halo that was about his cousin John.

The other one who knew, inevitably, and through means of her own, was Mistress Sophronia. She took the trouble to let Fontaine understand that she knew, foreseeing a possibility of turning it to her own advantage, some time, by being in a position to make demands upon this young man for assistance in her central scheme of life; which was, to possess herself of the soul of John Stevens. But she let him go with a hint that she was aware of his dangerous employment; for whether the English ruled in America, or were driven into the sea, was matter of small consequence to her.

One day in September, 1780, Nancy and Fontaine were seated on the small veranda that hung before the windows of the dining-room, silent, as was not unusual with them, when they heard the voices of Francis and Lieutenant Lucas, that moment entering the room behind them. Not being meal-time the two young men could have only one mission, and presently there was added to the sound of their voices the noise of glasses and bottles.

Now, when the house of Robert Stevens was built, fate intervened to the extent of providing the balcony in which Nancy and Fontaine were sitting, in a place directly opposite the one spot where the sideboard could fitly be placed. Wherefore it followed that Nancy and Fontaine, sitting silent and unperceived, were enabled to overhear all that was said during the mixing and drinking of Robert Stevens's wines and liquors.

As for Fontaine it was consistent with his honor, considering his occupation, to listen and play eavesdropper. As for Nancy, she never in the world would have permitted herself to do so, if the first words she heard from the lips of Francis had not stirred within her the last fiber of curiosity. This, also, is after the fashion of women.

This is what Isaac Francis said to Lieutenant Hempstead on that afternoon in September, 1780, in the hearing of Nancy Hempstead, his heart's desire, and Lieutenant Fontaine Stevens, spy. "Ecad! He hath slipped me more than once, but I am more than like to lay our brave Yankee major by the heels this merry time, if things fall not much awry!"

The two on the balcony looked at one another, quickly, inquisitively, each with the same thought, that this Yankee major against whom Francis planned was John.

"How so?" asked Lucas, in a tone displaying more interest than was usual with him.

"Why, i' faith, I have set Mistress Sophronia upon him!" cried Francis, in triumph.

"My troth, you have done well there," returned Lucas, applauding the other with a laugh.

The two on the balcony looked again at one another. It was John.

"She is not likely to do so again, for when we have finished with what we have in hand, the fellow will be as safely sealed up as though the grave had him!"

"Come!" cried Lucas, with more lively interest, "unravel me your pretty plot."

"By Heaven, that I will, Sir Lucifer; for you are a man of discretion, and my breast bursts with the glee of it," returned Francis, slapping the other playfully on the shoulder. "You already know of the business that has gone forward for some time between a certain American general and Sir Henry, in which I have been able to be of some slight service.

Of late matters have come to such a pass that the American conceived it to be expedient to send a private emissary to us, to take up certain matters.   Last night Major André, who has done most of the business, and myself, repaired to Friar David's, to a rendezvous with this emissary, and when we came there whom, think you, should we find awaiting us?"

LOOKING DOWN THE HUDSON FROM THE LOWER BATTERY AT WEST POINT

The two on the balcony looked hastily at each other, puzzled, expectant.

"By what has gone before, I should think it might be this same John Stevens," returned Lucas.

"By what comes after, so it was!" cried Francis.   "You should have seen the fellow stare, and blush, when he saw me.   But I made much of him, congratulating him upon seeing the error of his ways, and much to the same purport, hoping to set him at his ease; for already I had begun to have designs upon the fate that had thrust him thus into my hands."

"Think you the fellow has in truth come over to us?" asked Lucas, irrelevantly, with some astonishment.   "He seemed ever a sturdy patriot."

The two on the balcony looked apart, not daring to meet each other's gaze before that question; in the face of each was faith,— faith and anxiety.

"How else should he have been on this mission?" retorted Francis. "But that is beside the point of my story. I have done many things of which I am proud, my dear Lieutenant Lucifer, but what I did last night surpasses them all in cunning wisdom. I came straightway from the meeting, where we appointed to meet again to-night, and laid the whole matter before Mistress Sophronia, knowing that she would so far help me in ridding my love affair of his presence for purposes of her own; for she is as desirous of keeping Nancy and this man apart as I, and for a parallel reason."

From the lips of Nancy, listening, came a low cry, half fear, half anger, which Fontaine silenced with his finger-tips.

"Let me point out to you, my dear fellow, the delicate points of cunning in what I did. For my part, I should much rather see him hanged, for Sophronia would not be an evil fate for any man, but from that consummation, which seemed easily within my reach, I was deterred by certain considerations. In the first place, I need not hesitate to tell you that I was afraid the woman would again thwart me if I sought the fellow's life; for she has some strange hold upon this same Friar David, I perceive, and I was not safe in keeping secret from her the fact that John is there. Beyond that, was the apprehension that all our schemes would be spoiled by the fellow's tattling, if he should be arrested and brought for trial as a spy; and, though he could surely be made out to hang for it, nevertheless all our labor would be lost, and I should be wanting in the marked credit I hope to derive from this business. Again, I had a more subtle reason. It was apparent to me that if the fellow were put in the hands of Sophronia, it could be made to appear to Mistress Nancy, your worthy sister, that there was more between them than there yet is, whereby her own warmth for him might cool. And, by my faith," he added, with a chuckle, "there is like soon to be more."

Those on the porch desisted from glances; on Nancy's face was a deadly pallor. Fontaine flushed hot, longing to lay hands on the two within.

"You have done shrewdly enough," said Lucas, "but how is the matter to be done? That, it would seem to me, is the meat of the whole nut."

"Why, 't is simple enough, when such an one as Sophronia takes a hand," made answer Francis. "Look you, then, how it will be done. To-night, at five, soldiers go to Friar David's, and take one John Stevens, on charge of being a spy. In command of the soldiers is a certain sergeant, well known to myself, and by me to Sophronia. This certain sergeant will take the prisoner away with him; but as they go down the street, behold, a coach and four drives hotly up, the door is flung open, John Stevens is seized and whisked in, the door is closed, and the coach snaps away."

On the balcony was a stirring; quick, hard breathing, a woman half rising from her seat, a man, grim, tight-lipped, quivering with suppressed wrath and detestation.

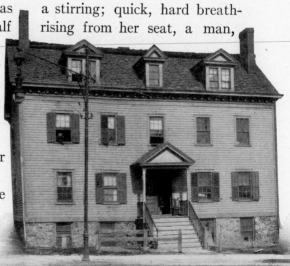

"Is the fair Sophronia, then, intending to kidnap our burly hero?"

"Ay, so the phrase goes!"

"I wish her more

HOUSE AT MORRISTOWN, NEW JERSEY. IN WHICH ARNOLD'S
COURT-MARTIAL WAS HELD

fortune than I have had with my beloved," rejoined Lieutenant Hempstead with a yawn.

Fontaine, on the balcony, made a sign to Nancy to listen further, being habituated to such a course.

"Eh? What may your misfortunes be, then?" asked Francis, clinking down his glass and smacking his lips.

"Why, you remember how I told you of sending a false note to that little minx in Boston, purporting to come from this same John Stevens, and telling her to come at once to his succor? Well, the child responded, in person; and my plans went so well that both was she captured by my gang of 'Skinners' and rescued by the 'Cowboys,' from whom, in turn, she was taken by another party and brought to this same Friar David's as being the most likely place for evil schemes in broad New York." The "Skinners" were bands of robbers operating in New York State, under pretense of being patriot partisans; the "Cowboys," so called because they were supposed to confine their attentions to cattle stealing, took advantage of the other side.

"Say you this Stevens fellow is there too?" cried Hempstead, leaving his languid habit of talk and speaking with quick anxiety, as though a thought had come to him suddenly.

"Ay, that he is."

Those on the balcony, looking at each other in wonderment at this new revelation, could not hear further. There was only the mutter of curses from the lips of Lucas, filled with new reflections, and the echo of their steps as the two left the dining-room. For a little Nancy and Fontaine sat still, stupidly, knowing nothing to do.

"Help me!" cried the girl, at last, half reeling, and throwing her arms about the neck of Fontaine, in the vehemence of her appeal. The danger in which her beloved was placed; the power of those who plotted against him; the thought of

his falling into the snare of this other woman; her own un-
conscious and innocent part in building up enemies against
him; the newly discovered perfidy of her brother in attempting to beguile Catherine Averill—for she made no doubt that
that was what he meant — were too much for her strength.
Trembling, weeping, she lay her head upon Fontaine's
shoulder, surrendering herself to dependence upon him.

Gazing for a moment at the lovely head, wistfully,
hopelessly, longingly, he lifted a
strand of the golden
hair in his fin-
gers, placed it
to his lips, soft-
ly, so that she
might not
know he did it,
and closed his
eyes, quivering
with emotion;
a low sigh
slipped from
his breast.

"Come,"
he whispered,
raising her
from his
breast; "we
will save him."

Looking up
into his face,
reassurance
came to her.

The Kosciusko Monument, Washington (*By Anthony Popiel*)

CHAPTER XXII

FRIAR DAVID'S

WHEN Lucas Hempstead left Robert Stevens's dining-room, much perturbed by the sudden realization that Catherine Averill and John Stevens were both in the house of Friar David, it lacked about two hours of the time when the plot was to be sprung against the American. Without pausing to consider what he was doing, he left Francis at the mansion, made his excuses, and set out at once for the place, fearful lest this man should in some way interfere with his own schemes.

As he hurried along his fear of the American rose, and with it his anger against him. He was not satisfied with the disposition Francis and Sophronia proposed to make of him; he had doubts of its success. As he hastened to the place where Catherine, through his villainy, was restrained, he suddenly hit upon a notion that caused him to pause abruptly in mid-career. For one moment he stood still; in another he faced about, and made his way toward headquarters. He would interfere with their little game, for his own greater security from this rampant Yankee. He knew John Stevens well enough to know that his arrest as a spy would not lead to a compromise of any one else, and that he would hang in dignified silence; it would not interfere with Francis's hopes. Therefore, he would reveal that part of the plot which

382

GENERAL ROCHAMBEAU (*From the engraving by H. B. Hall*)

contemplated John's escape to the proper officer at head-quarters, and have John apprehended as a spy, taking care, himself, to show no hand in it.

But who was this Friar David, whose house was the theater of so much trickery, and what was he? That can in part be answered. His cognomen was a bit of ironical pleasantry on the part of those who had dealings with him; for never was man further from what a friar should be than this scoundrel. If any low villainy were to be perpetrated, requiring the services of a purchasable person, otherwise disinterested, Friar David was more than likely to be that person.

His house was a fit habitation for him. It was a low, one-storied affair, with a low window, a low door, and a generally skulking appearance. Next the street, below the level of the pavement by a step or two, was a long, bare room, devoid of grace and comfort, furnished only with such necessities as a man in slender circumstances might be expected to provide for his own uses: a rough deal table, half a dozen plain chairs of straight, hard pattern, and a forbidding lounge of cheap design and material. The farther wall of the room was pierced by a battery of doors, mysterious, all alike, defying the imagination to conjecture whither they led. At one end of the room was a heavy hanging, beyond which no man was known ever to have peered.

At somewhat the same moment when Lucas Hempstead, filled with his new inspiration, was making his way toward headquarters, a coach and four, rather elaborate for the part of the city through which it was traveling, rolled along the narrow streets near the Battery and pulled up around the corner from Friar David's. There descended from it Sophronia Osborne, dressed severely, in a traveling gown, as though she looked forward to much hard journeying.

Lingering for an instant to pass some final word to the coachman, she hastened around the corner and into the Friar's cell, without pausing for the formality of knocking.

Friar David himself was seated at the table when she entered; a little twisted, narrow-shouldered man, with cold eyes that asked questions. At sight of the girl he arose

RUINS OF FORT PUTNAM, WEST POINT

abruptly, in some annoyance, not free from fear, and stared at her for a moment.

"What brings you here this time?" he said, presently. There was no welcome in his tone.

Nor was there indication of a desire for welcome in her manner of answering. "I come this time on affairs of my own," she said.

"In which, perchance, you are gracious enough to require my assistance," retorted the man, keenly.

"What I require, you shall shortly learn," rejoined Sophronia. "You have concealed here one in whom I have great interest. There are certain matters on hand to-day in which I have seen fit to concern myself. I shall expect nothing further from you than to do as I ask you, from time to time, as the occasion arises. For the present,

I shall ask you to let me avail myself of this concealment."
So saying, she took a step to the end of the room opposite
the hangings, and pressed a certain panel. As she did so,
a thin door, concealed by the paneling, swung open, revealing a narrow space, in which she entered, closing the panel
after her.

Her treatment of the man was amazing; she spoke as
one on a familiar footing with him, but as she might have
addressed an inferior, except that there was in her tone and
look a trace of contempt which one would not trouble one's
self to entertain toward a menial.

She had no more than ensconced herself, and Friar
David had not yet had time to resume his seat by the table,
when there was a measured tread of many feet in the street
outside, and presently a great knocking at the door. Before
Friar David could open it, or even bid those to enter who
summoned him thus, the door flew wide and a young British
lieutenant entered, at the head of a file of soldiers. The
time lacked an hour of that set for the consummation of
Francis's plot with Sophronia.

"Now, by my sword, Friar David, I had never thought
to come to take you for a spy," quoth the young lieutenant,
flippantly, snipping dust from his laced sleeve with a gloved
finger. "Though for my part," he went on, leering at the
man, "I should not find it amiss if that were my mission,
instead of taking one Master John Stevens, sometimes
known as a major of American infantry, and always, by
your leave, known as a sneak and a scoundrel and a blackguardly spy. Come now, Friar David, produce him, and
that at once; or you are likely to have the military authorities
down upon you; and that, you know, you could ill afford."

"I harbor so many wretches and spies and promiscuous
scoundrels, that I am fain to ask you which one you seek,"
retorted Friar David, with scornful sarcasm. He was bold

enough with this fellow. It was worthy of remark, the difference between his attitude toward this officer, followed as he was by a band of armed soldiers, and that other, the solitary and defenseless girl who had just hidden herself.

"Come, holy man," replied the lieutenant, disliking the other's humor, "Have done with this, and bring forth the man I seek."

"Whom do you seek?" growled Friar David, casting an uneasy glance from beneath his brows at the movable panel in the wall.

"One John Stevens, I tell you." The young officer was growing impatient.

"Is there any other name?" queried Friar David, slyly.

THE OLD FORGE AT TUXEDO PARK, NEW YORK, WHERE THE CHAIN WAS MADE

"What other name should there be?" gruffly demanded the impatient lieutenant.

"That I cannot answer, young man; but I can answer you that so far as I know there is no one of that name within this house."

"So far as you know, quotha? Come, you know him well enough, and can answer my fair question fairer than that, and without delay."

"Do you yourself know this John Stevens whom you seek?" Adroit, was Friar David.

"Nay; but you know him, and right well, at that," retorted the lieutenant, guilelessly.

LINKS FROM THE CHAIN ACROSS THE HUDSON

"Shall we search, sir?" whispered a grenadier, twitching with eager finger at his gun; for the searching of private houses was at once a pastime and a profit.

"Ay, presently, unless the rogue finds the man himself," said the officer.

"I know this John Stevens, and will help you in your search by so much as telling you he is not here, but has this hour returned to the American lines." It was Sophronia Osborne who spoke, standing in the middle of the room, whither she had come so softly from the paneled wall that none had perceived her, being greatly engrossed in the dialogue between the two men. She took a step toward the young lieutenant; as she stepped, she lifted the situation from Friar David by one glance at him, greatly to that gentleman's relief and satisfaction. In her face and manner were not the least sign of the surprise and dismay she felt, discovering another and premature squad come to arrest John; for these were not the soldiers she had bargained for.

"By your leave, Mistress Osborne," said the lieutenant, doffing his hat with an elaborate bow, for he was one of those who came at odd times to the Stevens mansion, "by your leave, and craving your pardon, I find myself under the painful necessity, imposed upon me by my commission, of being obliged to go further in this matter, despite your assurances, and to have the

OLD FURNACE AT SMITHFIELD, NEW YORK, WHERE THE ORE FOR THE CHAIN WAS SMELTED

premises searched, unless, haply, you can furnish us with
the man we seek."

"Why do you wish this man?" asked Sophronia,
apart from all point under discussion, but with such an
apparent innocence of curiosity that the young lieutenant
was beguiled by it. What Sophronia desired, above all
things else, and what she must obtain, was delay, until the
other squad could arrive.

"As a spy within our lines," explained the officer,
politely.

"Shall we search, sir?" The same soldier who had
spoken before, a round-headed, grizzled warrior of years,
muttered it in the ear of the young lieutenant.

"Hold your tongue, sirrah!" scolded the officer, piqued
at this show of insubordination before Sophronia. "Can
I ever hope for your forgiveness," to Sophronia, "if I carry
out my duties, and search this house?"

"The house is not mine, so what have I to forgive?"

"It is my duty," the officer continued to explain, con-
gealed by her last blast.

"You seem uncommonly averse to doing your duty,
then, to stand stammering before it a half-hour," returned
Sophronia, with a disdain that the officer attributed wholly
to his callow lack of tact in handling the situation. In her
heart was desolation. This was the wrong squad of soldiery;
there was some treachery abroad; it boded no good to John,
whatever it was; she was powerless to intervene; she could
only hope to lure this young man away.

Her irony struck the susceptible heart of the soft soldier;
even now he hesitated, reluctant to give the offensive order,
when the private who had already ventured twice into the
council of war gave a premonitory cough that settled the
whole matter at once. The lieutenant, with a wave of his
gloved hand, and a stern look toward Sophronia, who was

as unconcerned in the proceedings as the breeze outside, bade them make search.

They had not got so far as the first of the battery of doors when the outer door was thrown open once more, and Fontaine Stevens, with Nancy at his elbow, appeared on the heels of the searchers. They looked quickly about; he met their gaze boldly. "What goes forward?" he asked, calmly.

FORT CLINTON, NEW YORK

"We have come to seek one John Stevens, an American spy," replied the officer in command of the squad, eying him sagaciously. "Belike you may know him."

"In very truth, I am like to know him well," laughed Fontaine, "for I am he." At the words, Nancy gasped, turned pale, and cast a swift glance at the others. Sophronia looked as steadily upon the scene as though she had been hewn from marble; Friar David made no sign.

"Nay, that can hardly be," said the officer, making a show of doubt, out of sheer vanity, so that the women might perceive how shrewd he was, "for you I know to be of the household of Robert Stevens, and a Tory."

Nancy was trembling now; her hand was on Fontaine's

sleeve, clutching at it, as he answered. "You draw much knowledge from that, young man," he said, scornfully. "Think you I would be a lieutenant of Continentals in my cousin's house, having certain duties to perform?"

The soldiers observed Nancy's agitation, and drew inferences from it, which were wrong, they being mere men.

"You confess yourself a spy, then?"

"You confess yourself a dunce, to ask me the question," retorted Fontaine. "Have I not told you already that I am John Stevens?"

"Nay, I am John Stevens!" From one of the four doors rang the voice of the man himself; he stood there, framed by it, massive, magnificent, looking upon them all. "I am John Stevens! What will you have of me?"

At that the young lieutenant fell into such a state of astonishment and uncertainty that he was fain to rumple his hair; even the grizzled warrior with the round head seemed at a loss what to make of it. In the midst of it all, Fontaine made shift to give a sign to John across the room, and while they still stared, he spoke further.

"Have done your jesting, man," he said, sternly. "This is a wild fellow, who, finding me, as he thinks, in straits, would turn a trick to help me," he explained to the soldier, with a brave show of carelessness. "Come," he went on, "I have run my course; I am done. Take me away, I beseech you, without further delay."

"Nay, not so," cried John, advancing, puzzled, uncertain. "There is mischief here."

"This is no time for jest, Morton; go back to thy bottle," snarled Friar David, having a cue from Sophronia.

Uncertain still, John gazed from one to another of the three whom he knew so well. The countenance of Sophronia was as though she had never seen him before this time; Fontaine met his look fully, but without sign; Nancy,

General Rochambeau's Headquarters at White Plains, New York

trembling and the color of death, stared desperately at the British officer.

"Now, if God gives it to me to come through this without an addled pate, I shall turn friar too!" cried the unhappy officer. "For Heaven's love, set me right in this, you who know John Stevens," he added, appealing to the others. "What say you, Friar David, which is he?"

"Why, I say, as he says, that that is he," returned Friar David, unconcernedly pointing a finger at Fontaine.

"And you, Mistress Hempstead? Know you John Stevens?"

With the look of a lost soul, Nancy raised her eyes toward Fontaine, speaking no word; in them were unutterable gratitude, and a pitiable plea for his forgiveness; wherein he had his full reward.

The officer was growing satisfied.

"And you, Mistress Osborne?"

With a wail that set their hearts on edge, Sophronia staggered to the wall, burying her head in her arms, shaking with sobs.

Whereat the young lieutenant shut his lids as a sign of profound understanding, and pointed out Fontaine to his soldiers, with an elegant gesture of command.

In another moment there was the sound of departing feet in the street without, and the place of Fontaine was vacant in the room.

"In God's name, tell me the meaning of all this?" John Stevens, standing bewildered in the midst of the three left in the room, cried out to them.

"It means that you have been saved from an imminent danger," replied Sophronia, recovering her composure.

He gazed beyond her, at Nancy; as their eyes met, the girl, giving way to her emotions, tottered and would have fallen, had not Friar David gone quickly to her support.

Perceiving her emotion, John believed it to be because of
Fontaine. Long years it seemed to him since he had seen
her last. In that time, worked upon by the thoughts concerning her that Sophronia had placed in his brain, he had
abandoned all hope in her love for him, and had buried his
own love for her. For an instant, on seeing her now, it
had awakened both the hope and the love. But now they
vanished; he put her out of his contemplation once more.

"But Fontaine is in danger," he resumed, returning to
things real and present. "Why is it? What is it? Can
no one tell me?"

"He has given his life for yours," murmured Nancy,
finding her voice.

"Pish, nothing of the sort," rejoined Sophronia, making
light of Nancy. " 'T is merely a little device we have hit
upon to extricate you from the unpleasant dilemma of being
found a spy in the British lines. He will suffer nothing,
believe me. He has long been a resident here, living with
his cousin Robert, where his reputation as a turn-coat
patriot, and certain influences that can be set at work, will
suffice to take him clear of present suspicion."

"The lad is in danger," persisted John, recoiling from
the cool manner in which Sophronia viewed the situation.

He strode toward the door, as though to pass through.
Sophronia detained him by his sleeve.

"What will you do?" she asked, calmly.

"I will go and set matters straight; he shall not suffer
for the sins of John Stevens!"

"Brave and heroic in you," commented Sophronia,
"but what will you accomplish in that direction? If his
danger were real, which I maintain it is not, could you do
more than thrust your own neck into the loop? If he can
be proved a spy as Fontaine, could your proving yourself
a spy as John avail him anything?"

"But I have that which relieves me from the imputation of spy," expostulated John, thinking of the credentials that had brought him safely to the city.

"And meanwhile, the project which brought you here will fail through your unsoldierly care for the safety of another. Listen. If this man, your cousin, should fall wounded on field of battle at a time when the destiny of the fight, and perhaps of the war, were in your hands, would you give pause to the conflict to aid him, cousin though he be? And as for that, the man is in no danger. I protest he is not."

To all this Nancy, seated in the chair to which Friar David had led her, weak and trembling, listened in silence, with tense face, the Friar standing behind her in quiet observation of the scene.

He had no means of knowing that the commander-in-chief had left Tappan for Hartford on September 18, attended by Lafayette and Hamilton, to hold his first interview with General Rochambeau. So

OLD FERRY-HOUSE, NEW YORK

that the words of Sophronia brought before the mind of John the dreadful need that he must get back to the American lines, and that without delay, to acquaint Washington with the wild, fantastic project that Arnold contemplated. Everything must be sacrificed to that necessity. "My God!" he said, "my taskmaster is a cruel taskmaster!"

The words had scarcely passed his lips when the door that had admitted so much of tragedy on that afternoon opened once more, and Lieutenant Lucas Hempstead entered. At sight of those who were there, he stood staring about him, taken aback; before another word could pass, Sophronia was upon him, wrathful, an avenging fury, divining his part in what had taken place, letting go all restraint for the once.

SLEEPY HOLLOW, NEW YORK

"This, then, is your pretty meddling!" she cried, with voice that almost hissed. "Have a care, sirrah, lest you seek this man's life once too often! You have come to nought, through a good chance; if it had been otherwise, you should have paid heavily for it!"

Bereft of her presence of mind and self-control before by the situation through which she had passed, Nancy shrank and shriveled at sight of her brother, whose infamy she knew. John gave him hardly a glance, holding him in a contempt from which no sense of obligation to Nancy withheld him now. Lucas, still staring about him, was too much astonished to reply; nor had he much leisure for it, for Sophronia gave him slight respite.

"What evil brings you here, rogue?" she demanded, savagely. The frustration of her plans; the introduction of Nancy into the situation; the complications arising from Fontaine's conduct, opportune though the incident was, conspired to set her beside herself with wrath and chagrin. All her resentment was directed against this man, whom she knew as the marplot the moment she saw him enter, and whose complicity she could now no longer doubt, having witnessed his behavior under her accusations.

"Is it so strange that a young officer of the British army pays a visit to the cell of Friar David?" Lucas retorted, regaining his impudence by degrees.

"It would be strange if he came on any good," made answer Sophronia. "I choose to know your errand, lest it mean further mischief to us."

"And what if I choose not to tell you?"

" 'T is all one whether you tell me, or I learn elsewhere," she replied, calmly, turning toward Friar David, who trembled at the turn of affairs toward him.

"I know why he comes," cried Nancy then, arising from her chair with effort, and speaking in a voice that rasped harshly in her tense throat. Her face was without expression; her eyes without light; the thing had gone too far for her strength. She spoke stiffly, mechanically, almost unconsciously. "There is a young woman here he comes to see." For John's sake, and hers, she forebore to speak the name of Catherine.

"If that is all, then, I care not," commented Sophronia, "so long as Lieutenant Lucas confines himself strictly to his own affairs," she added, fixing him with a powerful, threatening glance.

"Nay, nay!" cried Nancy, tottering to the center of the floor, and pointing a dreadful finger at her brother. "See first who the girl is!" With that Sophronia turned again toward Friar David, perceiving by Nancy's emotion that it was a secret of import. "Bring her here," she commanded.

"On your life, an you do!" cried Lucas, taking a step forward.

The man looked imploringly at Sophronia, who replied with a curl of the lip and a terse nod of the head. He shambled off toward one of the four doors. As he started, Lucas sprang forward with an oath, forgetting all else except that he would not have Catherine brought forward in that company.

John he forgot, with the others. As he sprang past him, the heavy hand of the American was clutched about his throat, and his free arm pinned Lucas helpless. "Once you have felt my fingers," said John, in low voice. "Let me not be forced to put them to such use again!"

Lucas, brought thus to himself suddenly, subsided, waiting doggedly for what was to happen. Nancy stood in the center of the floor, swaying slightly, with clenched hands, fighting for her wits. Sophronia, standing beside John, eyed closely the several actors in the drama, having completely possessed herself again of all her fine faculties.

Through some tense moments they stood thus, statue-like. At the end of the time, the door by which Friar David had departed opened again, and he entered, leading by the hand, pale, weeping, trembling Catherine Averill. There was no word said; the matter had gone beyond words. With a glad cry, the girl threw her arms about the neck of John, who still held Lucas, and fled from him to Nancy, who received her with eyes fixed upon the two men; whether her grief was greater that her brother was the manner of wretch he was, or that this brave American had deigned her no look, no word, at any time since they had first come together thus, no man could have told.

Sophronia, mistress of herself once more, mastered the moment. "Hand me his hanger," she ordered Friar David, bending her head toward Lucas. She was obeyed. "Run fetch the coach!" Friar David disappeared through the front door with alacrity; it served his need to show this young British lieutenant that he could not but choose to obey this indomitable woman. "Unhand him now," she said, to John. "Is there anything you need against your going?"

ROCHAMBEAU'S HEADQUARTERS AT ARDSLEY, NEW YORK

"Nothing."

Catherine still wept on Nancy's shoulder; the English girl stared fixedly at her brother, unable to think.

There was the rumble of the coach in the street without; the door opened; Friar David returned. "The coach," he said.

"Come," said Sophronia to John. John paused, uncertain, looking at Lucas as though loath to leave him to further mischief. "Have no fear of him," said Sophronia, coolly. "He is not likely to make a noise concerning this affair; neither will he play villain further, having at heart a strain of virtue, which is soon to come to the top, for, if I mistake not, his spirit is broken by this."

Stopping only to press a kiss of comfort on Catherine's brow, John walked to the door; for his dread errand was heavy upon him, demanding, at any price, that he return to the American lines. Sophronia followed into the street.

Once there, she glanced swiftly up and down, and beckoned Nancy and Catherine to follow. They came, leaving the door open; through it John observed Lucas, sullen and defeated, sitting in a chair. Sophronia spoke to Nancy. "Make it known to my mother that I say it is necessary that Lieutenant Stevens should come to no harm," she said to her, in a low voice. She turned to John. "Are you ready?" she asked.

He nodded. "You have served me well," he said. "This is scarcely a time when I can find words for thanks. I place my hope for my cousin's life in your hands." He stopped for a farewell; she passed him and continued to the carriage. Nancy, with a great sigh half stifled in her heart, turned her head away, and led Catherine from the scene.

"You are not going?" John asked, astonished, forgetting to speak further word of parting to Catherine and Nancy, in the confusion of the minute.

"It is necessary," she replied.

"But my cousin? You must remain to save his life."

Her face turned toward his, and came close. In her eyes was a liquid fire; her neck pulsated. "Your life is dearer to me than his," she whispered.

John thrilled with the sound of her voice; for the love of Nancy was stilled in his heart.

"I cannot let you go," he protested. "You must save him."

"I have told you he would be safe, and you cannot but choose to let me go," she replied, tenderly, yet with a determination that he perceived was not to be shaken.

"May God forgive me," he muttered, and entered beside her.

The coach rattled down the streets, past the figures of two women who walked silently, with averted faces. The hour was 5 of the afternoon, — the hour when, in the first plans, this same coach was to have taken these two in rescue and flight from the city.

VERNON HOUSE, NEWPORT, RHODE ISLAND, HEADQUARTERS OF COUNT RO-CHAMBEAU

CHAPTER XXIII

THE TRAITOR

BLACK night hovered over the Hudson; the feet of
the highlands lay in ultimate shadow; the thickets
of fir and spruce fringing the shores were masses of darkness.
Above, the September sky was abysmal; only the stars
sprinkled through it saved the mind from thoughts of the
illimitable extension of the firmament.

Through the dense shadows of the night stole sounds:
the sigh and plash of the Hudson, rolling seaward; the moan
of the wind in treetops; now and then the watch calling the
hour on a ship that swung in the river; these, and the innumerable nameless sounds of the night that go to make
inscrutable silence.

But in a thicket of fir, at midnight, four miles below
Stony Point, there were more sounds than these. There
was the drone of human voices, speaking low;
rising now and then in sudden intensity, and
falling again to a monotone.

The blackness broke; far in the east it
broke into grey, a long, faint hue that swept
in an arc through compass points
north and south. In slow
silence the grey crept over the
land and out upon the river,
revealing a sloop-of-war
placidly at anchor not far
from the thicket whence the
voices had merged into the
night; disclosing the thicket

402

itself; disclosing, in due course, two men emerging from the thicket, one of them limping, with crippled leg; the other debonaire; both of them serious and earnest. One of them, he who was lame, was Benedict Arnold. It was the leg wounded once at Quebec and again at Freeman's Farm that made him limp. Now, after the night in the thicket, he suffered pain in it; a dumb expostulation against the deed he did.

They walked to the bank of the river, still talking earnestly, arousing a company of boatmen when they came there.

"I am ready to return to the *Vulture*," said the debonaire young fellow

"It is too late; the dawn has come. We dare not row you

MAJOR JOHN ANDRÉ   (*After a portrait attributed to Sir Joshua Reynolds*)

back to a British ship lying in the Hudson," said the leader of the boatmen.

"How, fellow, you will not do this?" growled Arnold, with his cloak about his chin, lest he be recognized.

The fellow doggedly shook his head; though the one who desired their transportation cajoled and threatened, he would not embark his men.

"Come, then," said Arnold, " 't is as well; there is still much that I would go over with you. We can repair to the house of Joshua Smith, two miles hence, where we shall be safe, Smith being of uncertain allegiance at best."

In due time the two were seated at the table of Joshua Smith, waiting to be served with breakfast. Into the small talk that was between them and Smith, an inquisitive, loquacious fellow, there burst the booming of cannon. The debonaire young fellow, passing to the window, looked back in some concern. "They are firing on the *Vulture*," he said, "and she is slipping down stream."

" 'T is that over-zealous Colonel Livingston, I warrant," said Arnold. "But have no care for that, John Anderson. If the worst come to the worst, there is land between here and New York where one many ride without wetting."

Until noon the two men were closeted in an upper room in the Smith house. At noon John Anderson placed six papers inside his stocking, beneath his naked sole. "Egad," he laughed, "how they tickle!"

But there was no mirth in his laugh; for his head was full of weighty matters.

A score of words with Joshua Smith, and the lame man left, to be rowed eighteen miles up the river to West Point, where he set himself to await the fruit of what had gone forward in the thicket. For it had been settled between him and John Anderson, who was Major John André, adjutant-general of the British army, that Clinton and Rodney were to ascend the Hudson as soon as André reached New York; that, under pretense of repairs, a link would be removed from the chain closing the Hudson, so that Rodney could bring up the vessels; that the American troops

MONUMENT MARKING THE SPOT WHERE ANDRE WAS CAPTURED AT TARRYTOWN, NEW YORK

would be so disposed in the works that the British could surround and capture them in detail; that, when there was apparent warrant, Arnold would surrender the stronghold at West Point, and the garrison of 3000 patriots.

Now he had only to wait. There could be no missing of the target. André, who had come to complete negotiations, had only to return to the *Vulture*, which had brought him up the river. And the *Vulture*, although it had dropped down stream when Colonel Livingston opened fire upon it, would wait for him, being so ordered.

One thing only gave Arnold anxiety lest his plot should miscarry. John Stevens, whom he had sent to New York two weeks before, in preliminary arrangement, and who had not taken kindly to the scheme, however deceived regarding its true import, had not yet returned. André had told how he had eluded a trap set for him by personal enemies, and had left the city the day following his arrival there. Beyond that, there was no word or hint of him, except a strange story that he had gone with a woman.

That tale Arnold could not credit. He knew that if there were anything in heaven or in hell that could swerve John Stevens from what he conceived to be his duty, that one thing was not a woman. Where then had he gone, and why, if he had in fact left New York? If he had not gone away from the city, but had been taken as a spy, the secret was safe. But might it not be that he had left New York and gone in search of Washington, who had departed to Hartford September 18, and whose absence had been taken advantage of for the consummation of the plot?

It was September 23, the day after he had left André at Smith's house, when Smith himself rode up to Arnold's headquarters, in the Robinson house, with a report. "I rode with him close to the American lines last night," said Smith. "By this time he is safe at home."

"You rode?" returned Arnold, uncertain what he meant, in the confusion of terms. "You mean, on a horse, or in a boat?"

"Ay, on a horse."

"And why did you not take him to the *Vulture?*"

"It had passed down stream, being fired upon by Colonel Livingston. I did not think it safe for either of us."

Arnold bit his lip. "Where did you leave him?"

"Close to his own lines," returned Smith; "I do not know precisely where." As a matter of fact, it was at the Croton River, far from White Plains, to which point he had been instructed to accompany "John Anderson." Arnold held his peace; the matter could not be improved now.

It was the morning of Monday, September 25. Benedict Arnold's household was in some disturbance, word having been received overnight that General Washington and staff might be expected to breakfast. Benedict Arnold was in greater perturbation even than the household preparing for the guest. Washington was returning two days earlier than he had intended — Arnold had made shift to learn that date explicitly; there was not the least sign or intimation of Clinton or Rodney; not one of the signals which he and André had concerted, had been observed. Moreover, John Stevens had not returned. Upon that circumstance he fixed much blame for the miscarriage of his plans. He abused his friend and confidant roundly, finding it needful to vent his impatience in some manner that was not observable.

The breakfast hour dragged on; Mistress Arnold, the beautiful Margaret Shippen that was, expressed lively fears that the meal would be past all hope if their guests did not make haste; Benedict Arnold spoke lightly, frivolously, unlike one having a great and concealed burden to bear. Pres-

Beverly Robinson Mansion at West Point: Arnold's Headquarters

ently there arrived Colonel Alexander Hamilton, aide to Washington.

"General Washington, General Knox, and General Lafayette stopped to ride over the works, accompanied by the rest of the staff," said he, entering. "They will be here anon." Arnold looked keenly at him, but saw no sign that the secret was known.

The meal went on; in the course of it Arnold found occasion to ask of Hamilton, quite naturally, if he had lately seen aught of Major John Stevens, knowing them to be friends.

"Why, is he not your own aide?" asked Hamilton, surprised.

"Ay, he is; but I sent him on an errand from which he has not returned, and I was not certain that it had not led him to General Washington; for it was of a roving character, so to speak, and one in which he had discretion."

An adjutant brought Arnold a dispatch. Mistress Arnold watched him as he opened and read it, perceiving by her husband's mood that something untoward was going forward.

"You will excuse me," said Arnold, coolly, folding the dispatch and placing it in his pocket, "but my presence is demanded across the river, in the works, on some business that cannot well wait."

He arose and left the room, ascending to his chamber, followed by his wife.

"What is it?" she whispered. She knew all was not right.

"Read," replied the man.

She read. It was a dispatch from Colonel Jameson, announcing that one John Anderson had been taken prisoner by three militia-men near Tarrytown, and that certain compromising papers, relating to West Point, had been discovered in his stocking. Colonel Jameson desired to acquaint his commanding officer with the circumstance, and begged to know what disposition to make of the prisoner.

"I am a ruined man," cried Arnold, when she had finished. "I must fly for my life!" His wife fell fainting upon the bed. Stopping only to call her maid, and to kiss his infant son, the traitor fled from the house, took barge, and was rowed down the river. Mistress Arnold, reviving, had presence of mind enough to send down word that she would not return, being indisposed. Washington arrived at noon, and breakfasted. Finishing the meal, and finding that Arnold had not yet returned, he crossed the river with his staff to inspect the works, thinking to meet Arnold there. Hamilton remained behind.

There came to Hamilton then a courier, bearing a message and papers for General Washington from Major Jameson.

"I have searched two States for you," said the courier, mopping his brow, for he had ridden hard.

"Ay, we came a different route from what might have been expected," answered Hamilton, taking the papers to examine them, think-ing it a matter of routine. With a white face, he

THE JOSHUA SMITH HOUSE, TREASON HILL, NEW YORK

turned and entered the house, pacing the dining-room, the parlor, the hall, in a fever of impatience, going ever and anon to look through the window of the door, across the Hudson.

Looking so at last, he perceived Washington and his staff approaching the house. "A dispatch," he whispered to Washington, when the party came to the portico of the house. His appearance caused Washington to look twice at him, as he took the papers and hastened into the house, followed by Hamilton.

They spread the documents upon the dining-room table. They were plans and maps of the defenses, notes, instructions, passports for John Anderson from Arnold. In utter silence they looked them over hastily. Pale and trembling, Washington turned to Hamilton.

"Arnold has not returned?" he asked, hoarsely.

Hamilton shook his head. Washington rang for a servant. "Pay my compliments to Mistress Arnold, and request her presence here," he commanded.

"Mrs. Arnold begs to be excused," said the servant, returning presently.

THE ROOKERY WHERE ANDRÉ
SPENT THE NIGHT BEFORE
HIS CAPTURE

"It is necessary that I should see her, and at once. Tell her so, with my apologies for insisting."

Her maid entered the room at the moment.

"Mistress is in a dreadful state, sir, if you please, sir," she said. "She is taking on dreadful, sir, laughing and crying till I am at my wit's end to know what to do."

Washington looked at Hamilton, in blank despair. "Make haste; cross the river. Seek him out. Arrest him. Bring him here. He must not escape."

"You think, then —?" Hamilton was beginning.

"What other meaning can this have? Make haste!"

Passing through the entrance to the porch, where Lafayette and Knox were talking, he approached them. "Arnold is a traitor, and has fled to the British," he said. "Whom can we trust now?" Tears flowed down his cheeks; his voice was thick and hoarse.

But in a moment he was composed. Ordering a barge, he crossed the river, mounted a horse, and rode about the works, preparing for defense; for Clinton and Rodney might even now be on the way up the Hudson; as, indeed, they would have been, if André had not been captured.

"Merciful God, see what the man has done!" he moaned, perceiving on all sides evidences of treacherous arrangements.

Seven o'clock, and he was seated in the same room which Arnold had quitted in such haste that morning, having done all that could be done toward restoring the defenses. There they brought him a letter from General Arnold, written from the cabin of the *Vulture*. It assured him of the innocence of Mrs. Arnold, and begged that she might be allowed to return to Philadelphia, or come to her husband, as she might choose.

"Go to Mrs. Arnold," said he, quietly, to one of his officers, "and tell her that though my duty required no means should be neglected to arrest General Arnold, I have great pleasure in acquainting her that he is now safe on board a British vessel."

The meal wore on in silence, broken only by snatches of talk; for the thoughts of all were heavy. Toward its close, Washington looked up suddenly. "I have not seen General Arnold's aide, Major Stevens," he said, to one of the fugitive traitor's former staff. "Can you tell me where he is?"

"He left West Point a fortnight since, sir," replied the officer, "traveling southward. Common belief is that he went to New York City."

"He has not come back?"

"There has been no word of him since, sir."

A look of fresh pain passed over the rugged features; he closed his eyes; his lips moved, but he spoke no word. Presently they heard his voice, sounding strangely.

"Colonel Hamilton, have an order made for the arrest on sight of Major John Stevens, late of General Arnold's staff, on a charge of treasonable conduct."

WASHINGTON'S ROOM, DEWITT HOUSE, TAPPAN, NEW YORK (*From an etching by W. H. Wallace*)

CHAPTER XXIV

PICTURES ON THE HEARTH

SOPHRONIA OSBORNE, in sending the message concerning Fontaine Stevens to her mother on the day she left New York with John Stevens, had not reckoned without her host. Fontaine was cleared of all charges through an influence that came from somewhere near headquarters.

In another matter that day Sophronia was right. Lucas Hempstead not only refrained from any attempt to work further evil against Catherine, or any one else, but his character underwent a change, strangely accompanied by a physical and mental disturbance. Isaac Francis, hearing of the miscarriage of the plot against John on the eventful afternoon when it was to have been carried into effect, and hastening to Friar David's for further information, found Lucas there in a weak, dazed state. He brought him to the Stevens home, unabashed by his transgressions against that worthy blood, where he was received with forgiveness by both his sister and the girl he had endeavored so foully to injure. There he fell into a fever, in which the two nursed him. Recovering from that, he surveyed his past life with revulsion and penitence, making what amends he could for the present by word of mouth, and sincerely promising much in behavior for the future. For Lucas was not wholly evil at heart. In the

414

beginning, he was nothing worse than weak, selfish, and vain. His villainy had been engrafted upon him by the life he led and by evil associations. Now that his naked soul was stripped bare, he saw it in all its blackness, and recoiled from the sight.

Still other changes were wrought in the immediate circle of Robert Stevens's household by the episode at Friar David's and the consequences of it. While Robert Stevens was kept in ignorance of much that had happened there, and sought to ascertain nothing that was withheld from him, he nevertheless was aware that members of the family had been involved in proceedings that were discreditable. This he resented against his wife, who had flagrantly defied his authority and ignored his wishes from the time the British first came to New York City, after the battle of Long Island.

He took no trouble to conceal his displeasure from her, and she soon found him less tractable and gullible than he had been. When, in due course, the treachery of Arnold became notorious, he connected it in some way with the affair at Friar David's, and implicated his wife in it. His suspicions that the plot had at least her tacit sympathy were strengthened to conviction when Mistress Stevens openly invited the traitor to his house as one of the guests of a dinner party she purposed giving to some of the British officers. Learning her intentions, he firmly declined to permit her to entertain the man, or the other guests she had invited. There was a violent scene between them. She resorted to every device which had served her in the past, to no avail. The man was aroused, and had his will in the matter. From that time forth there was an open rupture between them, but he maintained his position as head of the house with dignified stubbornness, from which she was unable to move him.

And one other shifting of human affairs took rise from

that same day at Friar David's. Catherine had not been long in the house of her kinsman before she learned the story of Fontaine's sacrifice for John. Though the last demand was not made upon his loyalty to her hero, and he came off free, she nevertheless was filled with an admiration for his generosity that livened and warmed to a closer feeling when Fontaine took up his abode once more under the same roof, after his nominal exoneration. She was the more prepared for such a change in her affections by a conviction she had been slow to gain, that she might never expect any regard from John other than the impersonal friendship

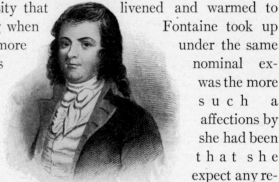

John Paulding, One of the Captors of André

which had begun between them when he was a lad and she a child.

Innocently, without guile, and thinking only to thank him for what he had done, she revealed to Fontaine more of her regard for him than she herself was aware of. Her very innocence and guilessness appealed to him; he was tender with her because of the unhappy situation in which she found herself; he pitied her for the ordeal through which she had been at the cell of Friar David; it was not long until he began to find in her a sweet comfort and solace for the other love that he had uprooted. In brief, they fell in love, sweetly, gently, building by degrees a new happiness out of the wreckage of their shattered hopes.

Sophronia Osborne returned to New York and the Stevens household some three weeks after her disappearance with John Stevens, riding in the coach that had borne them away. Where she had been, or what had befallen, she did not reveal, and there was that about her which gave pause to any who might desire to ask. Fontaine alone braved her, requesting word of John. He learned for his pains only that his cousin was alive.

The Arnold and André affair made much noise in New York. Knowledge of it burst upon soldiers and citizens suddenly. For some days before the scheme fell into ruin, an army had been embarking in the Hudson, — the army that was intended to carry out the plot. Word was persistently spread abroad that a movement to the Chesapeake was afoot, and was as persistently discredited. In the midst of the excited discussion of the mysterious preparations, came news of André's arrest and Arnold's defection, setting the town abuzz.

André's unhappy fate cast a gloom over New York. He was beloved in the army, by rank and file and officers. Arrested on September 23 by John Paulding, Isaac Van Wart, and David Williams, "Skinners," and brought to Colonel Jameson, he would have been sent by that officer to Arnold himself, had not Major Benjamin Tallmadge, Jameson's second in command, advised strongly against

ANDRÉ'S PRISON IN THE SEVENTY-SIX STONE HOUSE   (*From the etching by W. H. Wallace*)

it, suspecting some mischief. But the letter which Jameson had naïvely written to Arnold, informing him of the arrest, which enabled him to escape, was permitted to go forward.

On September 28 André was taken to Tappan, where the main army was posted. Tallmadge himself escorted him; Tallmadge, who had been classmate to Nathan Hale, hanged in New York City as a spy by General Howe, four years before. Fourteen generals sat in commission next day to weigh his fate. Greene presided. For their prisoner they felt a measure of sympathy, because of his generous nature and frank behavior; but there could be only one verdict. On October 2 he was hanged, after Clinton had vainly interceded in his behalf, and after a secret proposal to deliver him to the British in exchange for General Arnold had been rejected. His remains were interred near the spot where he gave up his life; but in 1821 they were conveyed with honor to Westminster Abbey, where they now rest.

Arnold was received coldly by the officers of King George. To them he was a traitor, who had sold himself for £6000 and a commission as major-general in the British army. That he had sought to work out their own purposes condoned nothing. His rank among them they treated with punctilious respect; himself, with scant courtesy.

Some there were in the British army who were not content with such mild protest. Major Hempstead, long grown sick at heart of the war against the people and liberties of America, and disapproving of the policy to wear them out by ravaging destruction, lately adopted by Lord George Germain, was so disgusted by this late event that he straightway resigned his commission, and returned to England, accompanied by Margaret, his wife.

Nancy remained, held by the fascination of John Stevens. Slight hope had she of seeing him again; less hope of more than seeing him. But as long as he might live, and more

WASHINGTON'S HEADQUARTERS, TAPPAN, NEW YORK

especially as long as he remained the subject of mystery
he had been since that day at Friar David's, she could not
bring herself to leave. She found good excuse for staying
in the need her other brother had of her, for he had not yet
regained his strength when Major Hempstead left.

But continued residence at the Stevens house was becoming unpleasant. Although Robert Stevens treated her with
a frank expression of high regard, and although she still
felt that she was personally welcome, she knew that all
things associated with the idea of the British army were
becoming more and more repugnant to him.

There was another reason why life in the household
was unbearable to her. That reason was Sophronia. Sophronia's attitude toward her was friendly, even warm; but
she could not divest herself of the thought that the woman
sought, and had thus far been successful in her seeking, to
intervene between herself and John. She did not regard
her as a rival, for there was not enough between herself
and the American to give basis for such a relation between
them; but she did look upon her as an enemy, none the less
hostile and dangerous because of her subtle avoidance of
open enmity, or because that for which they both might
have been in contention was beyond her attainment, at
least, and perhaps beyond reach of either of them.

Still another source of annoyance in New York was
Isaac Francis, who dogged her with his attentions and was
not to be put off. Flippant, impertinent, audacious, he
was deterred by nothing in his suit; not even by the direct
rudeness with which Robert Stevens now met his visits to
the house.

For these reasons, Nancy insisted upon accompanying
an expedition sent in December under General Arnold to
Virginia, to a place in which her brother's regiment was
assigned. The journey was made possible to her by the

circumstance that in Yorktown there resided an aunt on her mother's side, with whom she had been in frequent correspondence since coming to America, and who had pressed her with repeated invitations to pay her a visit.

She did not obtain, however, all the relief she hoped for by going with her brother to Yorktown. For Sophronia, under the cool excuse of being a companion on the voyage, and Francis, impudently, with no excuse whatever, both accompanied her; a contingency from which she was un-

THE DEATH-WARRANT OF MAJOR ANDRÉ (*From the painting by Chappell*)

able to extricate herself. Her annoyance and disappointment were great, on both counts; but greater than her annoyance was her surprise at the unaccountable attendance of Sophronia.

Catherine still stayed in New York, telling herself and Fontaine that she must wait now until spring when she might journey overland to Boston; for there was no safety in travel by sea. The two were more together than ever after the departure of Nancy and Sophronia with Arnold's expedition; so much together, that the new love in their hearts made itself known to each, through the timid pleasure they found in each other's company.

Christmas came, with all its cheer throughout the city. Balls there were, and pageants; fine lace coats; dresses of satin and silk; powders and puffs; drinking of punch. But in the house of Stevens was no loud merriment, for Mistress Stevens gave no more fêtes, her lord and master having come into his own, after much travail.

The fire burned low on the hearth in the great library, whence Robert Stevens had lately retired, and whither Mistress Stevens rarely came; never, when there were no guests. Catherine and Fontaine sat in the warm glow of the yule-log, beset about by mellow shadows; for the last candle had guttered and gone out, unheeded by them.

For a long time they sat, silent, innocently close to one another; she in her cousin's great chair, which she had appropriated when he left them; he on the rug at her feet, gazing into the twisted pictures of the flame. Only the rustle of the fire disturbed the stillness.

At last she spoke, softly, almost in whispers, for the silence was pleasant and full of meaning to them. "Where think you he is, to-night?" she said.

No need to say whom she meant.

"God knows," returned Fontaine; his words a prayer that all might be well with him.

Another silence. "You could never learn from her what befell him in her hands?" asked Catherine, presently.

"As well cry questions to the silent moon. You are much concerned to know?" he added, with a meaning she discerned, from his tone.

"Are not you?" she fenced, giving back an answering meaning that was not in her words.

"Ay; but one thing I would know concerning him above all others."

"And what is that?"

"How much he may have known of — the dire affair." He avoided more explicit expression of the traitorous deed that had been done, when his fears linked John with it.

She made no response; never before had their talk run so close to their dread.

"What think you of it?" he asked, seeing she made no motion to answer.

"I cannot tell." A little tremble ran through her slender body; she sighed sharply, in sudden agitation. "'T is strange enough," she went on, the tremor rising to her throat, "'t is passing strange, but I find I cannot think clearly of the matter."

"Being a woman, 't were better if you let your intuitions play upon it," he suggested, half playfully.

"Nay, that they will not," she whispered; her head bent toward him; in her eyes was the glow of the fire, warm, fluttering.

"Why so?" he said.

"Because," she murmured, faintly, "because, it would seem that my thoughts are all of another, now." Her hand crept timidly adown his shoulder, resting next his cheek.

At the touch of it, a tingle went through him. He would have turned and raised his head, but that she placed her other hand gently on his, as imploring him not to. At that, he took her fingers from where they rested on his sleeve, pressed them to his lips, and crept closer to her knees.

The fire, rustling softly in the hearth, making the silence sweeter, wrought pictures for them both out of its warm glows.

WASHINGTON'S HEADQUARTERS DURING ANDRÉ'S TRIAL (*From the etching by W. H. Wallace*)

CHAPTER XXV

MIDNIGHT—AND DAWN

THE campaign against Newport, Rhode Island, in 1778, was the last in the North. From that time until the close of the war there were only desultory fighting and marauding expeditions along the coast. Clinton was held fast in New York by Washington, and Washington was detained there watching him. But in the South the struggle was carried on with vigor, and abounded in incidents as heroic and romantic as any that marked the conflict about Boston, New York, or Philadelphia.

The transfer of operations to the Southern States was a part of Lord George Germaine's new policy to wear out the rebellious colonies. The attack on their center had failed; he now purposed to crumble away the edges of revolt. The first operations were in Georgia, which offered a promising field, being next the British colony of Florida. South Carolina bore almost equal opportunity of British success, having a liberal sprinkling of loyal inhabitants. The patriots, moreover, planters for the most part, were withheld from resistance to invasion by fear of their slaves. The blacks were of ugly temper toward their masters, and heavily outnumbered them.

General Robert Howe, the distinguished patriot of North Carolina, was the American general in command of the southern department. Against him was the British general Prevost, commanding in Georgia. In the autumn of 1778 Howe moved

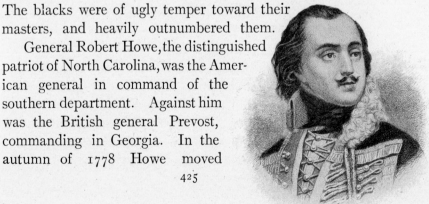

COUNT CASIMIR PULASKI (*From the etching by H. B. Hall*)

against Saint Augustine, hoping to put a stop to the numerous marauding expeditions sent out by Prevost. He got no farther than Saint Mary's River, however, because of a fever that decimated his troops. Returning to Savannah, he found that Colonel Campbell had arrived from New York with 3500 regulars. Although his own force numbered barely 1200, of whom half were militia, he gave battle. He was completely routed, losing 500 prisoners. The British immediately overran the State.

In December, 1778, General Benjamin Lincoln, who had done so well with the militia in the campaign against Burgoyne, superseded Howe in the South. The militia of South Carolina did not mobilize, fearing the slaves would mutiny if they were to relinquish the constant watch they kept over the blacks. But General Samuel Ashe came from North Carolina with 2000 men. These, with 700 Continentals, comprised Lincoln's force.

Presently an attempt was made by the British to wrest Port Royal from General Moultrie. It failing, Lincoln felt able to assume the offensive, and sent Ashe with 1200 men against Augusta. The British retreated, but turned on Ashe when he pursued, and administered a crushing defeat at Briar Creek, March 3, 1779. The Americans lost 400 in killed and wounded; less than 300 succeeded in making their way back to Lincoln. As a consequence of the disaster, the British set up the King's rule in Georgia, with Sir James Wright as governor.

Lincoln, thinking to erase the effect of his defeat, marched against Augusta. As soon as he left Savannah, Prevost started for Charleston, sacking and plundering as he went in a fashion that must have been highly satisfactory to Lord George Germaine. He drove Moultrie's insufficient force ahead of him, and threatened Charleston, which was saved by the arrival of Pulaski from the North, and the return of Lincoln, who was obliged to abandon his Georgia campaign.

In the August of 1779, D'Estaing arrived off the coast of Georgia with a French fleet, and a siege of Savannah was at once begun. For a fortnight it continued, when, the time of D'Estaing being limited, an assault was made on the British works. It was desperate and deadly, but futile. Pulaski was killed, and D'Estaing received two wounds. The Americans lost 1000 men.

COLONEL BANASTRE TARLETON

On the day after Christmas, Clinton and Cornwallis left New York for Georgia with 10,000 men, bringing the British forces there to 13,000. With them was Colonel Banastre Tarleton, a cavalry commander destined to achieve much notoriety in those parts. The force proceeded against Charleston, where Lincoln gathered all his resources and offered resistance. Tarleton broke his line of communications, and the place was besieged. In May, 1780, Lincoln, with his 3000, surrendered. Shortly after, Tarleton destroyed a force coming to the rescue under Buford, and there was not an organized army left in the South to oppose the British. Thereupon Clinton departed for New York, leaving Cornwallis with 5000 men to complete the work, already so far advanced, of subjugating the Southern States. South Carolina was immediately overrun.

Disorders broke out in South Carolina. Before he

left, Clinton issued an injudicious proclamation which forced
the inhabitants to take stand with one belligerent or the
other, by declaring all those to be rebels who did not help
in putting down the rebellion. Many who would gladly
have remained neutral were compelled by this to take up
arms. Clinton had overreached himself. The petty strug-
gles between the partisans extended through the country-
side; neighbor was arrayed against neighbor; there was
interminable bloodshed and outlawry.

Meanwhile, though there was no organized resistance,
South Carolina did not supinely submit to the invaders.
Leaders arose who, with bands of daring followers, struck
through the country, cutting down British outposts, inter-
cepting detachments, and keeping the foe in constant anxiety.
Foremost among them was Francis Marion, a man of few
words and of modest demeanor, delicately organized, of
untiring energy and quick intelligence, a knight in courtesy,
honor, and courage. He and his tiny troop, numbering vari-
ously from sixteen to seventy men, was a constant scourge
to the British, accomplishing feats of unparalleled daring.

Hardly second to him was Thomas Sumter, stern and
haughty, who operated in the upland country. His blows
were quick and startling; July 12 he destroyed a company of dragoons; August 6 he captured the post at Hanging
Rock, annihilating a whole regiment.
One of his followers in this battle was the
youthful Andrew Jackson, an
orphan boy of thirteen, as
staunch in the fight as any of his
comrades.

Andrew Pickens and James
Williams were two others who,
made life uncertain for the foe.

GENERAL FRANCIS MARION. (*From an engraving
by H. B. Hall*)

On June 20 Baron de Kalb, sent from Washington with 2000 Maryland and Delaware troops, arrived at Hillsborough. Gates, appointed to command in the South, arrived at Hillsborough on July 19, and prepared for a campaign against Camden, a town that commanded the highways into South Carolina. Obtaining this point, he could dislodge the British from all their inland possessions, and force them back on Charleston.

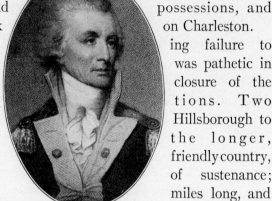

GENERAL THOMAS SUMTER (*After the portrait by C. W. Peale*)

His blundering failure to accomplish this was pathetic in its merciless disclosure of the man's limitations. Two roads led from Hillsborough to Camden: one, the longer, through a friendly country, fertile, and full of sustenance; the other, 160 miles long, and fifty miles shorter than the first, across a desolation of pine barrens, where the few plantations were owned by Tories. Considering only the necessity of haste, he took the shorter. The longer would have sustained him better on the march and offered a better line of retreat in case of disaster.

August 10, after a hard march of two weeks, his army reached Little Lynch's Creek, fifteen miles north of Camden, where his way was opposed by Lord Rawdon, with a greatly inferior force. He might now either strike the blow he had sacrificed so much to strike hastily, or pass to the other road, here near convergence with the one he was on, and reach Camden by Rawdon's rear. He did neither, but loitered for three days, unable to make up his mind. By the time he had decided to make the flank movement, and march to Clermont with that purpose, Cornwallis, unknown to Gates, had come up to Camden from Charleston, and the opportunity for which he had made such haste was gone.

His army now numbered 3052 men, having been reinforced at various points on the march, but they were mostly raw militia, and hardly more than a match for the 2000 trained regulars under Cornwallis. For a day and a night he loitered. Then, still unaware that Cornwallis had come up, but believing that he had only Rawdon to deal with, he sent 400 of his best men on a long march southward to coöperate with Sumter in an attempt to cut off the British communications between Charleston and Camden.

At 10 o'clock on the night of August 15 he started through the ten miles of woods between him and Camden, thinking to surprise Lord Rawdon. At 3 in the morning his advance fell in with a British column; Cornwallis had come out with the same purpose of a surprise. So much was learned from prisoners brought in. There was a skirmish, in which the Americans were worsted, and the two armies sat down to wait until morning.

The country in which they found themselves in the morning was rough and wild; huge swamps on either hand flanked them. Gates opened the battle by an attack on the British right, commanded by Colonel James Webster. The attack was made by militia, most of whom had never been under fire, and all of whom knew nothing of the bayonet. They did not even know how to advance properly. The result was immediate. Webster charged; in fifteen minutes the American left was a howling rabble.

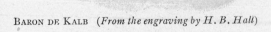

Meanwhile, the American right, the Second Maryland brigade, under De Kalb, twice repelled attacks by Rawdon, and at last pierced the British left, holding

THE BATTLE OF CAMDEN: DEATH OF DE KALB (*From the painting by Chappell*)

that part of the field. But Webster, leaving the fugitives for Tarleton to deal with, came behind them, driving the First Maryland off the field, and completed the defeat. De Kalb, indeed, fought through it all, directing his troops how to extricate themselves, until he fell dead, wounded eleven times. Gates had left the field early in the action, swept away by the fugitives; swept so vehemently that the impetus carried him to Hillsborough, 200 miles away, in four days.

The defeat was overwhelming in its consequences. South Carolina was left practically defenseless again, and nearly hopeless. Partisan warfare, indeed, still showed life; on the day before the battle Sumter captured the British supply train, with all its stores and 100 prisoners; Colonel James Williams, on August 18, at Musgrove's Mills in the western part of the State, defeated a force of 500 British and Tories, with heavy loss, and two days later Marion fell upon a detachment of the British army near the Santee, captured twenty-six of their number and liberated 150 Maryland troops, held as prisoners. But these successes seemed trivial in comparison with the greater event, and that of Sumter was neutralized on August 18 by Tarleton, who surprised him at Fishing Creek and took 300 prisoners.

The period following Camden was the darkest in the war. The detritus of the army in the South, for the second time in three months swept out of existence, gathered faintly about Gates at Hillsborough, barely 1000 strong; Washington could spare no reinforcements; the southern territory was drained of fighters. Civil matters throughout the country were in worse shape than they had been at any time. The Continental Congress was fallen into such disrepute as to be a source more of weakness than of strength; the thirteen States had not yet come together under the Articles of Confederation that had been before their consideration for three years. Their relations were not defined; there was no central power to exercise authority; such resources as the exhausted country still had could not be drawn upon and marshaled for use. There was no money of value. Congress continued to print currency and circulate it, but it fell so low in credit that it took four months' pay of a soldier to purchase a single bushel of wheat; Washington himself said that a wagon-load of currency could scarcely buy a wagon-load of supplies. The term, "not

QUEEN MARIE ANTOINETTE OF FRANCE
(*After the portrait by Madame Wren*)

worth a continental," coined to fit the times, had a bitter
meaning. Congress, in its requisitions on the several States,
no longer asked for money, but for specific supplies, — beef
and pork, flour and rice, salt and hay, tobacco and rum.
The army could scarcely be fed and clothed; Washington
was obliged to levy on the country
round about his army, paying
for supplies so taken in due-
bills receivable for taxes.
The army was on the
border of disintegration;
the desertions to the
British lines averaged
a hundred a month.
There was more than
one meeting of the
men. The French al-
liance, for which the
patriots had sacrificed
much in conscience, had
accomplished, so they felt,
nothing to reward them. Hope
was nearly dead.

Washington, writing to President Huntington in August, be-

LOUIS XVI OF FRANCE

fore news of Camden, said, concerning the morale of the
army: "The shadow of an army that will remain will
have every motive except mere patriotism to abandon the
service, without the hope which has hitherto supported
them of a change for the better. This is almost extinguished
now, and certainly will not outlive the campaign unless it
finds something more substantial to rest upon. To me it
will seem miraculous if our affairs can maintain themselves
much longer in their present train. If either the temper

or the resources of the country will not admit of an alteration, we may expect soon to be reduced to the humiliating condition of seeing the cause of America in America upheld by foreign arms."

But if hope was to be placed in the French alliance, nothing had been accomplished in that direction to give promise of reviving it. True, the embroiled state of affairs in European politics, to which the action of France had been a prelude, had so far taxed the resources of England that she could not give her whole attention to subduing her rebellious colonies in America; but France had done next to nothing, up to the present time, in actual operations in the United States.

In this tide, Lafayette went to France and obtained an audience with King Louis. "The money that you spend in one of your court balls would go far toward sending a serviceable army to America, and dealing England a blow where she would most feel it," he told his Majesty. The King received him graciously at court, and Queen Marie Antoinette begged him for "good news of our dearly beloved Americans." For several months the young enthusiast urged Vergennes to send 13,000 men under a good general; D'Estaing, returning to Paris after the defeat at Savannah, added similar advice.

In the end, Lafayette had his way. On July 10 Admiral Ternay arrived at Newport with seven ships-of-the-line and three frigates, conveying a force of 6000 soldiers under Count Rochambeau. Hope revived at that, and at the promise of more to follow. But the others promised never came, being blockaded and turned back by a British fleet at Brest.

Clinton, learning of the arrival of the French, started down the sound with 6000 men to attack them, but was held back by Washington, who moved suddenly toward

New York. Nevertheless, the French fleet was blockaded in Narragansett Bay by the British, and Rochambeau could do nothing more with his army than remain in Rhode Island to help the admiral. On the top of all this had come Arnold's treason, throwing the country into consternation and dismay.

But the fighting spirit was not dead in the South. Shortly after the depression of the country had reached its depths, there came out of North Carolina news of a victory that sent a quiver of joy throughout the entire country, and turned the people back to their task.

When, following the victory at Camden, Cornwallis began an invasion of North Carolina, he despatched Major Ferguson into the hill country to raise a body of Tory troops, with whom he was to join the main army

MECKLENBURG MONUMENT, CHARLOTTE, MECKLENBURG COUNTY, NORTH CAROLINA

at Charlotte. Ferguson took with him 200 British light infantry and 1000 Tories, and proceeded with them as far as Gilbert Town, in the present county of Rutherford.

But they were not all Tories in the country into which he had penetrated. Instead of the hospitable reception he had looked forward to, Cornwallis found himself in that famous Mecklenburg County which, just after the battle of Lexington, had launched its bold revolutionary declaration. Out of the mountains came a horde of defenders; staunch

KING'S MOUNTAIN MONUMENT

backwoodsmen, dressed in fringed leather hunting-shirts, armed with vicious knives, and with long rifles that could pick squirrels out of treetops. "These rebels," the British commander avowed, "are the most obstinate I have found in America," and he called their country a "hornet's nest." From the south came James Williams of Ninety-Six, with 400 like him; from the north, William Campbell of Virginia, Benjamin Cleveland, and Charles McDowell of North Carolina, with 560; from the west, Isaac Shelby and John Sevier, destined to win fame in the history of Tennessee. By September 30 there were 3000 of these "dirty mongrels," as Ferguson playfully called them, ready to set fangs in him; grim, determined, deadly.

Mongrels though they were, Ferguson became alarmed, and turned back. The Americans followed closely, snarling about his heels, shooting down his couriers that hastened toward Cornwallis with his cry of alarm. Ferguson was desperate. On October 6 he took refuge on King's Mountain, a natural stronghold. Three sides of it were steep slopes; the fourth a precipice, not to be scaled. The slopes were covered with huge bowlders, the crest with trees. "Well, boys, here is a place from which all the rebels outside of hell cannot drive us!'' cried Ferguson to his men.

But the Americans could climb hills and shoot as they climbed. Up the three sides they crept next day; Campbell and Shelby in the center, Sevier and McDowell on the right slope, Cleveland and Williams on the left. From bowlder to bowlder, from tree to tree, they dodged. Ferguson charged the center, the first to come within striking distance. It gave way, softly, skilfully; he rushed into the trap. From the right came a deadly enfilade from the long rifles. Thither he turned; into his rear came death from the left; on his flank the center returned destruction. The end was soon. Ferguson himself was slain. Three hundred and eighty-nine were killed or wounded, and 716 surrendered. The total American loss was twenty-eight killed and sixty wounded; but among the dead was the gallant Williams.

It was like Bennington. Gladness ran over the land. Cornwallis, alarmed, retreated to Winnsborough, and ordered General Leslie, whom Clinton had sent into Virginia, to join him. The country stirred itself again. Sumter and Marion swung like hawks through the land; Sumter in the northwestern part of South Car-

BATTLE MONUMENT ON THE FIELD AT COWPENS,
SOUTH CAROLINA

olina, Marion in the northeastern. On November 20 Sumter avenged himself on Tarleton, a worthy foeman, defeating him at Blackstock Hill; Marion dealt many a blow.

But who was that man of towering frame, shaggy, taciturn, careworn, with the look of grief, who rode with

BATTLE OF KING'S MOUNTAIN (*From the painting by Chappell*)

Marion now? They knew not who he was, nor asked, and he spoke no word of it. They only knew that he had come in a night, late in October, begging a horse and a sword, and that he was terrible in battle, like one longing to die. For them that was enough.

Came Morgan, in September, to the wreck of Gates's army, at Hillsborough. Morgan, the mighty, who had left war when he could endure the insults of Congress no longer, but who, after Camden, set aside all personal feeling in the great need of the hour. Congress, frightened, forgot its bickerings and gave him the rank he deserved; from which action Congress received greater reward than its intentions deserved. Came others, many of them, to join

Gates, so that, when Cornwallis had withdrawn in alarm, they were 1400 strong, — strong enough to move forward to Charlotte.

Hope was alive once more, and to hope was added, presently, General Nathanael Greene, sent to save, and, what he did not know nor care, to reap gratitude and undying fame. Since the spring of 1778 he had been quartermaster-general, and, as such, ill-treated by Congress, so ill, that in July, 1780, he resigned. Him Washington had desired to take the army when Gates was appointed, but Congress would have none of him, his merit placing him beyond their comprehension. But now, through Washington, he was given command, and arrived at Charlotte December 2.

COLONEL WILLIAM WASHINGTON (*From the engraving by J. B. Forrest*)

With him Washington sent Steuben as far as Virginia, to watch the traitor Arnold, who had been sent there by Clinton to replace Leslie's force. And with him Washington sent Kosciusko, and Henry Lee, "Light Horse Harry." At the same time there appeared another cavalry leader, known to this day,— Colonel William Washington of Virginia, a distant kinsman of General Washington's.

Greene proved himself the man for the moment. One element of greatness he had; he perceived and utilized the abilities of others, without jealousy. His army was too

small to risk a battle with Cornwallis, but he did not lie
idle.   Knowing the value of partisan warfare in the circumstances, he divided his force into two partisan bodies.
He, with the larger, comprising 1100 men, went to Cheraw
Hill, on the Pedee, to coöperate with Marion.   He took
with him Light Horse Harry Lee.   The other body, 900
strong, under the mighty Morgan, he sent to the westward,
to threaten the British hold of the inland towns and coöperate with the mountain forces there.

Lee and Marion, under Greene's direction, struck like
lashes of a whip upon the flanks of the British army, stinging,
cutting deeply, threatening Cornwallis's communications
with the coast.   One night they rode, those two, with their
followers, into Georgetown, and captured the commander
of the post.   That night he who was unknown to his
comrades under Marion, did deeds of daring that held the
breath even of those bold and reckless men, used to mocking
death.   William Washington, with Morgan, was not behind
them in boldness or ability.   He made a raid through the
very lines of the enemy, destroying a force of 250 men at
a single magnificent blow.   Those were times to stir the
soul and quicken the heart!   ·

Cornwallis, angered, could not strike back, for his
flanks were beset, whichever way he turned.   At last he
hit upon a way.   He, likewise, divided his force, moving
with 2000 men into North Carolina, hoping to draw Greene
after him, or at least to hold him idle.   At the same time he
sent Tarleton with 1100 to punish Morgan.

Evil hour for Cornwallis!   Morgan, playing well the
game of war, retreated to the Cowpens, near King's Mountain, and took stand before an impassable river.   "It is
what I wish," he said, when they told him the position left
him no retreat.   "My militia will know there is no use
in running away."   Cunning warfare!

Battle Monument on the Field of Cowpens: Tradition Says that at the Spot now Marked by the Tree in the Foreground, Tarleton Leapt a Wagon in His Escape from Colonel Washington

Before him was a long slope; up this the over-confident Tarleton attacked, January 17, 1781. On the top of the hill were the Continentals, old warriors. In front were militia, under Pickens; behind, William Washington, with his cavalry. There they waited; there Tarleton advanced to destruction.

The militia were driven; Tarleton, following, extended his line, threatening to overlap Morgan, who refused his right, and fell back a space. Tarleton, believing it only a matter of time, pressed on, too hastily, in some confusion. Pickens, re-forming his militia, moved around and fell upon the rear of the British left, bent forward to meet the refused American right; the Continentals, dealing destruction at thirty yards, gave them the bayonet. At the same time Washington swept around the hill and descended upon Tarleton's right rear. Thereupon the greater part of the British surrendered, and the remainder fled, those who could. Only 270 escaped, among them Tarleton, who fought for his life, hand to hand, sword against sword, with Washington. The British lost 230 in killed and wounded, 600 prisoners, 1000 stands of arms; the Americans, twelve killed and sixty-one wounded. It was more than Bennington, more than King's Mountain; in point of tactics it was the most brilliant engagement of the Revolution. And it deprived the hard-pressed Cornwallis of one-third his force.

Now what did the mighty Morgan do? His only road to rejoin Greene crossed the Catawba by certain fords; Cornwallis was nearer those fords than he. What did he do but reach the fords first, and, crossing, march northward, with the chagrined Cornwallis hard at his heels. Greene, hearing of the Cowpens and Morgan's movements, conceived a bold plan. He would draw Cornwallis north and north, until the attenuated line of support from the coast left him weak, and then fall upon him.

With this in mind, he set his main army in motion northward, under General Huger, and himself rode 150 miles to take charge of Morgan's force, that there might be no failure to coöperate. He found Morgan, and began leading Cornwallis on the chase. There had been rains; the streams were swollen; but Greene's army was amphibious. It carried boats on wheels between rivers, which boats bore it and the wheels over the rivers as they came to them. Always they marched on a line converging with Huger; always Cornwallis, maddened and baffled, followed, destroying his heavy baggage, insistent upon bringing his foe to bay.

At Guilford Court-House, in North Carolina, thirty miles from the Virginia border, Greene joined Huger. He had thought to bring about the fight, as soon as that was effected, but was disappointed in not receiving reinforcements from Steuben, who was too much occupied with Arnold in Virginia to spare them. Wherefore he kept on, crossing the Dan, behind which he rested, secure, to await more troops. At that point Morgan, falling ill, was forced to return home.

Cornwallis, baffled, made the most of it, proclaiming that he had conquered North Carolina and inviting the Tories to come to his standard. Greene would not suffer that, and recrossed

the Dan. There ensued a game of hide and seek, until, on March 14, having been reinforced until he numbered 4404 men, Greene, always the one sought, stopped at Guilford Court-

BARRACKS OCCUPIED BY CORNWALLIS AT CHERAW, SOUTH CAROLINA

House and permitted Cornwallis to fight him. He need not
win a victory; he need only strike a blow to damage his
enemy; for Cornwallis was far from home, and exhausted
after the long chase.

He did not win in the battle that was fought the next
day. He formed his army in three lines; first, the Carolina

THE BATTLE OF COWPENS: THE ENCOUNTER BETWEEN COLONELS WASH-
INGTON AND TARLETON (*From the painting by Chappell*)

militia; second, troops of Virginia; third, the regulars of
Maryland and Virginia,—they who had stood their ground
at Camden, and on many a field. The first line was swept
away, as had been expected; the second crumbled, after hard
fighting, which was foreseen; the third, held; precariously,
but held. A brilliant charge by Washington turned the day
there, and made uneven battle for the English. For a
space the British were discomfited, but in the end, fighting
gloriously, they held, and by night Greene withdrew, with
a loss of 400 dead and wounded.

But he did not lose. Cornwallis held the field; it had

cost him 600 men, and there remained to him only 1600 fighters. He was in the midst of a hostile country, 200 miles from his base, with a force that was hopelessly outnumbered. He dared not return through South Carolina; that would invite destruction, piecemeal. He could not stay where he was; every hour there was full of danger. Three days after his equivocal victory, he withdrew from Guilford, leaving his wounded, and made haste to Wilmington, the nearest point where he could expect aid from the fleet.

Now he was no better off. To go by sea to Charleston would be conceding that he had been defeated and would make it necessary to begin all over again. But Virginia offered a hope. Clinton had just sent General Phillips thither to augment Arnold's force; the three of them together would be able, perhaps, to overrun Virginia, which, he was assured, was teeming with loyalists. To Virginia, accordingly, he went, arriving at Petersburg and effecting a junction with the forces there.

ON THE BATTLEFIELD OF GUILFORD COURT-HOUSE, NORTH CAROLINA

Now did Greene crown his superb generalship with a master-stroke. He did not follow Cornwallis into Virginia. As far as Ramsay's Mills he pursued, a little above the fork of the Cape Fear River. There he cast him aside, leaving him for others to handle, and marched boldly, swiftly, into

MEMORIAL ARCHES ON THE BATTLEFIELD OF GUILFORD COURT-HOUSE, NORTH CAROLINA

South Carolina. For, should Cornwallis follow, North Carolina would be relieved, at least; and should he not, there was more than a fair chance that the British, left under Lord Rawdon, could be driven out of South Carolina, at least as far as Charleston.

The British held all the strategic points in the interior of the State: Camden, and Ninety-Six; and Augusta, in Georgia. Toward Camden, 160 miles away, the most important of all, Greene turned his army. Lord Rawdon was there, with 900 men. Between Camden and Charleston stood Fort Watson, guarding the line of communications. Against this Greene sent Lee, to coöperate with Marion.

The fort was on a knoll; round about it was flat country.

The Americans had no cannon, and there was no vantage-ground at hand. Out of the ranks of Marion's men stepped one, huge in bulk, silent, careworn — out of the ranks, and up to Major Mayham, one of Marion's officers. To him he spoke briefly, in low voice, and buried himself straightway in the ranks. Mayham, in high spirits, turned to Marion.

BRITISH BREASTWORK NEAR CAMDEN, NORTH CAROLINA

"Make a hill!" he cried. It was done. Out of logs, hewn in the forest hard by, and builded into a great crib, they erected a tower, an eminence; behind a rampart of logs leveled the rifles of the Americans, and Fort Watson was lost. The silent man from the ranks held a rifle that grew hot with speaking over the top of the logs that day, ere the flag of truce was flung out.

It followed that Rawdon could no longer hold Camden, howbeit he had won a battle in its defense while this other affair was going forward. Greene, finding the enemy too strong when he arrived, took a position on Hobkirk's Hill, where Rawdon assailed him, April 25, 1781. There a strange thing happened. The 2d Maryland brigade, that had stood so bravely at Camden, that had overwhelmed Tarleton at the Cowpens, that had saved the day at Guilford, behaved badly, having mistaken orders, and deranged Greene's plan of battle. He was driven from the field, retiring to Clermont; but the victor was already vanquished by the wooden hill at Fort Watson, and retreated to Monk's Corners, thirty miles from Charleston.

THE BATTLE OF EUTAW SPRINGS *(From the painting by Chappell)*

Then there were victories. Lee and Marion took Fort Motte and Fort Granby; Sumter took Orangeburg; on June 5 Augusta surrendered to Lee, and Georgia was recovered. Nothing was left but Ninety-Six. Here Greene laid siege for twenty days, until Rawdon came up from Charleston to the rescue. But he could not stay to make a permanent defense, having stripped Charleston of troops to bring with him. He withdrew the garrison, and retired upon Orangeburg on June 29, and inland South Carolina was freed of the British.

Through the summer the two armies rested, the Americans on the High Hills of the Santee, the British at Orangeburg. Rawdon, sick and tired, returned to England, leaving Colonel Stuart in command. On

THE PULASKI MONUMENT, WASHINGTON
(By Kasimir Chodzimski)

August 22 Greene broke camp and moved against the enemy, before Stuart was aware of his movements.

Stuart fell back upon Eutaw Springs. There followed a battle, on September 18, which, like all those Greene had fought in his marvelous campaigns in the South, was not a victory, but which again, like all the others, had the effect of victory, because of the rare strategy that preceded and led up to it. Stuart held the field, although once half driven from it; but after the fight he retreated without rest to Charleston, fifty miles away, starting the evening next after his victory. And though he had won the day, he was pursued for thirty miles by Marion and Lee.

From that time forth there was little fighting in the far South. The State government was restored, and the British cooped up in Charleston until the end of the war. Greene, in thirteen months, had taken a disorganized and discouraged army and recovered a territory overrun by a superior force, without winning one battle in the process, —a feat of strategy and intelligence that places him high among the world's great generals. What he might have done with better tools in a larger task it is interesting to conjecture.

What of the unknown fighter among Marion's men? He of the broad shoulders and downcast eye, taciturn and sad? From the moment when Marion turned in his pursuit of Rawdon, after Eutaw, and rode back to Greene, he was seen no more.

PRESIDENT TAFT AT THE DEDICATION OF
THE PULASKI MONUMENT

CHAPTER XXVI

IN THE REDOUBT

WHEN Cornwallis, turning into Virginia after the battle of Guilford Court-House, reached Petersburg May 20, 1781, and made conjunction with the other forces then in that State, his army was brought to 5000 men. Arnold, after some useless plundering and burning, had been recalled to New York, and Phillips had died of a fever, leaving Cornwallis in complete command. Lucas Hempstead's regiment remaining in the State, Nancy sojourned at Yorktown to be close as possible to him, though much against his will. With her stayed Sophronia and Francis.

The American forces in Virginia, numbering 3000 men, of which two-thirds were raw militia, were under the youthful Lafayette, whom Washington had sent down to watch Arnold. Cornwallis, looking forward with high hopes to subduing Virginia, and bringing large numbers of Tories under his standard as a preliminary, set out to capture "the boy" who was pitted against him.

But Lafayette was too shrewd to be forced into a fight. He marched from Richmond, where he had been posted, to the Rapidan, west of Fredericksburg, Cornwallis after him. Being reinforced there by 1000 Pennsylvania regulars under Wayne, he turned back, in

451

THE LAFAYETTE STATUE AT WASHINGTON
(*By Falguière and Mercié*)

time to interrupt a raid that Tarleton was making to Charlottesburg, to break up the legislature and arrest Thomas Jefferson, governor of the State. Jefferson, notified in time, got away from Monticello twenty mintues before Tarleton arrived. Tarleton, frustrated in that, would have seized the stores at Albemarle had not Lafayette intervened, with his increased force. Thereupon Tarleton joined Cornwallis, then at Richmond, and the British withdrew to Williamsburg.

Lafayette, further strengthened by 1000 regulars under Steuben, pressed closely after them. On July 6 an action was fought between parts of the two armies at Green Springs, near Williamsburg, in which the Americans were repulsed with a loss of 145 men. The campaign ended the first week in August, when Cornwallis occupied Yorktown, where his army was increased to 7000 by the addition of the Portsmouth garrison. Lafayette, with 5000 men, took position at Malvern Hill to await developments.

The developments were many and marvelous. Washington and Rochambeau, about New York, were already contemplating a joint movement against the city, awaiting only the arrival of a sufficient French fleet. Such a one was on the way,—twenty-eight ships-of-the-line and six frigates, carrying 1700 guns and 20,000 men, under De Grasse. On August 14 word came from the French admiral that he was starting for the Chesapeake; at the same time Washington heard from Lafayette that he was watching Cornwallis in Yorktown, where he had deep water on three sides of him.

THE ROCHAMBEAU STATUE AT WASHINGTON
(By F. Hamar)

Here were the elements of a grand drama. If Cornwallis could be blocked there by an American force, and De Grasse should coöperate by sea, he would be caught in a trap; for the naval strength of the British was no more than nineteen ships-of-the-line, carrying 1400 guns and 13,000 men. But whence should the army come that was to close the trap?

The thought was supreme, sublime; the army should be Washington's own army and that of Rochambeau!

On August 19 Washington's army crossed the Hudson at King's Ferry and moved toward New Jersey; in it were 2000 Continentals and 4000 French troops; the only time when the two land forces marched together. Lord Stirling, with a small force, remained at Saratoga; Heath lay at West Point with 4000; enough to hold Sir Henry if he attempted to move up the river from New York.

THE COUNT DE GRASSE (*From the drawing by Miller for the European Magazine*)

Swiftly they marched, no one knew whither, save only Washington and Rochambeau. Clinton, hearing of it, began to prepare a defense, and continued to prepare until he learned that instead of turning toward New York, in New Jersey, they had gone to the west and southward.

The American officers were puzzled; men in the ranks wondered much, finding many theories to explain the movement, as men in the ranks will. It was not until the patriot army was close to Philadelphia, with Clinton still marveling whither they went, that the purpose and destination of the march were understood, for the plan could no longer be concealed.

Then was there a madness of joy and excitement. News had come of Greene's masterly triumphs in the South; now Washington, the great, the beloved, was going to bag Cornwallis, and end the war! The fox was after the hound! Ladies leaned from windows as the ragged Continentals marched through the rebel capital; they blew kisses to the gay French troops. Strong men wept; old men shouted; boys stood still and trembling, dreaming of glory.

"De Grasse is in the Bay! He has reached the Chesapeake!" Washington, riding eagerly forward to Chester, received and sent back the news.

"Long live Washington! He has gone to catch Cornwallis in his mouse-trap!" the people shouted in the streets. Hope sprang abroad through the land. Liberty raised her head, and smiled.

It was August 30 when De Grasse reached the Chesapeake, sailing from the West Indies, where he had been fighting France's battles against England. The fleet of the great Admiral Rodney had followed fast; but Rodney was not aboard the flag-ship, having returned to England, ill, and Sir Samuel Hood commanded. Hood had outsailed the Frenchmen, called in at the Chesapeake, found nothing, and gone on to New York. Admiral Graves, commanding there, hastened back, but found the French fleet blockading the bay. There was a naval fight on September 5, Graves withdrawing at last, and leaving the enemy masters of the water there.

On that same day, September 5, the army began embarking at the head of Chesapeake Bay. September 18 they began arriving in detachments; until then Cornwallis had known nothing of what was preparing for him. He had need to know much earlier than that, for on September 7

Monticello, the Home of Thomas Jefferson

Lafayette, reinforced by 3000 French soldiers under Saint-Simon, set ashore from the fleet, had come down to Williamsburg, and the trap was set.

September 26! Sixteen thousand soldiers in front of Cornwallis! Behind him, the ocean, over which ranged the French, for all of Brittania's mastery of the sea!

It was not until September 2 that Clinton, still wondering what Washington was about, learning that the American army had crossed the Delaware, and learning from Hood that the French fleet was somewhere south of them, divined the nature of the operation, the very daring and magnitude of which rendered it secure from detection earlier.

He was at his wit's end; all he could contrive to do, by way of a counter-stroke, was to send Arnold into Connecticut with 2000 men, to harry and destroy,— a futile and brutal retort. Arnold captured Fort Griswold, guarding New London, massacring the garrison of 157 militia-men, old neighbors of his, and burned the town. That was the last of him in American history. As a diversion from the Yorktown situation, it was useless, for by the time word of it reached Virginia the combination against Cornwallis had been completed.

Yorktown was invested without delay; October 6 the first parallel of the American lines was opened by General Lincoln, who had surrendered Charleston to Cornwallis; October 11, the second parallel was opened by Steuben, within 3000 yards of the British works. On the right were the Americans; on the left the French. Their guns battered down the works of the beleaguered, dismounting cannon, silencing them. The night was streaked with the trail of bombs; the earth muttered with the constant roar of firing. Fiercely, incessantly, the besiegers battered at the gates of the city; doggedly the English answered as they could. And so the fight went on, in the springing of the trap.

It was 8 in the evening of October 14. Masses of men
were gathered behind the second parallel; two bodies of men,
one in ragged regimentals, the other in the bright uniforms
of France. Ahead of them, 300 yards away, looming black
into the grey night, were two redoubts that must be carried,
for they enfiladed the parallels, hindering the work of the
soldiers who built them. The eyes of the officers turned
from the redoubts before them to one place behind. From
that place presently rockets shot into the air; the masses of
men moved.

Colonel Alexander Hamilton led the American storming
party. Close behind him, with bent shoulders lifted above
his fellows, his steel-blue eyes flashing in the grey of the night,
stalked one whom no one knew. He had come to the army
lately out of the South; a man of silence, with a careworn
look, and a burden of grief upon him.

They did not stop for the abattis that crossed their path,
the Americans. They brushed it aside. That man of
silence among them twisted great split branches from the
felled tree, trampling them underfoot. Up to the parapet,
without firing a gun; for it was to be the work of bayonets!
Over it, Hamilton first of all, stepping on the shoulder of
a man who knelt to lift him, not heeding who the man was.
After him, the man himself: the man of silence, whom none
knew, save that he had come among them from the South
to join the fight, and was mighty in valor.

British soldiers, brave, gave way slowly; officers among
them encouraged them, fighting with sword and pistol.
One, a young man, slender, graceful, raised his weapon to
fire at the unknown, the careworn man of silence. Raising
it, a bayonet thrust him through, and he fell coughing,
turning his face to the skies.

As he fell, the one who had struck him down gave a
cry, and knelt beside him; surprise and dismay, remorse,

were in his tones; it
was the man of si-
lence, whom none
knew.

"Merciful God,
have I slain you?"
he said, beneath his
breath.

The eyes of the
wounded man lifted;
they were the eyes of
Lucas Hempstead.
Into them came a
half-look of recog-
nition, of bewilder-
ment.

"Ha, man?" he
breathed. "Who is
it speaks?"

"I would not

THE MARQUIS DE LAFAYETTE (*From the portrait
by Ary Scheffer in the Capitol at Washington*)

have slain you," said the other, compassionately. "Are
you hard hit?"

"Ay, mortally." He said it calmly, indifferently, being
close to death. "Hold a minute," he went on, speaking
faintly. "I am dizzy. Let me recall. Who are you?"

"You know me well," returned he who had struck him
down. "I am John Stevens." John Stevens, into whom
love of Nancy had surged back, making him forget and forgive, in this deadly moment when he had slain her brother.

"Ah, yes, I know you well," observed the dying man,
with no surprise; for death obliterates all lesser marvels.
"So it is you."

"I am sorry I have hurt you."

"Pish, 't is all in war. But why, pray?" thinking it

GENERAL MORGAN'S HOUSE AT WINCHESTER, VIRGINIA

strange to have such compassion from one both a personal enemy and a foeman.

John could not answer.

"Ah, now I have it," Lucas went on, after a pause. "My sister. My dear sister. Nancy,—Nancy."

Silence fell between them, and silence lay about them, for the fight was over, and the redoubt taken.

"Can I make you easier?" from the American.

"Let me rest my head upon your knee, then; there, — so. That is better. I would meet death looking about me." A bit of his old whimsy came back into Lucas's voice. "So it is you. Let me see. It has been many years. It is all confused. There is something I would have learned from you. I cannot think. Nay, I have it. We had an appointment to meet — great God, what a strange ending to it all — and you did not come, yet you are no coward, as I well learned. That I would know of you — that riddle."

He was in the last accumulation of strength, before the end.

John, pressing his hand upon the wound to staunch the blood, which, creeping now through his uniform, disclosed where the hurt was, spoke as though his thoughts were of other matters. "I was concerned with the Sons of Liberty, and word came of important matters demanding me in Boston, so that I had to leave at once," he said.

"You told no one that," suggested Lucas, feebly. "It put you under the imputation of being cowardly."

"It was a matter demanding secrecy; I could better afford being thought a coward than to tell my excuse." He said it simply, without bombast.

For a time Lucas looked at him; through the gloom of the falling night they could barely discern each other's countenances. "If I had known that that was the manner of men we had to contend against, belike I should have gone home to England ere ever we met again," he said, half to himself.

Another pause; cries of victory from the other redoubt told that it, too, was taken, by the French, who had been slower, being more formal in the manner of assaulting redoubts.

"Is there nothing I can do?" asked John, presently, struggling for his speech. His pity was for Nancy.

The eyes of the wounded man were shut. He opened them again suddenly, as though recalled by the other's voice. For a while he stared, collecting his thoughts. "Ay, that there is," he replied. "Seek out my sister. She is in yonder town, where you are likely soon to come. Seek her out. You may easily find her. Tell her I died gently, thinking of her, and repenting my sins. Do not tell her by whose hand," — his voice, fallen to a whisper, was wavering; the one kneeling above could scarcely hear what he said — "for that would be more than she could bear, poor girl. Promise me only that, John Stevens."

GENERAL MORGAN'S GRAVE AT WINCHESTER, VIRGINIA

With a sudden mad joy upspringing through his sorrow for what he had done in the fortunes of war, John bent closer.

"Why should I promise you that?" he asked, with trembling lip.

"Because," faintly, like a sigh, came the whispered voice of the dying man, "the — poor — girl — "

The answer passed into silence; Lieutenant Lucifer had passed to a better understanding of things.

La Fouche, the Old Everettsville Tavern: Here Tarleton's Breakfast was Delayed to Give Jefferson Time to Escape His Raid

CHAPTER XXVII

A MAGNANIMOUS MAID

IT was afternoon of October 19, 1781, and the thing was
done. That day, at 2 o'clock, the British soldiers and
sailors had marched forth, with colors furled and cased,
between the lines of the allied armies, to surrender. That
day, at 2, General O'Hara, acting for Cornwallis, who
remained behind indisposed, gave his sword to General
Lincoln in token of surrender; and the thing was done.
Another British army had been obliterated; American arms
and American strategy were triumphant once more, and
hope ran high throughout the land!

It had come swiftly after the taking of the redoubts by
the French and American troops on the night of October 14.
Cornwallis, even then, had not succumbed to the inevitable,
although his works could not show a gun against the American parallels. Two days later, in the morning, a small
party made a
sortie against
the batteries
being in-
stalled on the
second paral-
lel to spike
guns there,
which was
only partially
successful.
That same
night Corn-

Looking over the Breastworks at Yorktown, Showing the Redoubt Stormed by Lafayette

463

wallis endeavored to extricate his army by crossing to Gloucester Point, across the York River, whence he thought to break his way through and flee to Clinton. But a storm driving his transports after one division was across, he was obliged to abandon the attempt, bringing back the next morning those who had gone over.

On the same morning, at 10 o'clock, Cornwallis sent out a white flag, asking for parley. It was hopeless; he did not wish to submit his troops, that had stood by him so valiantly, to the horrors of an assault which could not fail to be successful. Clinton, who was expected to sail from New York about October 5, had not been heard from. Indeed, Cornwallis, after losing the two redoubts, had written him advising against his taking the risk of coming into the trap.

There were parleys and the interchange of proposals, brought to a close on October 19, when terms of surrender, drawn up by the Viscount de Noailles and Lieutenant-Colonel Laurens for the allied armies, and Colonel Dundas and Major Ross for the British, were agreed upon. At 2 o'clock the surrender took place, under the same terms that had been accorded Lincoln at Charleston. One concession, however, was made to the English; Cornwallis was permitted to send a vessel to Clinton with the news of the surrender, and with such troops as he saw fit to embark on it, it being promised that there should be no questions asked — this, as a means of getting rid of the troublesome problem of dealing with certain Tories in the town.

Now that it was over, Nancy Hempstead awaited word of her brother Lucas. Fearful, hopeless, she waited, walking the floor of the room in her kinswoman's house. All through the terrible siege she had been there, refusing to heed her brother's demands that she leave; giving only civil answer to the suggestions of English officers that she be sent into the American lines under privilege which they made no doubt could be obtained. She would not go, but waited to be near Lucas,— all she had left to her now. And she had not heard from him since that awful night when fugitives came running from the redoubt where he had been, and he was not among them.

With her in the town were Sophronia and Isaac Francis. Francis had not taken advantage of the one vessel which it was premitted Cornwallis to send to New York, for there was in him an audacity very like courage; and, now that Lucas did not return, he believed the time was not far distant when Nancy would capitulate to him. If only the detestable Yankee from Boston did not appear inadvertently meanwhile!

But now Nancy was alone, the others having gone forth since the Americans had entered the city, on their own affairs. What those affairs were was not revealed to Nancy in the excuses they made to her for leaving. Neither did she greatly concern herself about them, for it was only news of her brother that she took interest in.

Pacing the floor with quick breath, in her anxiety, she heard the sound of two men approaching

THE MOORE HOUSE AT YORKTOWN, VIRGINIA: HERE THE TERMS OF SUR-
RENDER WERE DICTATED

through the hall without the room where she was, and her
heart leapt, thinking it might be Lucas coming under
liberty of the parole granted the surrendered British officers.
A moment more, and the door opened. Isaac Francis
entered the room, followed by John Stevens.

"Belike this fellow will tell you somewhat of your brother,
having recently seen him," said Francis, turning abruptly,
almost hastily, and leaving them alone in the room, as
though he had other and urgent business; taking care,
moreover, to close the door after him. Confused as she
was at the sight of John, and the ominous introduction,
Nancy did not fail to mark the strangeness of Francis's
action and to marvel at it. It was not long before she understood better what it signified.

In the first moment of being thus alone, the two looked
silently at each other. Through his mind there flashed
those other scenes when they had been together; the night
before Lexington, in his mother's cottage; that other night,
in the same cottage, when he had kissed her brow; that
day in the New York den, when Sophronia had taken him

REDOUBTS AT YORKTOWN

away in a coach. There came to him, too, keenly, cutting him like a knife, memory of that other time when Sophronia had rescued him from a danger into which this woman's zeal had brought him, as he believed; that time when, knowing he lay wounded in the house, she had not come to him, but had betrayed him. Upon it all there tumbled memory of her brother's broken words.

But the hope, fantastical, fatal, he had built on their limited meaning left him now, and only the thought of his errand with her enabled him to face her. That same thought sent him dumb; for how should he tell the woman he had loved that he had slain her brother? He was brought to the necessity presently, when she broke the tense silence.

"You have news of him, then?" asked Nancy, steadying her gaze to meet his, which he held upon her through sheer strength of will.

John could not answer yet, though he tried to voice words. She saw his struggle to speak, and put the dreaded meaning in it. "He is dead?" she whispered.

"God forgive me, I myself have slain him."

The woman staggered, clutching at a table edge for support. "You! You!" she repeated. "You have killed him?"

"I did not know," said John, in a voice that was half a moan. "I did not know. I struck down one who would have slain me; it was night. I could not see. Had I known, I would have —" He did not finish. What right had he to say it?

She bent eagerly forward. "You would have —?" she murmured.

"I would rather it had been I who perished," he answered, suddenly afire from the look he saw in her face.

She put her hands before her eyes. "No, no!" she

sobbed. "It is horrible. 'T was in fair fight?" she asked, with a new horror, taking her hands aways to look as him. "In battle, I mean?"

"Ay, at the redoubt."

"God has dealt heavily with me," she said, looking away.

"And with me," answered the man.

"Nay, say not so; for you were not to blame for what war brought forth. Merciful Heaven, when will this war cease?"

Her perturbation, something in her tone, brought a mad hope into the breast of the man. "You can forgive me, then?" he asked.

"I have nothing to forgive, but fate," she answered. "If only it might have been that you had not struck so hard!" Her gaze met his again, emboldening him.

"Or that it had been I who fell." He blushed for the advantage he took of her grief; but a rash hope drove him on.

"No, no, no; I would not have had it so!" she cried, reaching forth her hands, all a-tremble. "'T is a wicked thing, and may Heaven forgive me, but if it had to be one of you, — I am glad that it was not you." The storm of her emotion swept her away; she raised tear-dimmed eyes to his; she held forth her arms. With a cry that was half a sob of relief, he moved toward her. But before he reached her the sound of some one entering gave him pause. He turned, and beheld Sophronia Osborne on the threshold.

The eyes of the woman, fixed on his face, read there the truth. She smiled, coldly, calmly, shrugged her shoulders, laughed. "Well, then," she said, "let it be so. I have fought a good fight for rich stakes. Having lost — let it be so."

Before there was further word among them the door opened once more, and Francis reëntered, followed by Colonel Hamilton of the American army. "Here, then, is the arch-traitor," he said, with a leer, pointing out John to his companion. This, then, was why he had brought John there, and left so hastily; a final piece of artistic cruelty to her and him.

For one brief, teeming moment Hamilton looked at John, grief and abhorrence in his eyes. "It is my painful duty, Major Stevens," he said, stiffly, "to inform you that you are to consider yourself under arrest as a traitor to your country."

Nancy was the first to break the following silence. "'T is false! 'T is false!" she cried, advancing till she confronted Hamilton. "There is none braver! There is some ugly error here!"

To her the American officer returned a low bow. "That is a matter that Major Stevens will have opportunity to demonstrate," he said.

John spoke calmly, with full possession. "Would it be consistent with the exercise of your duty to inform me on what the start- ling charge is based which you lodge against me?" he asked.

"It is irreg- ular in me to answer that," returned Ham-

THE NELSON HOUSE: CORNWALLIS'S HEADQUARTERS AT YORKTOWN

ilton, "but out of respect to your past services, of which I am not ignorant, I will so far transgress propriety as to reply that it is in conjunction with the lamentable and detestable treachery of Benedict Arnold."

At that John flinched. "I am aware that my behavior at that time lays me open to such a suspicion." he said.

WASHINGTON'S HEADQUARTERS AT RICHMOND, VIRGINIA

"If you have any care to say anything to those who are present, believe me, I shall not be so inconsiderate as to prohibit it," replied Hamilton, perceiving who it was before whom he would speak, and why.

"I will freely confess," said John, "that I came to New York on a mission for General Arnold, shortly before his treasonable act, and at a time when he had it in contemplation, and, further, that I came on that business, to confer with Major André and this man here," indicating Francis, who acknowledged the identification with a leer, "whose principal interest in the matter seemed to arise from the circumstance that it was a nefarious and wicked plot, involving much black treachery. In so coming, I was misled partly by General Arnold, who, while he acquainted me with the plot, assured me that it was nothing more than a ruse to entice Clinton out of New York to his destruction, and partly by my own zeal to thwart it, if I could, without stirring up a scandal in the army. For, while I scarcely conceived the possibility that Arnold contemplated treachery, I was doubtful of the propriety of his plan, devised as it was without the knowledge or sanction of his superiors, and of its successful issue, in case it should be pushed to a climax."

His earnestness, his frankness, his calmness, impressed Hamilton no less than it did Nancy, who listened with parted lips, having much marveled over these things. As for Francis, he contented himself with sneering and leering at John, with many grimaces, Sophronia the while remaining calm and quiet beside him, as though the matter had slight interest for her.

"It may occasion some surprise," John continued, "that, knowing of the plan, and the dangers it involved, to say nothing of the possibility that Arnold did not act in good faith, I did not at once apprise General Washington of the whole matter, and so end it. Let me plead in extenuation of that an affection I had held for Benedict Arnold since the time when I marched with him against Canada through the frozen woods of Maine, and the time when I stood beside him during those terrific hours when his bravery and devotion wrought the destruction of Burgoyne. Let me plead further a reciprocation of the affection, and an intimate confidence between us of a nature that rendered it highly distasteful to me to bring him into any mischief with his superiors, or with the army in general, — a result that must have followed my divulgence of his plan.

For these reasons, if they can be received as reasons, and because I gave him the benefit of any doubt of his sincerity, I hit upon the alternative of accepting his mission, hoping to be able to thwart a consummation of the scheme by a counterplot, which I had not formed in mind, but which, I hoped, might suggest itself in the course of my visit to New York. Failing in that, I was determined, as a last resort, to inform General Washington."

"Ay," broke in Sophronia, still indifferent in manner, "and was prevented in that by myself."

Those who heard looked at her in surprise; even Francis gasped at the revelation she seemed intending, knowing what it was.

"It may be a matter of conjecture why I intervened in the carrying out of Major Stevens's plans," she resumed, smiling slightly with self-amusement. "That is a matter of small relevancy to the point at issue. It is needful for me merely to tell that, on the eve of his departure from New York, to inform General Washington, for he failed in his other project, I devised his abduction in a coach, in an approved and romantic manner, and so contrived matters that we fell into the hands of certain prearranged bands of cowboys who detained us for such a space of time that the mischief was done, and Arnold had escaped before Major Stevens had opportunity to communicate with any one whatsoever. Had you beheld his restlessness, you would have known how the thing galled him. He was a very caged lion, and at the last broke from restraint, and was off, we knew not whither. But then the mischief was done."

John, who had been thrown into some embarrassment at the beginning of her narrative, grew in astonishment as she proceeded. When she finished all else gave way to rage.

"Was it you, then, who held me there?" he cried, for-

THE SURRENDER OF CORNWALLIS   (From Trumbull's painting in the Rotunda of the Capitol at Washington)

getting she was a woman; in which, perhaps, he was justified, for she was more than a woman in strength. "Were
you a party to the despicable scheme?"

"If you mean to the treason, I can answer no," returned
Sophronia, easily, "but if you mean to your detention, I
answer yes."

"In Heaven's name, then, what was your purpose?'

"Had you not been utterly blind, you might have divined my purpose," she replied, smiling reminiscently.
"I had one, believe me, which was above and more than
the affairs of hostile armies."

To all the other woman said, Nancy listened with drawn
breath and parted lips, wondering whether the thought that
had first come into her brain was near the truth. Now she
knew she had guessed right. With the knowledge came a
fear,— the fear of a danger that was past. With a little
broken gasp she reached forth and laid a tense hand on
John's sleeve.

It was Francis who broke the silence that held them
when Sophronia finished; Francis, from whose face the
leer had passed, to be succeeded by a look of chagrin and
malignity. "Egad, Mistress Osborne, 't is a pretty tale
you weave, and prettily told," he said. "I know not
whether to admire more your cunning in the invention or
your courage in endeavoring to save this man for the arms
of another. But your labor will be lost, for the case is
plain against the rogue, as Colonel Hamilton well knows."

"By your leave, Colonel Hamilton chooses rather to
speak for himself in the matter," said that gentleman
decisively. He went on:

"Major Stevens, I am pleased and proud to acknowledge
that what I have heard places your case in a different light,
and I shall take upon myself the responsibility of refrain-
ing from completing the errand that brought me here, only

asking of you, on your honor, to hold yourself in readiness to report to General Washington at your leisure; or at his desire, should he fail to take the same view of the situation that presents itself to me. Sir," he added, advancing toward John and extending a cordial hand, "permit me to tender my respects, and to express my sympathy for you in the unfortunate position in which circumstances placed you. Mr. Francis, I bid you good day. If you consider that you have anything further to divulge in this matter, allow me to request that you report to General Washington himself, who, I promise you, will be ready to listen with just reason to all that you many find you have to say. Mistress Osborne, may I ask you to be ready to repeat your story, if occasion requires? Madam," to Nancy, "I beg of you to accept my reassurance that all is likely to

come out as you would wish it." With that he turned and left the room, followed by the dazed gaze of John and Nancy, and by a whimsical smile from Sophronia.

"And now, Master Francis," said Sophronia, when Hamilton was gone, "since there seems to be no further need of us in setting ill matters aright, I would suggest that we had better leave these two, and turn our attention to other things. But before we go," she added, bethinking herself, "there is one more matter in which I would absolve myself, having fully lost the fight. It was not Nancy here, Master Stevens, who disclosed your presence in your cousin's house, when you lay wounded, for she, through my good care, knew not you had been there until you had gone with me, driving through the streets in livery of green." With that she swept from the room, taking Francis with her, half by force. To those they left he said nothing, contenting himself with a leer; for his spirit had returned.

For a space they stood silent, alone in the room, gazing upon each other, bewildered, half doubting. It was John who spoke. "Beloved," he said, "the war has ceased."

She made no answer other than to creep to his side and raise her radiant face to his.

On the morrow, John sought out General Washington, anxious to be understood. The commander-in-chief had heard the story from Hamilton, and received him cordially. "My joy could not be more complete," he said, frankly, "for I have ever held you to be one of our best and truest."

"I could wish, sir, that I might be put upon a trial, for the sake of my good name," said John, manfully, acknowledging the other's kindness with a pressure of the hand.

"Nay, Major Stevens," returned Washington, "I think I can insure your reputation without that. But there is one question I would ask you, for the benefit of my own curiosity," he went on. "Where did you go when you found yourself free from the toils involving you, and why did you not come at once to me?"

"Therein I erred," conceded John, "for I put a bad face upon a matter already ugly enough. But my grief at learning of General Arnold's perfidy, whom I loved and honored, and my self-reproach, drove me from the sight of

those I had known. I made my way to the South, where
I joined Marion's band, coming hither after the battle at
Eutaw Springs to be in the midst of the glorious affair that
I knew was soon to take place."

Washington smiled gratefully. "And are we to consider that you have been taken captive by the enemy, or
that you have made a captive?" he asked, still smiling.

"You are to consider, sir, that the war has ceased,"
replied John Stevens, smiling back.

And so it had. When the news reached England, in
November, the British people recoiled from the thought
of prolonging the conflict. Lord North knew there was no
further hope. "Oh, God!" he cried, pacing the room and
throwing his arms about, "it is all over! It is all over!"
Only the stubborn and stupid King still persisted, demanding that Georgia, Charleston, and New York be held.
But the English people gave him no support. For a long
time the war against America had been growing in unpopularity; now the opposition to it rendered the King powerless to proceed. Lord George Germaine was dismissed;
the House of Commons talked of a vote of censure on the
administration; a motion of Conway's, petitioning the
King to stop the war, was lost by only one vote. The
country squires, who had most strongly supported the war,
went to the other side; the two sections of the Whig party
joined issue against it. On March 20 Lord North, bowing
before the storm, resigned as prime minister. Lord Rockingham succeeded him, and with him came into office
Shelburne, Camden, Grafton, Fox, Conway, the duke of
Richmond, and Lord John Cavendish, all staunch friends
of America, whose appointment involved the recognition
of the independence of the United States.

In America the war saw only one more campaign.
In the winter of 1781, Wayne, acting under Greene, drove

the British from Georgia, and Greene held them safe in Charleston until the war was officially declared at an end. Clinton, who had left New York with a powerful fleet and 7000 men on the very day that Cornwallis surrendered, returned thither when he learned of the event. He was succeeded by Sir Guy Carleton; but the British forces re-

WASHINGTON AT YORKTOWN

mained idle until the evacuation of the city, November 25, 1783, after peace was formally declared.

The news of the fall of Yorktown was received with unparalleled joy throughout the States. Early on a dark morning in late November an honest old German, pacing the streets of Philadelphia on his night watch, called out: "Bahst dree o'clock, und Cornvallis ish dakendt!" That is how the story broke in the capital. Congress received dispatches from Washington in the forenoon; word spread over the country as fast as couriers could carry it. Every village green was ablaze with bonfires; homes that had been desolate for seven long years rejoiced; the heavy burden.

borne with such sacrifice through all the weary time, was
removed at last.   For, though peace was not yet declared, and
British armies yet remained in the States, none doubted
that the end was near.

Orders were sent to the British generals in America
to cease hostilities. Savannah was evacuated in July of
1782 that year; Charleston, December 14.   November 30,
1782 a   preliminary treaty of peace was
signed at Paris, Adams,
Franklin, Jay, and Laurens
representing the United
States; Strachey, Os-
wald, and Fitzherbert,
England.   On Septem-

THE YORKTOWN MONUMENT,
    YORKTOWN

ber 3, 1783, a definitive
treaty was signed at Versailles, by which England acknowledged the independence of the United States.   On
November 25 following, New York, the last position held
by the British on our coast, was evacuated.   And the thing
was done.

Over the land of the free the Stars and Stripes were
thrown upon the pleasant winds of early autumn.   The cares
of the war, the exhaustion of resources, and the preoccupation
of the people with a struggle for life or death had left them
little time for thought of the new emblem.   So it was that,
outside of the army and navy, comparatively few knew the

flag and, as the celebration of the establishment of peace generally included the raising of the beautiful national standard, it is most often referred to in the writings of the time as "The Peace Flag." And, as the Flag of Peace, long may it wave!

On Christmas eve of that year there was a merry gathering about the hearth in the Averill home, in Boston. Catherine was home from Virginia with Fontaine, her husband. With them were John and Nancy, who had married the day after Yorktown surrendered.

Sitting about the fire, the talk ran to the war that had been; it came to pass that they spoke of Sophronia, and the part she had played in their lives.

"It is a strange thing that she has gone so entirely from our view," said Nancy, with cheek resting on her husband's sleeve.

There was silence for a space. It was Fontaine who spoke. "Belike I can tell you somewhat of her," he said. "My tongue has been sealed, but now that our cousin Robert of New York has passed this life, and is beyond the reach of scandal, I may speak, in this company, to tell you of one more good thing she did before she passed from our knowledge. I have no need to tell you that the woman who fastened herself upon our unfortunate cousin in New York, Mistress Osborne, was a designing adventuress.

"It seems that the woman never was legally Robert's wife; that she had a husband living at the time of her pretended marriage to him, and that her marriage was part of a plot to plunder him, in which the real husband had his share. Sophronia was aware of it, the man being her father, but was complaisant, having little scruple to live a life of easy luxury in the New York mansion, even at the cost of fraud and infamy. But in the end, when she had done you a good turn, she returned to New York and told

Robert, gently and with great tact, of the trick that had been played upon him. It was that disclosure that caused the departure of Mistress Osborne from our cousin's house. But who, think you, was the man, her husband?"

They made no guess. "Why," continued Fontaine, "it was none other than our rascally acquaintance, the Friar David, which was the reason of the power Sophronia had over him. But there is more to it than that; for who think you this same Friar David was?"

Again they made no guess. "He," said Fontaine, slowly, giving them time to prepare for a surprise, "was none other than one David Stevens, of Virginia, own half-brother to Robert, and a kinsman of ours, a great rascal, of whom many stories are still told in Fredericksburg."

A little ripple of horror; and the talk fell back to pleasant things, until, when the log was low, Nancy and John departed for their home,—to that cottage in a little lane where first she had learned what manner of man he was; and where he had kissed her upon the forehead; where all things had their beginning; where their life now lay in peaceful lines, full of blessings and many a promise.

THE STARS
AND STRIPES: THE
BETSY ROSS FLAG

THE END

INDEX

INDEX

A

ADAMS, JOHN
defends Captain Preston, 69
portrait of, 77
chosen chief justice, 146–147
one of committee appointed to draft Declaration of Independence, 189
Congress sends, to confer with Lord Howe, 202
at signing of treaty of peace, 480

ADAMS, SAMUEL
protests against Stamp Act, 20
writes letters attacking Parliament, 20
portrait of, 36
effects the removal of soldiers to Boston Harbor, 69
organizes committees to resist King's decree, 69
calls Continental Congress to meet in Philadelphia, 72
makes stirring speeches at Concord, 74
threats of arrest for treason made against, 77
order goes forth to take, to England for trial, 85
British regulars prepare to arrest, 85
Revere and Dawes make ready to warn, 86
accused of stirring up strife, 98
at the house of Reverend Mr. Clarke, 103
Paul Revere gives alarm to, 104
Gage offers pardon to colonists if Hancock and, will lay down their arms, 126
suggests that colonies declare themselves independent, 144
indorses Thomas Paine's pamphlet, 173

ALBANY, NEW YORK
Burgoyne to proceed to, 250
Burgoyne and Saint Leger to meet at, 250

ALBEMARLE SOUND
Clinton waits for Parker in, 174

ALEXANDER, WILLIAM, see STIRLING, WILLIAM ALEXANDER, LORD

ALLEN, ETHAN
sets out to take Ticonderoga and Crown Point, 125
takes Fort Ticonderoga, 125

AMBOY, NEW JERSEY
the British retain, 243

AMERICA
Continental Congress claims free power of legislation for, 51
people will not permit tea to be brought to, 69
the first Revolutionary monument in, picture of, 120
hiring of foreign troops arouses bitter anger in, 162
Parliament closes ports of, to the world, 173

AMERICA — *continued*
French alliance not wholly popular in, 320
reasons for unpopularity of French alliance in, 320
cause of, suffers for lack of efficient navy, 353
navy of, does damage to British shipping, 354

ANDRÉ, MAJOR JOHN
portrait of, 403
adjutant-general of the British army, 404
comes to complete negotiations with Arnold, 405
captured with compromising papers, 409
the Rookery where he spent the night before his capture, picture of, 411
fate of, casts a gloom over New York, 417
beloved in the army, 417
prison of, picture of, 417
taken to Tappan, 418
secret proposal made to exchange, for Arnold, 418
is tried and hanged, 418
remains of, taken to Westminster Abbey, 418
reading the death-warrant to, picture of, 422
Washington's headquarters during trial of, 424

ARMSTRONG, GENERAL JOHN
at the battle of Brandywine, 277, 280
at the second battle of Saratoga, 297–301
is wounded, 301

ARDSLEY, NEW YORK
headquarters of Rochambeau at, picture of, 339

ARNOLD, BENEDICT
organizes company of volunteers, 123
marches to Cambridge, 123
realizes importance of getting possession of the Hudson River, 124
obtains commission as colonel, 124
given authority to capture Ticonderoga and Crown Point, 124–125
joins Ethan Allen's company as private, 125
characteristics of, 142
an officer with Washington, 142
proposes plan for expedition against Quebec, 161
leaves Boston to coöperate with Montgomery, 165
reaches Claudière River, 165
leads his force out upon the Plains of Abraham, 165
forced to wait for Montgomery, 165
challenges British to fight or surrender, 166
and Montgomery decide to assault Quebec, 166
leads division of army against Quebec, 166
wounded at Quebec, 167
Carleton drives, back into New York, 188
Carleton threatens, by way of Ticonderoga, 188
in tribulation through intrigues of Gates, 268–269

485

Q

R